# DIAGNOSING

# MENTAL ILLNESS

# Other Books by Drs. Freedman and Kaplan

COMPREHENSIVE TEXTBOOK OF PSYCHIATRY
*Alfred M. Freedman and Harold I. Kaplan,* EDITORS 1967

PSYCHOPATHOLOGY OF ADOLESCENCE
*Alfred M. Freedman (with Joseph Zubin),* EDITOR 1970

COMPREHENSIVE GROUP PSYCHOTHERAPY
*Harold I. Kaplan (with Benjamin J. Sadock),* EDITOR 1971

STUDIES IN HUMAN BEHAVIOR
*Alfred M. Freedman and Harold I. Kaplan,* GENERAL EDITORS

DIAGNOSING MENTAL ILLNESS: EVALUATION IN
PSYCHIATRY AND PSYCHOLOGY 1972

INTERPRETING PERSONALITY: A SURVEY OF
TWENTIETH-CENTURY VIEWS 1972

HUMAN BEHAVIOR: BIOLOGICAL, PSYCHOLOGICAL,
AND SOCIOLOGICAL 1972

TREATING MENTAL ILLNESS: ASPECTS OF
MODERN THERAPY 1972

THE CHILD: HIS PSYCHOLOGICAL AND
CULTURAL DEVELOPMENT 1972

VOL. 1: NORMAL DEVELOPMENT AND
PSYCHOLOGICAL ASSESSMENT
VOL. 2: THE MAJOR PSYCHOLOGICAL DISORDERS
AND THEIR TREATMENT

# DIAGNOSING
# MENTAL ILLNESS

## Evaluation in
## Psychiatry and Psychology

---

### ALFRED M. FREEDMAN, M.D.

Professor and Chairman, Department of Psychiatry,
New York Medical College

AND

### HAROLD I. KAPLAN, M.D.

Professor, Department of Psychiatry, New York Medical College

EDITORS

---

## Studies in Human Behavior

New York   ATHENEUM   1972

The editors express their appreciation to the following publishers and publications for permission to reprint portions of the works cited.

American Psychiatric Association: Committee on Nomenclature and Statistics, *Diagnostic and Statistical Manual, Mental Disorders*, Washington, 1952.

Basic Books, Inc., Publishers: Final Report of the Joint Commission on Mental Illness and Health, *Action for Mental Health*, New York, 1951.

Basic Books, Inc., Publishers: Rollo May, Ernest Angel, and Henri F. Ellenberger, editors, *Existence*, New York, 1958.

Ohio Psychological Association: George Albee, "A Declaration of Independence for Psychology," Worthington, Ohio, 1964.

*Bulletin of the Menninger Clinic:* R. P. Knight, "Borderline States," Topeka, Kansas, copyright 1953 by The Menninger Foundation.

The Viking Press, Inc.: Karl Menninger, M.D., Martin Mayman, Ph.D., and Paul Pruyser, Ph.D., *The Vital Balance*, New York, copyright © 1963 by Karl Menninger, M.D. All Rights Reserved.

# *Preface*

This book is one of a series of volumes based on the First Edition of the *Comprehensive Textbook of Psychiatry*, which we edited for use in medical schools. Dr. Helen S. Kaplan served as Assistant to the Editors of that edition. The *Comprehensive Textbook* resulted from our part in setting up the undergraduate and graduate programs in psychiatry at New York Medical College. New articles have been written for these volumes, and certain subjects have been updated or eliminated, in an effort to reach a wider audience.

The responsibility for teaching psychiatry has made us acutely aware of the whole spectrum of current progress in the continuing search for the causes of mental disorders. Recent scientific research has placed at the disposal of the clinical practitioner new knowledge that must be incorporated into existing theoretical and therapeutic methods. Our aim is to include in these volumes all such major contributions in the basic and social sciences that have an influence on the teaching and practice of psychiatry. We have attempted to derive a balanced and current summary of psychiatric thinking in a variety of fields.

The interaction with distinguished and creative colleagues in the preparation of the material contained in these volumes has been most gratifying. We have had a unique opportunity to engage in a stimulating exchange of ideas and to establish rewarding personal relationships as well.

Many people have given us dedicated and valuable help, and we wish to express our deep appreciation to them. We would mention in particular Lois A. Baken, Elaine Cohen, and Pauline DeMarco. And we give special thanks to Joan Welsh for her invaluable help in editing and stylizing this series.

A. M. F.
H. I. K.

# Contents

**AREA B**

*Assessment of Children*

**AREA C**

*The Field of Clinical Psychiatry*

# Introduction

Problems of psychiatric and psychological evaluation are central to the practice of psychiatry. Diagnostic tools are a major part of the psychiatric process. Their proper deployment from the beginning of treatment and throughout its course is of the greatest significance for the patient's welfare and for the psychiatrist's effective use of his own time, efforts, and skills.

The psychiatrist's evaluative techniques are varied, and their effectiveness has been empirically validated. Some date back to the relatively early days of the science in the late nineteenth century, while others are much more recent. Some involve the assessment of the patient by the examining psychiatrist alone; others call on the training and skill of interpreters of such factors as intelligence, social environment, and various psychological parameters. The psychiatrist can simplify his diagnostic problems by employing a battery of tests and by calling on other evaluators to supplement or modify the results he obtains during the early interviews when he takes the patient's psychiatric history and examines his mental status.

This book provides a survey of the diagnostic tools at the psychiatrist's disposal. It is divided into three areas. The first and by far the largest concerns itself with the entire problem of assessment in psychiatry, with the varying techniques used by the psychiatrist and others, and with classification systems. A second area is devoted to the special problems that arise during psychological testing of children and the special techniques used to resolve these problems. The third area considers the relatively new mental health specialty that is closely allied to psychiatry, the field of clinical psychology. Together these three areas provide a comprehensive picture of the problems and potentials of psychiatric evaluation and of the many specialized techniques available to the psychiatrist.

This survey of psychiatric evaluation includes the classification of mental disorders provided in the second edition of the *Diagnostic and Statistical Manual of Mental Disorders* (DSM-II), published in 1968 by the American Psychiatric Association. This revised classification brings the reader up to date in nosology as used in this country today. Classification is in some ways relatively simple with the use of DSM-II. But the situation is more complex, for the classification scheme used in DSM-II is but one among many. It is the standard classification scheme in the United States, as its predecessor DSM-I was during the period from 1952 to 1968, when DSM-II was adopted, but it varies considerably from classification schemes used with relative effectiveness in other countries. Furthermore, like DSM-I, it has been criticized vigorously.

These criticisms are, on one level, disagreements about the classification systems and about the artificiality of certain diagnostic distinctions in those systems. On another and much more profound level, these criticisms take issue with the very definitions of mental disorder that appear in the manual and with the distinctions made between neurosis and health, between neurosis and psychosis, and between psychosis and the borderline states. A comprehensive view of these radical critiques is beyond the scope of this book, which is primarily a survey of present knowledge in the field; nevertheless, throughout the book attempts are made to provide perspective by examining these problems.

One chapter of this book is devoted to the history of psychiatric classification and to an examination of various classification systems, with special attention to the elements that make these systems scientifically valid. The new diagnostic nomenclature, as set forth in DSM-II, differs in several key ways from the nomenclature that was used in DSM-I. The modifications reflect the way in which psychiatrists now look at mental disorders, and there has been much debate over the various changes. Both Chapter 9, "A Guide to the American Psychiatric Association's New Diagnostic Nomenclature," and Chapter 10, "The New Diagnostic Nomenclature: Definition of Terms," concern themselves with these changes. They describe the major changes, explain their purposes, and examine the reasons for their adoption. Chapter 11 provides a comparative listing of the classifications in DSM-I and DSM-II. These chapters on DSM-II are not derived from the *Comprehensive Textbook of Psychiatry*, on which most of this book is based. They provide a unique contribution, considerably increasing the value of this book and giving it a unique perspective.

The remaining chapters in the area devoted to assessment concern various other aspects of the psychiatric examination. The psychiatric interview is the primary way in which the psychiatrist approaches his patient. The early interviews set the stage for the entire course of treatment. They help the psychiatrist evaluate the patient's intelligence, the depth and type of his mental disorder, the life situations that may complicate treatment and personality development, the probable intensity of the transference—in short, the diagnosis and prognosis of the case. Of course, it is not always possible to obtain a valid diagnosis and a reliable prognosis from these early interviews; often ancillary tools must be brought into play. Nevertheless, the psychiatric interview lies at the core of the relationship between the patient and the psychiatrist.

Problems of transference and countertransference arise during the first interviews, and with them the advantages and disadvantages inherent in the transference phenomenon. The psychiatrist must be aware of the early transference situation and of all its ramifications, for difficulties posed by countertransference can impede the diagnosis, particularly if the psychiatrist cannot establish rapport and the patient does not divulge certain material. On the other hand, this particular difficulty can be a valuable diagnostic tool, since one of the diagnostic criteria in certain mental disorders is that the patient is difficult to empathize with. At the same time, a psychiatrist insufficiently aware of his own unresolved conflicts may persistently ply the patient with unimportant questions to avoid encountering subjects he finds threatening, or he may stress material that is important to himself rather than to the patient. Needless to say, this sort of interview does the patient little good.

The first chapter in this book is a comprehensive examination of the psychiatric interview, with guidelines for conducting it properly—both with the patient who presents few difficulties in the interview situation and with the patient who presents many difficulties because he is depressed, overanxious, delusional, or manic, or manifests some other severe disorder. This chapter sets forth the techniques of conducting the interview, assesses the amount of interpretation that can be given in various situations, and describes the way in which the interpretation ought to be given. Some attention is paid to the question of note-taking; here practice varies widely according to the psychiatrist's individual inclination. Questions about the psychiatrist's own attitude during the interview and the amount of appropriate interaction with the patient are also discussed.

Generally the patient's recorded psychiatric history and mental status are based on the first few interviews, although the psychiatric history may be continued, modified, or expanded after subsequent interviews. A discussion of the psychiatric history and mental status examination appears in Chapter 2 of this volume. Proper evaluation requires a history of each period of the patient's life in as much detail as possible. Sometimes, for a report on the patient's infancy and childhood, several interviews with his family are needed. The more thorough the history is, the more certain the psychiatrist can feel about both diagnosis and prognosis. Genetic, environmental, economic, social, and educational factors are all important, and none of those factors ought to be ignored. Often the history of the patient's family of origin is significant; and, if he is married, the detailed account of the marital relationship should also include information about the spouse's family of origin.

Many critically important factors ought to be included in the mental status examination. Here it is helpful to read Chapter 2 in context with Chapter 7, which describes the clinical manifestations of psychiatric disorders. The mental status examination report should note manifestations of disorders of consciousness, difficulties in abstract thinking, hallucinations, obsessions, compulsions, phobias, and disturbances in perception, affect, and motor behavior. Emotional reactions, thought content, and orientation should all be carefully noted, as should the patient's behavior, posture, facial expression, and general appearance. Particularly important is the physical examination, which is often skipped with outpatients. From the mental status examination and the psychiatric history, the psychiatrist can make a diagnosis and prognosis, which can then be checked against the assessment derived from ancillary evaluation techniques.

These techniques are discussed in the remaining chapters of this area on assessment. Chapter 6 covers the relations between psychiatric treatment and the medical examination that should be required of all psychiatric patients. If the cause of the disease is physical, this can usually be discerned from the medical examination. Some brain damage can be discerned by psychological testing, and Chapter 4 discusses the testing techniques for determining whether certain manifestations are neurological or psychological in origin. Chapter 5 examines the role of the social worker, who can be of considerable therapeutic importance, particularly with children and adolescents and with the relatives of psychiatric patients.

The wide variety of available psychological tests—their goals, their advantages, and their limitations—are discussed in Chapter 3. These tests can examine intellectual ability and personality, and can provide clues that may help determine the direction of psychiatric treatment. Numerous personality tests are available; their employment depends on the experience the psychiatrist has had with each of them and on how effective he has found them as guides or tools for corroborating his diagnosis. Their use also depends on what the psychiatrist is interested in learning. One projective personality test examines neurotic conflicts; another, the Rorschach, gives the examiner a clear picture of the patient's personality defenses; a third, the Thematic Apperception Test, is valuable in providing a description of the patient's relationship with his parents. Of these tests, the best known is the Rorschach, which has a long history of successful application in evaluating personality, and a sophisticated and complex series of formulas for interpretation. There is disagreement regarding the value of some of these tests, but the Rorschach is widely accepted.

The tests are usually given at the beginning of treatment as aids in assessing diagnosis and prognosis. They are sometimes given again— though much less frequently—during the course of treatment or as the treatment is drawing to a close in order to measure the changes that have occurred in the patient's personality. Many psychiatrists feel that, since the tests' primary value is for diagnosis, there is little need for retesting as treatment draws to a close.

The psychological testing of children presents different problems from those encountered in testing adults. The tests for infants and preschool children provide less reliable results than those for older children. Furthermore, younger children do not respond well to tests that last a long time; yet short tests are less reliable. Problems of administering tests vary with the type of patient and with the age of the child. Many of the tests are used not only for psychiatric purposes but to examine normal development in children as well. Recently, much attention has been devoted to the problem of constructing tests that are valid no matter what the cultural background of the child. Chapter 13 examines these problems in depth and provides a survey of current knowledge in this complex field.

This book, then, provides the reader with a comprehensive and uniquely up-to-date study of the tools with which the psychiatrist can evaluate the problems of his patients. The subject is of major importance, and the authoritative overview presented here will be of value to both layman and psychiatrist.

# AREA A

---

# *Assessment in Psychiatry and Psychology*

# CHAPTER ONE

# *Psychiatric Interview*

## HERBERT S. RIPLEY, M.D.

THE INTERVIEW is the main tool used by the psychiatrist to gain a knowledge of the patient and what is wrong with him. Obtaining a mental status, eliciting a history of the patient's present illness and past life, and carrying out psychotherapy are dependent on a perceptively conducted interview. In fact, all these begin with the initial contact with the psychiatrist. An understanding of the patient in health and sickness comes chiefly from his account of his life events, attitudes, and emotions and of the development of his symptoms. The diagnosis and prognosis are based on these data and the additional information obtained from the patient's relatives, the physical examination, psychological tests, and any other special examinations. With this knowledge, treatment objectives can be formulated, and a plan of therapy that is realistic for the patient can be instituted.

In recent years there has been increasing interest in the psychiatric interview, and important refinements in its use have been developed. The traditional formal examination outline of general medicine has been replaced by greater emphasis on encouraging the patient to tell his story in his own words. The question and answer technique leads to brief and sterile responses and failure to elicit an elaboration of his background. Psychoanalysis has had a great influence on the improvement of techniques in interviewing. Freud in 1905 pointed out that he began treatment by asking the patient to give him the whole story of his life and illness.

The psychiatrist needs to consider not only the implications of the patient's conscious, realistic statements but also the unconscious or transference aspects. By transference is meant the reactivation outside the individ-

ual's awareness of attitudes and feelings toward people who were important to him earlier in his life. Infantile feelings of parental omnipotence or
of rebelliousness toward parents are frequently directed toward the psychiatrist, who may have trouble understanding such reactions since they
are no longer appropriate, as they may have been in the patient's childhood. In his puzzlement, the psychiatrist may feel that his own behavior
has been seriously amiss, or he may become angry and blame the patient.
The studies of transference relationships by Freud and subsequent investigators have been particularly illuminating of the relationship between the
physician and the patient.

## PHYSICIAN-PATIENT RELATIONSHIP

The physician-patient relationship is the core of the practice of medicine.
It is of concern to all physicians and needs to be evaluated in all patients.
Although personality factors are most significant when emotional and
mental problems are the core of the illness, they also affect the care of the
patient with structural disease. A good relationship, even more than a
cure, is expected by the patient; it is common experience that patients are
apt to be tolerant of the therapeutic limitations of medicine. Physicians
work with sick people, not just disease syndromes. As Alan Gregg put it:
"There are no diseases. There are only sick people." Therefore, it is in-
cumbent on the psychiatrist to consider the nature of the relationship, the
psychodynamic factors in both himself and his patient that influence the
relationship, and the manner in which good rapport can be achieved.

Rapport is the spontaneous, conscious feeling of harmonious responsiveness that promotes the development of a constructive therapeutic relationship. It implies that there is an understanding and trust between the
psychiatrist and his patient. With rapport, the patient feels that the psychiatrist accepts him and recognizes his assets, even though they may be
outnumbered by his liabilities. Frequently, the doctor is the individual to
whom the patient can talk about things he cannot tell anyone else. Most
patients feel that they can trust psychiatrists to keep secrets. This confidence must not be betrayed. The patient's feeling that someone knows
him, understands him, and accepts him is a source of strength for him.

### PHYSICIAN'S ATTITUDE TOWARD PATIENT

Failure of the physician to establish good rapport accounts for much of his
ineffectiveness in the care of his patients. Alexis Carrel pointed out that
the young physician all too frequently loses sight of the whole man and
instead regards his patient as the corpse dissected by the anatomist, the
cells and fluids studied by the physiologist, or the consciousness observed
by the psychiatrist. However, a live patient brings in a new factor that the
medical student's first patient, the cadaver, did not have: transference.
The young physician may, in turn, develop a countertransference—that is,

an emotional reaction to the patient based on the physician's own needs and conflicts. The physician identifies with the patient to a greater or lesser degree. Physicians consciously or unconsciously know something about the patient's needs, for everyone has been sick, at least as a child. Thus, the physician develops empathy, which means that he has the capacity to put himself in the patient's place to such a degree that he is able to experience the meaning of the patient's feelings, wishes, and thoughts.

"The secret of the care of the patient is in caring for the patient," remarked Francis Peabody, who was a talented teacher, clinician, and researcher. If a doctor dislikes a patient, he is prone to be ineffective in dealing with him. Emotion breeds counteremotion. For example, if the physician is hostile, the patient becomes more hostile; the physician then becomes even angrier, and there is rapid deterioration of the relationship. If, on the other hand, the physician can rise above such emotion and handle the resentful patient with equanimity, there may be a victory in the interpersonal relationship, and the patient may become a loyal and cooperative individual. Physicians are bound to like some patients more than others. It is not uncommon for physicians to be emotionally upset by certain personalities or illnesses. However, it is important to try to give a full amount of understanding to all. If the physician feels antagonism, he should try to evaluate the basis for this feeling.

## PATIENT'S REACTION TO PHYSICIAN

The reaction of the patient toward the psychiatrist is apt to be a repetition of the attitude he has had to previous physicians or to parents, teachers, or other authoritative persons who have figured importantly in his life. His reaction may be positive, negative, or ambivalent.

Because the traditional role of the physician is one of taking action and giving advice, patients are sometimes reluctant to tell their stories to a psychiatrist. They come to him with the expectation that all their difficulties will be promptly resolved with no further effort on their part except for a passive compliance with the physician's directions.

Although it is easy for the patient to identify the psychiatrist with another person in his life when there are realistic factors, at times the transference needs are so great that unrealistic factors will serve. For example, a young man can easily look upon an older psychiatrist as a father figure. However, when unresolved conflicts with his father are strong, he may even endow an attractive young woman examiner with personality characteristics of his father.

The psychiatrist's words and deeds have a power far beyond the commonplace because of his unique authority and the dependence of the patient on him. What the particular physician feels has a direct bearing on the emotional and physiological reactions of the patient. One patient repeatedly had high blood pressure when examined by a physician he considered cold, aloof, and stern. He had normal blood pressure when seen by a physician he regarded as warm, understanding, and sympathetic.

Not only individual experiences but broad cultural attitudes of patients affect their reactions. In one survey of 700 patients, there was substantial agreement among the patients that physicians did not have the time or inclination to listen to and consider the patient's feelings, that they did not have enough knowledge of emotional problems and of the socioeconomic background of the family, and that they increased fear by not giving explanations in nontechnical language. Since psychosocial and economic factors exert a profound influence on human reactions, as has been emphasized by Blum and others, it is desirable for the physician to have as much understanding as possible of the subculture of the patient. Differences in social, intellectual, and educational status have been found to interfere seriously with rapport. Understanding—or lack of understanding —of the patient's beliefs, use of language, and attitudes toward illness influences the character of the physician's examination.

## THE INTERRELATIONSHIP

Lewin pointed out that there is a core of the howling, enraged child in most patients, even in good patients, who are usually defined as cooperative patients. The physician is required to cope with the patient's aggressions. Counteraggressions also arise, but they are usually sublimated rather than expressed directly, as they were in the days when Dr. Willis flogged the psychotic George III, with the considered approval of a good part of the medical profession. The physician's unconscious guilt, an outgrowth of his incapacity to deal with the patient and his illness, may be alleviated by an accusatory method of questioning, which carries the implication that the patient is responsible for his illness.

Gaining conscious insight into the relationship between the psychiatrist and the patient requires constant evaluation. The better understanding the psychiatrist has of himself, the more secure he feels and the better able he is to modify destructive attitudes. The psychiatrist needs to empathize but not to the point of assuming the burdens of his patients. He should be able to leave the problems of his patients when away from the office or the hospital. Otherwise, he will be handicapped in his efforts to help the sick person, who needs sympathy and understanding but not sentimentality.

The physician is prone to have some defensiveness, partly with good reason, for many innocent doctors have been sued, attacked, and even killed because they did not give some patients the satisfactions unconsciously desired. As a protective defensive pattern, the psychiatrist may assume a habitual attitude toward all patients. Although such rigidity may create some comfort and efficiency, it is frequently inappropriate to the particular patient and situation. Greater flexibility leads to a responsiveness to the subtle interplay between two individuals.

The psychiatrist must avoid sidestepping issues that are important to the patient but that he finds boring or difficult to deal with because of his own sensitivities, prejudices, or peculiarities. For example, one medical student insisted on questioning a patient about her relationship with her 23-year-old son. It was evident from the playback of a tape-recorded interview that she wished to talk about her problem with her husband. When the patient was later interviewed by the supervising psychiatrist, she said: "The doctor was a nice fellow, but I could see he was having trouble with his mother. It made me understand my own son more."

In such a complex interaction as the interview, mistakes are usually not disastrous to the relationship if they are relatively infrequent. When the patient senses interest and goodwill on the part of the interviewer, he is apt to be tolerant of considerable ineptitude. The enthusiasm and interest of the young psychiatrist is likely to counterbalance his inexperience. The unhappy patient is chiefly concerned with getting relief, and the approach of the psychiatrist is more important than his age.

## TECHNIQUE

### GENERAL CONSIDERATIONS

The attitudes of both the patient and the physician are significant in determining the type of interview and its success. The patient comes to the psychiatrist for expert assistance. He may have a relatively realistic attitude characterized by some insight, awareness of the limitations of medical knowledge and skill, trust and confidence in a properly chosen psychiatrist, and capacity to cooperate. On the other hand, he may, like a helpless child, yearn for a parental type of guidance and expect magic from the psychiatrist. When there is such immature involvement on the part of the patient, the psychiatrist may either reinforce this illusion of magic by using a suggestive type of approach or try to dissipate these beliefs through an analysis of the problem.

Some patients come to the psychiatrist under duress because they are sent by relatives or friends. They are prone to be angry, inhibited, and unreceptive. The psychiatrist, through tact and understanding, may win such patients over and develop rapport in spite of such initial difficulties. When the patient shows marked inhibitions, the examiner aims to put him at ease and allows him to talk freely. A receptive manner is helpful. If the patient has questions, they should be answered frankly. Explanations should be given in keeping with the patient's capacity to understand. Such factors as intelligence, sophistication in regard to personality reactions, and degree and type of illness should influence the vocabulary and content of the psychiatrist's response. Every effort should be made to convey to the belligerent patient both understanding and tolerance for his feelings. If such a patient does not respond and does not wish to talk to the psychiatrist, it is advisable to discontinue the interview and resume contact with him at a later time.

The status of the examiner in the professional hierarchy influences some patients. Those who have had problems with authority may talk most easily to those of lesser status, and those who need to have their security bolstered require attention from a psychiatrist of recognized reputation.

A psychiatrist's knowledge of psychodynamics is of great use in helping him comprehend what is going on and in altering his approach to the patient. For example, if the patient is overbearing, it is likely that he is frightened. The interviewer needs to cope with this underlying fear in order to dissipate the overcompensatory anger. If the patient feels the psychiatrist has empathy, he is likely to talk more freely. It is frequently possible to capitalize on the patient's sense of humor in getting him to talk more easily. Smiling with him helps him feel a sense of rapport. Needless to say, laughing at him alienates him.

In guiding the interview, the examiner should allow the patient's free expression of thoughts and feelings, and he should let the patient tell his story. Gaps can be filled in later in the initial interview or in subsequent interviews. Listening is a major tool. Minimum activity encourages the patient to expand on his thoughts and enables him to bring up relevant topics. Attention must be paid to what the patient omits as well as to what he says. Undue emphasis or exaggeration, overt signs of emotion, and changes in manner and tone of voice may give clues to a distortion. For example, when a woman volunteers that her husband is absolutely perfect, her statement should raise suspicions about the soundness of the marital adjustment. But it is not advisable to challenge such dogmatic and emotionally charged statements immediately. These areas can be fully explored later, when the patient feels more secure with the psychiatrist. Misrepresentation and misperception of the facts due to conscious denial or lack of awareness can be clarified gradually.

Evaluating the social pressures existing in the patient's earlier life helps the psychiatrist understand the susceptibility of the patient better. For personality reactions, healthy or unhealthy, are the result of a constant interplay of biological, sociological, and psychological forces. Each stress leaves behind some trace of its influence and continues to manifest itself throughout life in proportion to the intensity of its effect and the susceptibility of the particular human being. Emotional reactions resulting from strain should be determined insofar as it is possible. The significant point may not be the stress per se but rather what that particular stress means to the person.

The patient must be an active participant when dealing with personality reactions. There is no short cut; he must find out about himself by frankly discussing himself. Patients should be encouraged to discuss the advantages and disadvantages of different possible ways of dealing with a problem. In this way, they learn to make their own decisions and take independent action; and they gain inner security, which will aid in dealing with future problems.

Usually, interviews should not last longer than an hour, although with some alert, receptive patients the initial interview may be prolonged to one-and-a-half hours. Longer subsequent interviews may also be scheduled, especially if it is not possible or appropriate to see the patient frequently. With sicker patients, fatigue and limited productivity indicate that the interview should be shortened.

The ultimate aim is to help the patient change his underlying attitudes and accept emotionally what he has heretofore refused to accept. The patient's confidence in the psychiatrist and his desire to improve can overcome resistance to such change. Resistance implies a conscious or unconscious need to withhold discussion of emotional conflicts. It may be due to shame, guilt, fear of rejection, distrust of the psychiatrist, or a need to hold onto symptoms that provide secondary gain. Frequently, the patient is apprehensive that the anxiety initially associated with his problems will be revived if his repression is removed. Resistance may be shown by talking about irrelevant topics or by directing the conversation to the psychiatrist himself. When patients ask personal questions of the psychiatrist, he may point out that he is interested in the reasons for this curiosity about his personal affairs. However, questions about the psychiatrist's qualifications should be answered frankly.

## QUESTION TECHNIQUES

Questions can be injected when the patient gives appropriate leads. When asked tactfully, questions do not contradict the patient's conception of himself. For example, if a patient who has had three wives complains about the resentment of his present wife, the psychiatrist should not ask him if he has always chosen hostile wives or if he always arouses anger in women. Rather, the psychiatrist should ask whether there have been similar problems with his previous wives.

Leading questions and interpretive comments should be avoided. For instance, if a patient complains of nausea, the psychiatrist should not say, "You must have your nausea when you're at work." He should ask the patient when he has his nausea and inquire about his environment and his feelings at the time it occurs. The patient himself may then see a connection between the stressful situation and his symptoms. Thus, instead of becoming defensive because he feels accused, he will be encouraged to develop his own insight.

The perceptive examiner asks questions that will help the patient develop understanding of himself as an individual. The examiner avoids influencing the patient to comply with preconceived theories that do not apply to him. For example, the psychiatrist may want to put all patients with peptic ulcer in the category of those who have unsatisfied infantile dependency needs. Instead, the psychiatrist's questions should lead the patient into an analysis of the development of his symptoms. With this approach, the patient gains an understanding of the hidden meanings of his personality reactions. When sufficient evidence in support of an interpretation has been given, the physician may use this data in making a more direct interpretation. Reformulating the patient's own interpretations may help in clarifying and consolidating insight. There is great variation in the capacity to make introspective observations and to understand their meaning. Those with little ability to revive unconscious thoughts and comprehend inner meanings need the most guidance from the psychiatrist.

## NOTE-TAKING

It is usually desirable to record some verbatim statements as aids in the evaluation of the patient and his illness. Notes should be taken as unobtrusively as possible and should not be so extensive as to interfere with the free flow of the patient's talk. Reassurance that the notes are confidential should be given, especially with patients who feel uncomfortable about them.

Psychiatrists should be alert to the reaction of the patient. When the interviewer feels uncomfortable about taking notes or belabors getting all the data on paper, the patient is likely to have an unfavorable response. If the patient objects to note-taking, it is best to discontinue it. On the other hand, many patients object when the psychiatrist fails to take notes. They may consider note-taking as a sign of the physician's interest and appreciation of the importance of what is being said.

When notes are not taken during the interview, the physician should take the time to record the data immediately after the patient leaves. However, if no notes are taken during the interview, there is danger that the interviewer's own personality reactions will excessively contaminate the patient's record. So if the psychiatrist doesn't take notes, he might consider sound recordings, which have several advantages over written notes: They are more complete, and they interfere less with spontaneous, easy communication.

## ATTITUDES OF THE PSYCHIATRIST

The psychiatrist needs to listen without reacting, even though he may be reminded of his own disturbing problems or experiences. Therefore, he himself should be relatively well adjusted and have sufficient sources of satisfaction and security. His attitude toward his conflicts must be clarified so that they do not interfere with his emotional stability and his capacity to concentrate while listening to his patient. The psychiatrist's self-respect is of significance, since ability to respect others is dependent to some degree on one's own self-respect.

Complete passivity on the part of the psychiatrist leaves the patient feeling helpless. However, some psychiatrists go to the other extreme: They pontificate and give interpretations based on their own personal reactions rather than those of the patient. When the patient expresses asocial attitudes, such as murderous impulses toward members of his family, the psychiatrist must avoid showing that he is shocked.

The psychiatrist should keep in mind that it is his medical training and experience that sets him apart. His patients may or may not have greater personal assets than he. The fact that a person needs help with his emotional difficulties by no means constitutes any basic inferiority. So an authoritarian attitude on the part of the psychiatrist is uncalled for and interferes with the patient's ability to talk easily. Indeed, it is likely to constitute a traumatic repetition of a cultural or parental pattern. Yet many psychiatrists succumb to the temptation to exert authority as retaliation for annoying authoritarian domination to which they themselves have been subjected.

## INITIAL INTERVIEW

Since patients are usually anxious and may find it difficult to talk, even under the best of circumstances, the setting should be one where there is quiet, privacy, and freedom from interruption. A comfortable chair should be provided for the patient. The psychiatrist should introduce himself and invite the patient to be seated. A courteous, interested, respectful, considerate, and tolerant attitude on the part of the psychiatrist helps put the patient at ease. The emphasis should be on developing a good relationship, since the relationship determines to a great degree the kind of information the patient will give, and the psychotherapeutic interaction depends on the rapport established.

The psychiatrist should avoid seeming to be in a hurry, since such an attitude inhibits the patient. A stilted, detached, or cold attitude or evidences of anxiety, anger, or indifference alienate the patient. The psychiatrist may develop empathy by trying consciously to put himself in the patient's place.

Asking the patient about the chief problems that brought him to the psychiatrist or hospital is usually the best way to start the interview. The patient can then be encouraged to tell the story of his present illness in his own words. All too frequently, patients complain to psychiatrists that other physicians have not permitted them to talk freely about what they consider important. Listening carefully and perceptively is a major ingredient of the interview. When the patient has the psychiatrist's undivided attention, it stimulates him to unburden himself. One patient said that he discontinued going to a certain psychiatrist because the doctor read his mail during the interview, and another patient could not tolerate a doctor who habitually munched on oranges.

The conversation should be guided rather than pursued in the manner of a prosecuting attorney. The latter approach leads to frequent "yes" and "no" answers and a failure to gain a depth of understanding of the problem. Simple explanations, reassurance, and praise may be used to obtain information when the patient needs to have his anxiety alleviated. The use of simple English rather than technical terms helps to overcome barriers in communication. However, the physician should avoid the use of slang or swear words. The patient should be accepted in terms of his own ethical and moral values. The psychiatrist should avoid being moralistic, prejudicial, dictatorial, or punitive. He should convey an atmosphere of being authoritative but not authoritarian.

Free expression is a valuable tool. In describing the associative anamnesis, Deutsch and Murphy emphasized allowing the patient to talk freely and making sound recordings for later close scrutiny of what he has said and how he has said it. What is said and the way it is said are of primary significance, but also to be noted are such nonverbal aspects as gestures and facial expressions. Therefore, the patient is asked to give the bodily sensations accompanying his ideas so that the somatic and psychic components can be observed simultaneously. A comparison of the emotional setting of previous attacks and illnesses with the manifestations occurring during interviews gives clues to which factors are more or less coincidental and which are dynamically related to the syndrome under observation.

The patient is frequently more able to talk about himself during the first interview than later, when he has mobilized defenses and resistances. Quiet attentiveness on the part of the physician lessens the development of anxiety, which leads to blocking and silences. But when the patient does stop talking, the psychiatrist should ask a question or two; prolonged silences are apt to be disconcerting. In asking questions, the psychiatrist should repeat the patient's phrases as much as possible so as to minimize the personal distortions of the physician.

What the information obtained means to the patient is highly important. There should be follow-through on the leads the patient gives. When the meaning is not clear to the psychiatrist, tactful questioning is indicated. Skillful, discreet, diplomatic questioning enables the interviewer to bring up intimate topics the patient might otherwise be reluctant to discuss. The psychiatrist whose demeanor is comfortable and nonapologetic can be accepted when he asks highly personal questions about such subjects as sex. The more intimate topics can be introduced by asking less emotionally charged questions, such as those concerning physical development. As a natural sequence, the patient's attitudes and feelings about the topic can be brought up. If the patient becomes unduly upset, the subject should be dropped.

When the patient belabors a subject, change the topic. If he persists in dwelling on it in a garrulous or circumstantial way, it is appropriate to say, "There are other important things for us to cover." Then bring up another subject of possible significance.

There is need for flexibility and individualizing. Flexibility implies altering techniques to suit different patients and to suit one patient at different times. The psychiatrist should develop variations in technique that are suited to his personality. Psychiatrists taught a specific method of interviewing usually deviate in certain ways, although they may conform to the general approach.

## INTERPRETATION

Discussion of present problems gives the psychiatrist an opportunity to ask whether there have been similar problems in the past. This approach gives him more information about the past and also gives him insight into the origin of sensitivities. In the first contact with the patient, however, interpretations are to be avoided or, at most, given with the greatest caution, unless the patient has provided unusually strong evidence in support of them. It is better to let the patient reach his own conclusions because then they have more meaning for him.

Avoid pointing out inconsistencies until later interviews, when rapport is well established. Patients need to maintain self-esteem and self-respect. Bringing up his deficiencies is difficult and painful. Since the patient has a need to feel pride in himself, the psychiatrist should not embarrass him.

## TERMINATING THE INTERVIEW

The patient may be warned that only a few minutes more time is available. Such a statement should be given during an appropriate pause rather than injected in the middle of a discussion that seems highly meaningful to the patient. The psychiatrist may point out to the patient that he has asked many questions and then ask the patient to raise questions of his own or to mention something else that he feels is particularly significant.

If no further interviews are anticipated, the psychiatrist can give a brief summary and recommendation. If further interviews are contemplated, the psychiatrist may state that there is need for more discussion, express continued interest, and suggest that the patient think over the topics covered and what he might wish to add during the next interview.

Recommendations for further interviews should be accompanied by a proposed plan for investigation in order to reach a decision about treatment. Or, if there has been sufficient clarification, the psychiatrist may recommend a tentative or specific plan of treatment. It can be simply stated that more time is needed in order to give an adequate opinion. This can be reassuring to a patient who does not want a premature formulation based on insufficient knowledge.

## SUBSEQUENT INTERVIEWS

Subsequent interviews should continue the understanding and therapeutic approach initiated in the first contact. The patient should again be permitted to express what he wishes. If there is a lag in getting started, the psychiatrist may ask him what has been on his mind, how he has been feeling, or what has been happening. The patient may be encouraged to expand on topics introduced during the first interview, or inquiry may be made about areas that were insufficiently covered or were not discussed at all. If during the initial interview there was interruption of a topic that seemed highly significant, the psychiatrist may reintroduce the topic and suggest that they continue where they left off.

To avoid giving excessive direction, the psychiatrist should permit pauses so that the patient can organize his thoughts. If the pause becomes awkward, a question can be asked about the previous statement. Long silences are apt to indicate preoccupation with the thought content concerning personal conflicts, anxiety about revealing too much, or exhaustion of the subject under discussion.

When the patient is having difficulty bringing out pertinent data, questions that will cover his background and clarify his problem are indicated. A play-by-play account of his daily twenty-four-hour pattern is useful. Note under which circumstances the patient feels at his worst and at his best. How do the symptoms affect the patient? Do they fluctuate from day to day? From morning to evening? From hour to hour? Are they affected by eating, exercise, work, social, or other particular situations? What brings relief, temporary or otherwise? Are there known precipitating factors, such as worry, accidents, disappointments, bereavements, financial difficulties, or other stresses? Did relatives or friends have similar symptoms, and what feelings did the patient have about them and their illnesses? The aim of understanding and modifying disordered patterns should take precedence over a descriptive classification of the patient. A dynamic formulation of the whole problem is the most significant part of the complete diagnosis.

If the patient shows some asocial behavior, the psychiatrist should continue an attitude of analyzing and understanding; he should not condone or condemn. The patient is apt to withdraw further if blame is placed on him or his relatives. There should be respect for his defenses and opinions. Attention should be paid to the patient's strengths as well as to his problems. The psychiatrist should focus on relevant material, so that coverage is as comprehensive as possible. When rapport has become well established, some challenging of the patient's ideas may be interjected.

## SPECIAL TYPES OF INTERVIEWS

Interview techniques need to be varied according to the personality reactions of the patient, the type and degree of illness, and the objectives of the interview. Varying degrees of permissiveness and directiveness may be used. Different approaches to different patients are indicated, and the approach to the same patient should be changed when appropriate.

### NONDIRECTIVE INTERVIEW

This method, as espoused by Rogers, emphasizes minimal activity on the part of the interviewer. When there are pauses, the interviewer repeats the last words of the patient. Rogers has called attention to a significant defect in much interviewing: All too frequently the psychiatrist talks too much, expounds on his own ideas and philosophy, and implants his own ideas through suggestion. When the doctor monopolizes much of the interview time, the patient has no opportunity to express himself.

However, extreme nondirectiveness leaves the patient feeling abandoned and is likely to create considerable anxiety. Only a limited number of well-oriented, intelligent patients appear to be suitable for a strictly nondirective approach. Most patients need guidance from an experienced interviewer and are stimulated and reassured by some verbal interchange.

## CONSULTATION INTERVIEW

In a consultation, where it is necessary to give an opinion after a limited period of interviewing time, a more directive approach is required than when a long-term therapeutic contact is planned. Therefore, as much essential information as possible must be obtained during the interview. However, such interviews usually lack depth of understanding and therapeutic value to the patient.

## STRESS INTERVIEW

This type of interview has its advocates and has a minor place in the armamentarium of interview techniques.

Most patients feel some degree of anxiety or other emotion when talking to a psychiatrist. Through his manner or a word of reassurance or praise the psychiatrist often can decrease this emotion so that the patient can continue to tell his story. However, certain patients are monotonously repetitious or show insufficient emotionality for motivation. Apathy, indifference, and emotional blunting are not conducive to discussion of personality problems. In patients with such reactions, stimulation of emotions can be constructive. These patients may require probing, challenging, or confrontation in order to arouse feelings that will promote progress in furthering understanding. For example, the *la belle indifférence* of the hysteric may be converted into anxiety so that the patient can experience enough discomfort to talk about his conflicts.

## INTERVIEW WITH ANXIOUS PATIENT

In patients with anxiety attacks, attention should be paid to what thoughts and environmental strains precipitate or increase the anxiety. When the stresses are not evident, prolonged careful investigation may be necessary to elucidate the sources of the emotion. Repressive or suppressive forces may have to be gradually overcome and analysis made of the current situations that evoke feelings. The original stimuli may have been applied symbolically to other people, and much time and patience are necessary to disentangle the complicated elaborations that have developed. Revival of unconscious mechanisms through such techniques as free association, dream analysis, and hypnoanalysis may eventually result in definitive insights. Endogenous factors and a series of exogenous circumstances, rather than a single traumatic event, are usually responsible for the illness.

Frequently, only vague feelings of apprehension or the bodily accompaniments of anxiety are evident. In such cases, the painful emotion may have been repressed, but it may continue to operate in the unconscious by producing psychopathological reactions.

## INTERVIEW WITH PATIENT DISPLAYING PSYCHOPHYSIOLOGICAL SYMPTOMS

Psychophysiological symptoms are present in a wide variety of clinical syndromes, whether the illness is primarily structural, psychological, or psychophysiological. Such symptoms may be related to either overt or hidden emotions. Careful study of the correlations between stresses, resultant feelings, and bodily symptoms leads to an understanding of the mechanisms. Much psychosomatic research has been concerned with the documentation of such reactions.

When the temporal coincidence of stress, emotions, and physiological reactions is unknown, enlisting the aid of the patient as a collaborator is helpful. Skillful use of this approach in interviewing and demonstrable measurement of physiological variables frequently overcome lack of awareness of the psychophysiological relationships and result in clarification of reactions and in therapeutic progress.

## INTERVIEW WITH DEPRESSED PATIENT

Depressed patients have a short attention span and should have relatively brief interviews. Their tendency to reiterate in a destructive, self-deprecatory way may require active interruption by the psychiatrist. Many patients with depressive illnesses do not make clear statements of mood disorder. Instead they may express their illness through physical complaints or such symptoms as insomnia, diurnal changes in feelings, irritability, or difficulty in concentration. Clarification of the affective nature of the disorder may come by obtaining expressions of futility, hopelessness, self-depreciation, shame, and thinly veiled hostility.

The possibility of suicidal preoccupation should be investigated. The patient may be asked about his interest in life, whether life has seemed to be worth living, and whether he has had thoughts of dying or of taking his own life. If there have been suicidal attempts or thoughts, questions should be asked concerning what he thinks about the reactions of others to these attempts or to his death and what means of suicide he has contemplated.

Since death is a sensitive, taboo topic, the psychiatrist may fear that talking about it will result in an increase in anxiety, depression, or suicidal preoccupation in his patient. He may, therefore, avoid frank discussion of it. But if questions about suicide are asked tactfully, they are not disturbing and do not increase suicidal ideas. On the contrary, many patients feel relieved to be able to talk to a confidant about such thoughts. Verbal expression may lessen the need to take action. Words of reassurance, such as a statement that death is frequently considered as a possible solution to emotional problems, can be helpful.

### INTERVIEW WITH DELUSIONAL PATIENT

The psychiatrist should show interest, understanding, and receptiveness. He should try to show that he realizes the patient is expressing thoughts and feelings with significant meaning, although the meaning may not be clear at the time. Since the psychiatrist should represent to the patient a person soundly based in reality, he must not subscribe to the patient's delusions. He should neither agree with nor contradict the patient. Rather, he should try to find out more about the nature of the delusional thoughts and who the patient feels is responsible for them. A skeptical attitude may help raise doubts in the patient's mind and may eventually lead him to an understanding of the delusions as an irrational outgrowth of his conflicts or illness.

### INTERVIEW WITH THE WITHDRAWN PATIENT

If a patient is absorbed with his inner world of fantasy and is unable to talk spontaneously about his feelings, the psychiatrist must be active in asking questions. He should pay close attention to the patient's reactions and should change the subject when there is difficulty in discussing certain areas of conflict. Shifting to subjects that are less disturbing helps the patient accept the psychiatrist and paves the way for the establishment of rapport, which can be used later in discussing topics initially avoided.

In extreme withdrawal, as found in the patient with catatonic stupor, there should be frequent, brief visits. When there is no response to questions about the patient's feelings, the physician may express an interest in talking later to the patient and explain in a kindly manner that he will be available to help when the patient is ready to communicate with him. The mute patient may be acutely aware of what is going on, and care needs to be exercised to avoid saying anything to him or about him to others in his presence that may antagonize and further alienate him. Some seemingly inaccessible patients may show some signs of reacting to the talk of the psychiatrist through gestures or changes in facial expression. Such nonverbal communications should be carefully observed and should influence what is said to the patient. They may be precursors to verbal contact.

### INTERVIEW WITH MANIC PATIENT

Good rapport is not possible with a highly excited patient. The examiner should maintain a calm, receptive attitude and note carefully the thought content. Overtalkative disturbed patients give valuable information about underlying conflicts that they are not likely to bring up when they regain better control of themselves.

## INTERVIEWING RELATIVES

The families of patients can give much valuable data to help the psychiatrist understand the illness, the prognosis, and the therapeutic potentialities. It is important to have contact with them to give them some understanding of the problem and to enlist their cooperation. Similar help can often be gained by obtaining information from friends, associates at work, or other significant people in the patient's life. Most relatives of patients, particularly those of hospitalized patients, want to be acquainted with the psychiatrist and to obtain information about the illness, such as its probable duration and the plan for treatment.

It is essential to interview relatives of children, the mentally retarded, psychotic patients who cannot give a clear history, and patients with character disorders, who notoriously misconstrue or misrepresent facts. Relatives of patients with other illnesses can give significant supplemental information and express points of view that add to the understanding of the problem. When a patient has marital conflicts, it is necessary to see the spouse. Distortions due to thinking difficulties, repressions, and emotional coloring of the data can then be clarified or corrected. For example, a person with a depressive illness may state that he has never been happy and has always been a failure, whereas he has really been successful.

The patient should usually be told about contemplated interviews with relatives before they are held and should be reassured that his confidence will not be betrayed. It can be pointed out that emphasis will be placed on gaining additional information that will be helpful in understanding him and that, during the interview, the relative will be encouraged to do most of the talking. When the patient is strongly opposed to the psychiatrist's interviewing his relatives, the interviews should usually be deferred or not held at all, unless the patient is a child or grossly psychotic. When the patient objects to having his own doctor interview his relatives, the interviews can be carried out by another staff physician or by a social worker, if one is available.

The psychiatrist who identifies with his patient and has heard sharp condemnations of relatives may find it difficult to avoid being antagonistic to the family. Contrariwise, the psychiatrist who is irritated by an uncooperative, hostile patient may be excessively sympathetic with relatives. In guarding against such reactions, he must keep in mind that an understanding tolerance is due both his patients and their relatives.

There are likely to be many discrepancies in the accounts given by different individuals. Relatives are often fearful and antagonistic and strongly influenced by shame because of psychiatric illness in the family and guilt over real or fancied mistakes they have made in relating to the patient. The information from various sources must be evaluated carefully. History obtained from relatives may have greater validity than that given by the patient. Although it is important to learn what the past events were, it is even more important to know what they meant to the patient and how they affected him. In weighing the data, the psychiatrist must consider the fact that the patient's fantasies may be of greater significance than reality.

## REFERENCES

Blum, R. H. *The Management of the Doctor-Patient Relationship*. McGraw-Hill, New York, 1960.

Carrel, A. *Man the Unknown*. Harper & Row, New York, 1939.

Deutsch, F., and Murphy, W. F. *The Clinical Interview*, vol. 1. International Universities Press, New York, 1955.

Ebaugh, F. G. Evaluation of interviewing techniques and principles of psychotherapy for the general practitioner. J. Omaha Mid-West Clin. Soc., 9: 29, 1948.

Finesinger, J. E. Psychiatric interviewing: Principles and procedure in insight therapy. Amer. J. Psychiat., 105: 187, 1948.

Freud, S. The dynamics of the transference. In *Collected Papers*, vol. 2, p. 312. Hogarth Press, London, 1946.

Freud, S. Fragment of an analysis of a case of hysteria. In *Collected Papers*, vol. 3, p. 13. Hogarth Press, London, 1946.

Gill, M., Newman, R., and Redlich, F. C. *The Initial Interview in Psychiatric Practice*. International Universities Press, New York, 1954.

Lewin, B. D. Counter-transference in the technique of medical practice. Psychosom. Med., 8: 195, 1946.

Menninger, K. *A Manual for Psychiatric Case Study*. Grune & Stratton, New York, 1952.

Peabody, F. W. *Doctor and Patient*. Macmillan, New York, 1930.

Rogers, C. R. *Client-Centered Therapy*. Houghton Mifflin, Boston, 1951.

Stevenson, I. *Medical History-Taking*. Hoeber Medical Division, Harper & Row, New York, 1960.

Sullivan, H. S. *The Psychiatric Interview*. W. W. Norton, New York, 1954.

Whitehorn, J. C. Guide to interviewing and clinical personality study. Arch. Neurol. Psychiat., 52: 197, 1944.

# CHAPTER TWO

# Psychiatric History and Mental Status

## WILLIAM L. SANDS, M.D.

THE PURPOSE of the psychiatric history is to furnish the psychiatrist with an understanding of his patient's personal development, the environment in which it occurred, the significance of the principal figures in that environment, and the patient's adaptive techniques, such as defense mechanisms and security operations. In short, the history attempts to answer the question: "How did this patient become the person I see before me now?"

The history is also a current commentary. It includes a description of the patient's present environment and the stresses and sources of pleasure that characterize it. It also contains a description of the persons who are significant to the patient and who now have an influence on him.

There is no one correct form for eliciting or recording the psychiatric history. However, it is important for a student to have a form, so that he learns to cover the important developmental areas. When the student has gained enough experience, he will doubtlessly modify whatever form he has learned to suit his own personality and his own approach. The outline suggested below is offered in this light.

The patient presents himself to the psychiatrist, or he is brought by his family, because of some difficulty he is experiencing. This is the matter that is usually uppermost in his mind during the initial interview. Sometimes, however, a patient who is denying the life difficulty or is unaware of it has uppermost in his mind a desire to impress the psychiatrist with the normality of his behavior and the exaggerated concern of his family. No matter how the patient is presented to the psychiatrist, the current situation or problem is his chief concern. This should always be recorded in the patient's own words and be recognized as the *chief complaint*.

The patient's concern with his present situation does not always match the psychiatrist's desire to understand how the present problem evolved from the past. The psychiatrist's chief asset in eliciting the history is his ability to listen critically. The less threatening he is to the patient, the more the patient will trust him with the details of his personal life. Therefore, the order in which the psychiatrist obtains the history will usually have to differ from the order in which he will record it in final form.

The psychiatric history should be a written document. By recording his data, the psychiatrist is compelled to organize the facts he has obtained into a meaningful story. The most useful form for a history is often a chronological one in which the present illness is shown evolving as part of the individual's life story. When reviewing the written history, the psychiatrist may note what information he has failed to obtain. This review can enable him to become aware of the areas which have not been satisfactorily covered and the questions which may still lack answers. Such study may indicate areas which the patient may have avoided or which the psychiatrist himself may unconsciously have omitted. Becoming aware of these gaps should lead to inquiring after the reason for their existence. This, in turn, may yield fruitful clues for the approaching therapeutic endeavor.

A written history is also a source of information to others. This is particularly true in an institutional setting, where the psychiatrist may be employed only temporarily. Together with the mental status examination, the history should provide a picture of the patient at that particular time, which may be of importance in the future.

The beginner often asks: "How many sessions should be spent eliciting the history?" The answer depends to some extent on the purpose of the psychiatrist's encounter with the patient. For example, an interview to determine an individual's fitness for military service will differ from one that leads to outlining a course of therapy. The latter demands a more accurate diagnosis and evaluation of the individual's personality structure and patterns of adaptation.

In an institutional setting, the psychiatrist may be able to spend several hours a day with the patient to elicit his history and then organize and record the data within the first few days of admission. With an outpatient, this is not usually feasible. Moreover, the outpatient is usually quite concerned with how his current stresses and discomforts interfere with his job or home situation. Therefore, the first few sessions represent a combination of maneuvers, permitting the patient some time in which to focus on the present situation but also, for a part of each session, directing his attention back to the developmental periods so that the psychiatrist may arrive at a dynamic formulation, establish a tentative diagnosis, and plan the optimal therapeutic approach. This is usually done with the indication that, once the history has been obtained, the therapist will have fewer direct questions and the patient will be expected to carry more of the sessions' direction by sharing the thoughts that come to mind.

The psychiatric history may arbitrarily be divided into eight sections: (1) identification of the patient; (2) chief complaint and present illness; (3) personal history; (4) family history; (5) mental status examination; (6) physical examination; (7) psychodynamic formulation; and (8) diagnosis, prognosis, and recommendations.

## IDENTIFICATION OF THE PATIENT

This should include the following details: name, age, sex, ethnic and cultural background, marital status, occupation, and means of referral. It may include a statement about the patient's housing situation. If the patient is being admitted to a hospital, the section should indicate whether this is the first such admission or whether this admission represents a rehospitalization for his psychiatric disorder.

## CHIEF COMPLAINT AND PRESENT ILLNESS

### CHIEF COMPLAINT

This should always be stated in the patient's own words. Although the patient's family may view the problem quite differently, the manner in which events are perceived by the patient himself will be of the greatest importance to the examiner. There will be times when the subtleties of the patient's perceptions may not be apparent to the psychiatrist until some time after their collaborative effort has been under way. A verbatim record of the chief complaint permits the psychiatrist to review it periodically in the attempt to learn why events appeared as they did to the emotionally disturbed patient. Improvement in the psychotic patient may be gauged in part by his own ability to reconsider earlier perceptions of his situation. As the patient improves, he and the psychiatrist may acquire understanding of how distorted perceptions came about. Although both patient and doctor may not succeed in achieving this understanding, they should certainly strive to acquire it.

### PRESENT ILLNESS

This section must set forth the story of the present illness as the patient has become aware of it.

*Interviewing the patient.* The psychiatrist will rarely obtain the history of the present illness in chronological order. The usual patient will be somewhat repetitious in discussing his illness, giving emphasis to those aspects that most trouble him. He usually intersperses his story with digressions and follows association trails that may be extremely informative to the psychiatrist even though they are not directly related to the present illness.

In eliciting the history, the psychiatrist must listen patiently, permitting the patient to tell his story spontaneously, and must carefully observe the patient's behavior, changes in posture, intonations, facial expressions, and emotional reactions to the various subjects discussed. If the patient is spontaneously productive, it is wise to permit him free rein in giving his account of what has befallen him and to limit questions as much as possible. The patient must be aware of the psychiatrist's sympathetic interest and willingness to be helpful; and, it is hoped, he will perceive the psychiatrist's respect for him as an individual. Especially at this stage, the patient must learn that, no matter what he has to report, the psychiatrist, in contrast to his family or friends, will listen uncritically and will not argue or scold, attempt to deny the patient's perception of events, or ridicule him for reporting strange ideas.

If the patient does not report any stresses or events which may have precipitated the present episode, the psychiatrist must inquire about them. He must obtain a clear description of each symptom or sign of illness of which the patient is aware. Where a symptom constitutes a prominent part of the illness, the details of its first occurrence must be obtained. The social context in which symptoms arose must be presented clearly.

*The report.*    From the wealth of data that the examiner has obtained, he must extract and organize those items which will provide an intelligible and sequential presentation of the development of the present illness. This presentation is rarely in the same order in which the psychiatrist has obtained the data. Not infrequently, organizing the data into such a structured history will bring to notice significant connections of which the patient may not have been aware and which may have therapeutic import.

This section should record whether the patient has encountered such difficulties before. If there were previous occurrences, the dates and outcome of each episode should be included. If there were earlier psychiatric treatments or previous hospitalizations, they should be recorded here, giving the name and address of the psychiatrist or the hospital and dates of admission and discharge. With written consent from the patient, summaries of previous hospitalizations should be obtained. The mode of therapy employed and outcome of each hospital admission should be recorded. If there were hospitalizations for nonpsychiatric illnesses, they should be indicated in the next section, the personal history.

A psychotic patient may be unable to give a description of the current problem and may even deny that any exists. In such a case, the informant who supplies the information should be clearly identified, his relationship to the patient stated explicitly, and the problem reproduced in *his* own words. It may occasionally be advantageous to have statements about the problem from several informants.

## PERSONAL HISTORY

The history of each period of the patient's life—infancy, childhood, adolescence, and adulthood—should be described separately. If the history is written in this chronological fashion, the behavior patterns which the individual has developed as he has matured emerge clearly; the environmental forces that have helped form them will also become apparent. Similarly, limiting physical or social factors can also be appreciated and their effects understood in relation to the period in which they occurred. The present illness may then be seen as the inevitable consequence of the patient's life story. For each period, the psychiatrist should record his survey of the patient's social, sexual, and vocational functioning, along with the inhibitions imposed by excessive or inappropriate fears and guilt, and the sources of the patient's successful pursuit of pleasure.

### INFANCY

Here firsthand data can be obtained only from parents. The patient and other informants can merely report what they have been told. The psychiatrist wishes to learn all he can about the physical and emotional climate into which the patient was born. Therefore, he attempts to learn whether the patient was a planned child; what the physical health of the mother was during pregnancy; what the nature of her relationship with the father was at that time; some details concerning the labor and delivery; the health of the patient during the neonatal period; the age at which he first sat up, walked, and talked; the method of toilet training used and the age at which sphincter control was achieved. An attempt should be made to discover what the patient's patterns of eating and playing were and what his parents' attitudes were to his behavior as an infant.

*Physical motility.* Infants display considerable variation in physical motility. Some are relatively passive; even when hungry, they may display little more than increased eye movement or head turning. Others inform their mothers of hunger or other discomfort with loud noises, much crying and thrashing about in the crib, and sucking movements that may eventually carry the baby's whole fist into his mouth. There are indications that much of this variation is inborn, but parents may respond to it with attitudes ranging from guilt or displeasure to pride, depending on what they think their baby *should* display. When the infant's behavior does not meet the parents' expectation, a cycle may be established: disapproval from the parent, stemming from his own anxiety, engenders anxiety in the infant, which then causes more anxiety in the parent. Such cycles sometimes constitute the dominant pattern of interaction between parents and growing children and often have serious emotional consequences.

*Sleeping patterns.* A similar inquiry should be made into sleeping arrangements. It is desirable to know what they were during infancy, and whether and when they were subsequently altered. If an infant shared the intimacy of his mother's bedroom but was displaced by his father's return from military service or the birth of a sibling, the displacement could play a major role in his subsequent emotional development and affect his relationship with his father or sibling.

**Significance.** A child's normal emotional development is related to his mother's ability to nurture him. Therefore, information concerning the mother's emotional and physical health during pregnancy and during the patient's infancy is of great importance. Whether the mother was able to feed and care for her baby in a patient, tender, and loving manner is of more significance than whether he was bottle-fed or breast-fed.

The way in which toilet training was carried out probably exemplifies the subsequent relationship between the patient and the mother. The mother who is severe in this matter is often equally strict in setting other standards for the child to meet during the first decade of development.

Serious physical illness during the first year of life, in which such vital functions as respiration or feeding are threatened, may initiate life-long anxiety in the child. Physical illness that leaves permanent residue or congenital defects that limit the attainment of physical skills damage the growing child's self-confidence and self-esteem, qualities which will be necessary for his success throughout the remainder of childhood and, indeed, into adulthood.

## Childhood

This section can be divided into two periods: from age one up to entry into school, and from then until the onset of puberty. Here, as in the section concerned with infancy, the psychiatrist needs to gain an understanding of the physical and emotional climate in which the patient was raised. He attempts to learn what the patient's personality was like during those childhood years and whether there were marked changes in dominant personality patterns and, if there were, what caused them. He tries to elicit a history of the usual childhood illnesses and how they were tolerated by the patient and his parents; a history of other illnesses, injuries, or hospitalizations, with emphasis upon the emotional reaction to them by the patient, his parents, and other people important to him; and a history of serious illnesses or deaths in other members of the family and how they affected the patient. The psychiatrist attempts to learn the patient's reaction to beginning school and to the subsequent school years; the history of any truancy, school phobias, academic difficulties, or outstanding achievements; the level of his academic performance; the pattern of his relationship to peers both in school and outside; his reaction to any moves from one school to another; and family attitudes toward such activities as school performance, religious instruction, church attendance, music lessons, athletic participation, etc.

It is important to note whether the parental expectations were consistent with community norms or significantly deviant. If the latter, how did the parents justify themselves to the child, and how did he accept the parents' standards? What was the relationship between the parents during this period? To what extent did the child observe affectionate display between his parents, and to what extent was affection openly given to him? The variation in family attitudes toward open display of affection or candid acceptance of children's sexual curiosity is still very great in our society. What was the parents' attitude to the child's sexual curiosity and to any questions he may have asked about sex? How did they react to childhood sexual experimentation?

Other data to be described in this section include the patient's reaction to the birth of younger siblings; the nature of the siblings' relationship as they grew up; whether the child played alone or usually with playmates; and whether there were enduring friendships or infrequent changes of playmates. In stress situations, did the patient show somatization responses? If so, of what sort were they, and were they recognized as being emotional in origin by the parents?

The psychiatrist also attempts to learn evidences of the patient's sexual interest or activity. What outlets were permitted him for expression of hostility; what evidences of excessive or inappropriate fearfulness became manifest; was there a history of nightmares, temper tantrums, enuresis, or nail-biting; what avenues for pleasurable experience were provided; and what techniques did the growing child employ to bolster self-esteem and self-pride?

Here again, as in the section concerning infancy, an inquiry into sleeping patterns and sleeping arrangements must be made.

**Significance.** In childhood, as in infancy, attainment of appropriate skills increases pride and self-confidence and encourages the individual to experiment further with his ever-expanding universe. During this period, the accepted standards of society must be learned so that the child can function away from home, at school and at play, and learn that he can operate successfully without the constant surveillance of a protecting parent.

In learning the rules of his particular society, the child inevitably undergoes some frustrations. If the consequent anger is not to be internalized, he must be permitted outlets for its expression. The psychiatrist must learn what the patient was forbidden by his family and what he was allowed, and how successfully this formula was integrated into his personality. What techniques were available to the growing child for expressing anger? Were his independence and self-reliance fostered or inhibited? Some of this information will come to the psychiatrist as concrete evidence; but some he will have to deduce. He should, of course, distinguish between concrete information and deduction in his report.

The significance of childhood illnesses depends particularly on the reaction of the parents and on how much anxiety they may have transmitted to the child. The child's life-long attitude toward illness is determined in large part by what happens during these formative years. For example, there are some individuals who respond to illness as though they were invulnerable or even immortal and others who react to a minor upper respiratory infection as if it were a serious disease. Some people minimize physical illnesses, while others dramatize them and appear to delight in telling friends the details of every symptom. These different attitudes originate early in life, as a result of attitudes toward medical treatment and relationships within the family.

A further illustration contrasts treatment attitudes. A generation ago, all children who had rheumatic fever were kept in bed for periods of six months to a year, with their physical activities permanently restricted thereafter. Now practice calls for continued activity, depending on the patient's physical condition. The emphasis is on maximum participation in all the activities in which the child's peers engage so that his self-image is not damaged and he does not develop false ideas of required immobilization.

## ADOLESCENCE

The same questions asked about previous developmental periods must be reviewed here. The goal is to ascertain the adolescent's adaptive techniques for building self-pride, coping with anxiety, and expressing anger. The particular demands made upon him during this period are both biological and social, the one relating to the onset of puberty and the appearance of sexual impulses and the other to his scholastic preparations for a career.

The psychiatrist attempts to learn what the patient's reaction was to the physical changes of puberty: for the girl, emotional reactions to breast development, preparation for menarche, circumstances of and reaction to first menstruation, pattern of reaction to subsequent menstrual periods; for the boy, preparation for nocturnal emissions, reaction to them and to spontaneous erections; for both sexes, masturbation fantasies and behavior, homosexual episodes, heterosexual behavior, and dating patterns. The reaction of the patient's family to his adolescent sexual behavior is also an important part of this historical development. Was the family's attitude consistent with that of the community or at variance with it? Did the parents instill feelings of guilt in response to the patient's inevitable sexual curiosity? The absence of memories of sexual thoughts during adolescence indicates an inhibition fostered by parental attitudes that condemned sexuality on moral grounds. How much guilt was engendered by masturbation? Under what circumstances did the patient acquire sexual information? In what situations did sexual behavior first occur, and what was the adolescent's subsequent emotional reaction?

The psychiatrist should also ascertain whether the adolescent was isolated or whether he was accepted by his peers and found membership in some group, thus building self-esteem. Were there abrupt changes in the patterns of relating to others?

School performance may be one guide to the adolescent's general functioning. It is also an indication of his ability to organize his energies into constructive patterns and of his capacity to plan meaningfully for adult responsibility. How much day-dreaming occurred, and to what extent did fantasy fulfillment take the place of realistic goal-planning? What were the evidences of rebellion against family standards in the patient's attempt to forge his own identity? Or were family standards accepted, and to what degree?

**Significance.** The adaptive patterns the individual unconsciously develops to survive in his particular environment become clearer as he nears adulthood. Many emotional difficulties become apparent during this period if the adaptive techniques prove inadequate to the increasing social, vocational, and sexual demands made on the adolescent by his body or his environment. If the adolescent encounters defeats in some areas, he may be less inclined to try again. Withdrawal from social relationships or from previously enjoyed activities are clues to malfunction. If the adolescent avoids activities in which his peers participate, the reason for the avoidance should be elucidated. The psychiatrist may suspect the existence of excessive or inappropriate fearfulness and attempt to confirm his suspicions. This, in turn, should lead to an identification of the substitute activities through which the adolescent attempted to compensate for the social defeats represented by his withdrawal and for the consequent damage to his self-esteem and pride.

The relative amounts of passivity and self-assertion that characterize the patient become clearer during this period and establish themselves more firmly as patterned behavior. The psychiatrist should learn how these modes developed in the patient. Which were subtly or openly encouraged by the family? Which techniques did the patient apparently find successful in achieving acceptance by parents and other significant figures? If the adaptive patterns that were successful in achieving emotional security in the family are unsuccessful in coping with others in the outside world, the child often becomes confused and uncertain. The psychiatrist must learn whether the patient resolved this and similar conflicts by adopting more successful survival techniques or by withdrawing from the competitive struggle.

Withdrawal always signifies defeat and results in decreased self-esteem.

In order to participate successfully in society as an adult, the adolescent must integrate into his personality those techniques necessary for achieving a relatively happy and mature adaptation. These include such qualities as healthy self-assertion, vocational capacity, a realistic self-image, and an ability to form relationships with others characterized by candor, trust, and sincerity. It is important to note that societies other than our own may emphasize other qualities. The standards that an individual must aspire to are determined largely by the society of which he is a part.

Among the experiences that increase self-confidence are those that require some initiative. Often these include some experimentation with behavior which the adolescent knows does not meet strict parental approval. In every generation, such experiments and other adolescent rebellions have engendered anxiety and reproach among adults. When the United States was primarily a rural country, such rebellion was exemplified by smoking cornsilk behind the barn and sparking in the family buggy. Today, in our largely urban society it appears to be manifested mostly in sexual behavior, echoing society as a whole, which has moved away from the double standard.

The psychiatrist must learn whether the patient was able to experiment with new ideas during adolescence. These need not have been in the sexual area only. It is not unusual for adolescents to question religious practices or affiliations. The psychiatrist must learn whether such attempts by the adolescent to forge his own identity were acceptable to parents or whether they were condemned and, if so, how severely. If adolescence was entirely free of such rebellious episodes, it may mean that self-assertion was inhibited. Such inhibition should then show up in other behavioral foci. Evidence of guilt should be noted, along with evidence of exaggerated conformity after attempts at rebellion which had been defeated by what the adolescent perceived as excessive parental disapproval. If the patient did conform in this way, the psychiatrist must look for signs of disproportionate fear in his subsequent behavior.

Mature, emotionally secure parents recognize that adolescents need to learn from experience, and they permit experimentation while providing guidance when it is sought. The parents' own practices, which sometimes differ from what they preach, are known to the adolescent. His ability to adopt parental standards as his own eventually or to reject them is an indication of a secure parent-child relationship.

## Adulthood

The onset of adulthood is arbitrarily delineated for the purposes of history-taking. Graduation from high school may conveniently end the section on adolescence, but adulthood may truly be said to begin when the individual moves from his parents' home and becomes self-supporting. Entry into college is frequently associated with leaving home, and for many individuals it represents the beginning of adulthood.

Whether the patient goes from high school directly into college, into the labor market, or into military service, the history must record whether or not the move was a result of his own desire and planning, and what his reaction to it was. It must show how the patient attempted to satisfy prestige needs; how he coped with fears, anxieties, and hostilities; and whether his techniques for doing so differed from methods employed earlier. Did he allow himself to become aware of anxious and hostile feelings, or did he have to deny them? Were these feelings accompanied by excessive or inappropriate guilt, and did this represent a change from previous patterns?

Career planning, sexual experimenting, courtship, and marriage—all should be described in this section; their pattern will probably be consistent with the patterns for handling emotional drives which have been seen evolving throughout the history. The psychiatrist should be alert to repetitive patterns manifested in job performance and in social relationships. If there were many job changes, why did they occur? Does the patient always ascribe the precipitating cause to factors outside himself, or does he recognize his own degree of responsibility? Is the patient able to develop close relationships, or are his relationships always casual? Does he maintain friendships, or are they always short-lived and changeable? What evidence is there of his capacity to love others? Is he exploitative toward his girl friend, wife, or children? Does he give as well as take? The history must record evidences of emotional crises and difficulties as the patient progresses through adulthood; it must tell how they were resolved and whether they recurred. It should also note, as in earlier periods, the effect on the patient of physical illness and of the diseases and deaths of parents and other people who are important to him.

*Marriage.* If the patient has been married, a detailed history of the relationship must be included. What first attracted the patient to the partner? Which person took the lead during courtship? What difficulties were encountered? Did either family object to the relationship? If so for what reason? To what extent did the couple understand each other's goals for the marriage? Were they able to discuss such potential areas of difference as church affiliation? Were children desired? Since raising a family is a cultural expectation, it is of great importance if either partner did not want children. If both desired to have a family, did they agree on its size? Were they in agreement about contraceptive techniques?

What has been the history of the sexual relationship during the marriage? Merely recording the fact that the patient enjoys sexual intercourse does not provide the type of information the psychiatrist requires. What is the usual coital pattern? Who takes the lead in initiating sexual activity? Are both partners orgastic? Is there a history of impotence or frigidity? Have there been abortions? How did the patient react to each pregnancy and each childbirth? Which were planned and which were not? What is the history of extramarital episodes? What was the patient's emotional response if either he or his mate proved to be sterile? Did the couple adopt children? If so, how did they go about it?

*Significance.* The psychiatrist must view alleged motivation critically, knowing that manifest behavior often serves to hide unacceptable impulses and tendencies. For example, marriage may sometimes represent refuge to an individual tormented by unacceptable homosexual impulses. Marriage may represent an easy escape from the frightening challenge of college discipline, or it may express spiteful defiance of parents. Of course it may also represent a mature readiness for self-realization and the ability to take an adult place in the community. A detailed history of the courtship and marriage can indicate to the psychiatrist the extent to which the patient relies on wishful thinking instead of planning maturely to reach his goals. When wishful thinking does occur, its effects are usually evident in other areas of behavior as well.

The significance of abortions may not be revealed until later periods of emotional depression. During depressions occurring in the fifth or sixth decades of the patient's life, the psychiatrist frequently hears expressions of remorse and guilt concerning abortions that occurred twenty or more years earlier.

When listening to descriptions of children, the patient's psychiatrist must also be alert to any correlations that there might be between the patient's attitude toward them and his attitudes toward his own siblings or other significant persons in his family of origin. Often, the patient's attitudes toward his children represent unconscious displacements of emotion from significant figures of his childhood.

## FAMILY HISTORY

This section should include a description of the parents and siblings in the patient's family of origin. Although some mention of these important persons probably occurred in the patient's account of his life history, they should be described individually and in greater detail here. Their names, ages, occupations, economic and social status, marital records, and history of physical and emotional illness should all be recorded. In particular, the psychiatrist should inquire about the possible occurrence of depression, psychiatric hospitalization, suicide, alcoholism, drug addiction, mental retardation, convulsive disorders, or syphilis.

In addition to these factual data, this section should indicate how the patient felt about each of these relatives, what the nature of their relationship was during the patient's childhood, and what it is like now. If there were divorces or marital separations, what was his emotional response? Was it different from that of his parents? A similar description of the patient's spouse and children may be made here or in the preceding section.

## MENTAL STATUS EXAMINATION

The purpose of recording the mental status examination is to enable the psychiatrist and others who may need to review the chart to obtain a precise picture of the patient's emotional status and mental capacity and functioning. Therefore, verbatim samples of the patient's speech and thought content should be included.

For clarity, the mental status examination should be recorded in a certain order and organized according to certain categories. However, these need not be the order in which the examination itself is conducted, for that order usually depends on the circumstances under which the patient and psychiatrist meet, the degree of cooperation of which the patient is then capable, and the degree of intactness of his sensorium. In any particular situation, the examiner must exercise his own judgment about which parts of the mental examination are to be emphasized.

Even if a patient is inaccessible or stuporous, it is nonetheless important to attempt the mental examination and to record the findings. Not only does this provide a picture of the patient *at that time* to someone reading the case record later, but the description of the patient is valuable as a base line for future comparison.

### Interview Behavior

*Relationship to psychiatrist.* Was the patient cooperative, indifferent, or withdrawn? Did he welcome the opportunity to present his views to the psychiatrist? Did he recognize the purpose of the interview? Was he openly hostile or assaultive? Did he display a friendly attitude? If so, was it excessively friendly or inappropriately "chummy"?

What is needed here is a general view. A specific description of the patient's emotional reactions is to be presented below.

*General appearance and grooming.* Was the patient dressed with normal neatness? Were the clothes he wore appropriate to the season and the occasion? Were they clean and in good repair? Was the patient clean? Was his hair combed? Were his fingernails cut?

*Motor behavior.* Here the psychiatrist presents a picture of the patient's overall motor behavior during the interview. Were his motor acts appropriate to the situation? Were they smoothly coordinated, jerky, or awkward? Was there hyperactivity? If so, give a careful description.

Was his motor behavior purposeful or seemingly aimless? Was any motor act self-injurious or destructive of objects in the room?

Was the patient willing to shake hands in greeting? Was his handshake of normal firmness or was it abnormally limp? Was there evidence of cogwheel rigidity or waxy flexibility? Did the patient display wringing of the hands, tics, twitching, or a tremor? If so, was it constant or "on intention" only?

If the examiner suspects that the patient is abnormally slowed, he may time the patient's reactions by giving him simple commands, such as asking him to walk across the room, to untie and tie his shoelaces, or to write out a dictated sentence. In the report, the examiner should give the time it took the patient to respond. The patient should be given a simple explanation for the test, such as, "I want to see how long it takes you to do certain things."

**Posture.** Was the patient normally relaxed, stiff and guarded, or limp and sprawled out in the chair?

**Gait and carriage.** Did the patient carry himself erect or slouched over? Was his gait normally brisk, slow, desultory, dilatory, unsteady, or poorly coordinated?

**Facial expression.** Was the facial expression appropriate to and consistent with the subject under discussion? Did it change appropriately with change of subject? Was the patient's face unexpressive and flat? Did he look to be normally attentive, apathetic, or indifferent? Did the patient at any point show elation (to what degree: mild pleasure, appropriate smile, or uncontrolled laughter); fear (to what degree: mild anxiety or apprehension, crying, or absolute terror); or anger (to what degree: frowning, scorn, or rage and fury)?

**Voice and speech.** Evaluation of the patient's speech should include consideration of the following factors: (1) Intensity. Was the patient's voice normally audible, excessively loud, or excessively soft? (2) Pitch. Was his voice monotonous or did it show any abnormal changes in pitch? (3) Speed. Did the patient speak at the usual rate of speed, very slowly, or rapidly? (4) Ease of speech. Did the patient speak easily, under much pressure, or hesitantly? (5) Spontaneity. Was his speech spontaneous, did he respond only when questions were put to him, or was he mute? (6) Productivity. Did the patient speak with usual verbal productivity, or was he garrulous, or laconic? (7) Relevance. Were his productions relevant, flighty, or easily distractible? (8) Manner. Was his manner of speaking pedantic, excessively formal, relaxed, or inappropriately familiar? (9) Deviations. Was there evidence of neologisms, echolalia, clang associations, or verbigeration? (10) Reaction time. Was it appropriate or abnormally slow? If significantly slow, the psychiatrist should time the interval between asking a question and obtaining the patient's response. (11) Vocabulary and diction. Were his vocabulary and diction consistent with his social and educational background?

Disturbances in speaking may occur at certain times during the interview, depending on the material under discussion. Themes of special emotional significance to the patient may produce alterations in any of the above qualities. Special note of this should be made when it occurs.

## EMOTIONAL REACTIONS

These are best recorded in the patient's own words. It is important to note the consistency of his stated emotion and its appropriateness to the subject under discussion. The examiner must note any inconsistency between the emotional reactions which the patient reports and those which he is observed to be having.

If the patient does not report his feelings spontaneously, questions designed to elicit a statement about them may be helpful. If asking the patient how he feels does not obtain the desired information, more specific questions should be asked. Are you sad? Happy? Fearful? Are you worried about something? Does something hurt you?

For the unresponsive patient, the examiner must note signs that suggest certain feelings. These include his observations of the patient's facial expressions and their changes, pulse and respiration rate, tearfulness, sweating, and blushing.

## CONTENT OF THOUGHT

What does the patient speak about spontaneously? How does he account for having come to the hospital or to the psychiatrist's office?

It is preferable to let the patient give an account of his problems without interrupting him with questions. However, there may be times, as with a patient who is easily distracted, when the examiner wishes to focus the interview more sharply. In examining a patient who does not voluntarily share his thoughts, the psychiatrist may ask: What are your worries? How did they come about?

Are there subjects about which the patient refuses to speak? Evasions and outright refusals to speak are as significant as the patient's answers, and they should be noted.

*Persecutory trends.* These may be elicited by asking: Do you think anyone is against you? Do people say things about you behind your back? What does it seem they say? When you get on a bus or a train, do you feel the other people turn around to look at you? Do they watch you during the entire ride? Is anyone trying to control your mind? How are they attempting to do this? Why do you think this is happening?

*Hallucinations.* To test whether the patient is hallucinating, the psychiatrist can ask: Have you ever heard anyone call your name aloud and, when you turned around, found no one there? Do you hear other things without discovering their source? What things? If the patient can identify a voice or voices, then the examiner should ask: Whose voice is it? Is it a man or a woman? Do you hear more than one person? Do you hear this in both ears? What is the person saying? Is it pleasant or unpleasant?

Do you ever *see* strange things? Do you ever see things you know are not really there? How do you think that comes about? What do these things look like? Do they frighten you? Are they moving or still?

Do you *smell* strange odors or *feel* things on your skin when you cannot see anything there? Do you have unusual *tastes* in your mouth? When does that occur? What brings it on? What is the strangest experience you ever had?

The examiner may believe that the patient is responding to hallucinations even though he denies it or declines to confirm the examiner's suspicions explicitly. In such instances, the examiner must carefully record what he has actually observed. Did the patient turn his head suddenly? Did his eyes appear to be following something in motion? Did he stare at a particular place in the room? Did his gaze return to a particular place at intervals during the interview? Did he mumble or appear to be conversing with a third person?

**Hypochondriacal trends.** These may be elicited by asking: How is your health? How do you sleep? Are you often ill? How frequently do you usually visit your doctor? Are there any special foods in your diet? Do you take any medicines regularly? What do you keep in your medicine cabinet? The examiner may wish to be even more precise in certain cases and ask questions such as: How is your heart? Your bowels? Blood? Sexual organs? Brain?

**Schizophrenic trends.** Ideas of unreality, which may characterize an incipient schizophrenic episode, should be asked for. Do you ever feel outside yourself? When crossing a street, do you ever feel as though someone else is moving your legs? Does the world look different to you? How? Do things about you sometimes seem not to be real? Does their size seem to change?

**Depressive trends.** When present, depressive trends are usually mentioned by the patient himself. However, it may be helpful to ask: Do you think you are going to get well? Are you blue? Have you ever thought of hurting yourself or committing suicide? Did you ever try to do something like that? Do you think you are a wicked person? Why?

If the patient is *severely depressed,* he is rarely spontaneous in describing his ideas. Severely depressed patients will often acknowledge nihilistic thoughts. These may be elicited by asking: Do you think everything is hopeless? That the world has stopped? That things outside no longer exist? That tomorrow will not come?

**Ideas of grandiosity.** When present, grandiosity is usually indicated by the patient himself. He may describe himself in exalted terms. He may exaggerate the amount of his wealth or the number of automobiles or homes he owns. It may be helpful to ask: Do you receive messages from

God? Do you have any unusual powers? What is your real rank? Do you think people recognize who you really are?

**Compulsions.** These may be asked about with questions such as: Are there any habits that you have? Are there any things you feel you must do in a certain way? More specifically, the examiner may ask: Do you have to wash your hands in a particular fashion all the time? Or bathe or shower in a certain way? Or use the toilet in a certain way? Is there anything you must do first in order to be able to fall asleep?

**Obsessive thoughts.** Such thoughts may be elicited by asking: Are there any thoughts that continually run through your mind? Are there certain prayers or particular slogans you feel compelled to say to yourself? Under what circumstances?

**Phobias.** When present, phobias are usually spontaneously described. However, the examiner may inquire: Do you have any particular fears? Do you have any morbid fears? Are there any places you feel you must avoid? Why? Are you able to use elevators? Do you feel you cannot go to the upper floors of tall buildings? Or into subways? Or to church? Or to any particular neighborhood or street intersection? When did you first become aware of such a problem?

## SENSORIUM

This section describes the patient's state of consciousness and his ability to perceive his environment correctly. The following items must be tested:

**Orientation.** *Time.* Does the patient identify the date correctly? If not, is he approximately correct? Can he give the month? Year? Season? Time of day? If he is in a hospital, does he know how long he has been there?

*Place.* Does the patient know where he is? If he is in a hospital, does he know its name and location?

*Person.* Does the patient know who he is? Does he know who the examiner is and what he represents? Does he perceive the hospital staff and other patients correctly?

**Recent memory.** This may be tested by asking the patient: Where do you live? What is the address? What are the names of the other people who reside there? How did you come here? With whom did you come? What have you eaten today? Where did you go yesterday? What was in the newspaper or on the radio news program today?

The particular questions to be chosen for testing recent memory depend on whether the patient is hospitalized or is being seen as an outpatient.

**Remote memory.** This may be tested by asking the patient: Where were you born? What was the date? Where did you grow up? What was the address? Where were your elementary and high schools located? What were the principals' names? How far did you go in school? How old were you when you took your first job? Where was that? How long have you lived at your current address? When were you married? What was your wife's maiden name? What are the names and birth dates of your children? What are the names and addresses of your siblings?

Questions must be appropriate for the particular patient. Thus, if the patient has been hospitalized previously, he may be asked when and where that was, the names of previous physicians, and the locations of their offices.

For foreign-born individuals, dates of immigration and naturalization are important and should normally be within recall. Similarly, questions designed to reveal their mode of travel to the United States may be included.

**Retention and immediate recall.** These faculties may be tested by giving the patient a date or the name of a person and asking him to remember it, as he will be asked for it later in the interview. The examiner should then test him after five minutes and again after twenty minutes or toward the end of the interview.

Auditory memory span may be tested by asking the patient to repeat a series of numbers. The patient should be able to recall and recite at least seven numbers forward and five numbers backward without error.

Visual memory span may be tested by pointing to an object or to the time on a watch and asking the patient to remember them. The examiner should then test the patient after five minutes and again after twenty minutes or toward the end of the interview.

**Counting and calculation.** Intactness of these functions may be tested by asking the patient to count to 20 forward and backward; to subtract 7 from 100 and to continue subtracting serially. The examiner should note whether the patient makes mistakes and is aware of his errors. When the patient is finished, the examiner should ask him whether his remainder is correct? How does he know whether it is correct? Can he check his answer? Simple tests involving multiplication and division should be given.

It is important to note whether the patient performed these simple functions within an appropriate time span or whether his mental functioning was abnormally slow. If the latter is true, the time interval between question and answer should be noted. The examiner's impression of the patient's effort to be cooperative must also be noted.

**General knowledge.** The examiner must form an impression of the patient's intellectual capacity and his general knowledge. The measurement of intellectual capacity is a function of the clinical psychologist, employing tests that have been statistically validated. However, a rough estimate of the patient's intellectual capacity forms a part of the psychiatrist's mental examination. It may be estimated by testing for his general knowledge, keeping in mind the level of schooling he has completed.

Sample questions (in order of difficulty) include: What do we do with food? Name some foods. What are houses made of? Cars? Clothes? Name some rivers, mountains. Who is the President of the United States? Who was President before him, and before him? Who was the President during

World War II? During World War I? Who is the governor of the state? The lieutenant-governor? For how many years is the President elected? What is the boiling point of water? What is its freezing point?

*Abstract thinking.* An impairment in the ability to think abstractly is found in several thought disorders. Any disorder that tends to make thinking more rigid, such as schizophrenia and some organic brain syndromes, may reveal this phenomenon. It may be tested by asking the patient the meanings of some of the more common proverbs. If asked the meaning of "Don't count your chickens before they're hatched," the normal subject answers in some general terms about the hazards inherent in drawing premature conclusions. If abstract thinking is impaired, the answer may well approximate a concrete restatement of the original proverb.

## INSIGHT

This represents the patient's ability to comprehend his current situation correctly. Does he believe himself to be ill? Does he feel the need for help? Has he come voluntarily or unwillingly to be examined? If he is in a hospital, why does he think he is there? If he does believe himself to be ill, how does he account for the illness? To what extent does the patient evaluate himself realistically? To what degree does he understand the dynamics of his own personality and the origin of his problems?

## JUDGMENT

This refers to the individual's capacity to interpret his environment correctly and to orient his behavior in it appropriately. The psychiatrist wants to know how the patient has been functioning in school or at work, and whether he has been exercising prudence in these areas and in his family relationships.

## RELIABILITY

This refers to the examiner's impression of the patient's veracity or capacity to report his situation accurately. An estimate of the patient's reliability is an important part of the case record.

## PHYSICAL EXAMINATION

Every patient requires a complete physical examination, which must include a neurological examination. It is imperative that the psychiatrist recognize that somatic disorders may present themselves through behavior disturbances. This may be more obvious when the structures of the central nervous system are directly involved. Involvements outside the nervous system may range from disturbances in circulation or nutrition to toxic manifestations of infectious diseases. The list of possible causes of behavioral disturbances is extensive. Therefore, all indicated physical and laboratory examinations must be included in the diagnostic investigation.

## PSYCHODYNAMIC FORMULATION

Having elicited the psychiatric history and performed the necessary physical and mental examinations, the psychiatrist must then attempt an amalgamation of the knowledge he has acquired. This section of his psychiatric work-up attempts to answer the questions: How did the patient become the person he is today? What were the environmental and genetic influences that shaped his personality during his early years? How did he express his fears and angers? What were his sources of pleasure and pride? How has the reality of his life circumstances produced his current situation?

This section includes an assessment of the patient's adaptive techniques and an evaluation of their effectiveness. It should attempt to explain the causes of his psychodynamic breakdown.

## DIAGNOSIS, PROGNOSIS, AND RECOMMENDATIONS

For psychiatric therapy to have a rational basis, it must be built on an accurate understanding of the patient's development and life history and on the results of the physical and mental examinations. These are the elements on which an accurate diagnostic description and psychodynamic formulation are based, and they, in turn, lead to the prognosis and recommendations for appropriate therapy.

### DIAGNOSIS

In an attempt to maintain uniformity, diagnoses should adhere to the standard nomenclature of the American Psychiatric Association. Where the psychiatrist feels that this is not satisfactory, he may supplement it with whatever qualifying terms he feels apply. However, the necessity of categorizing within one nosological system can be helpful in developing a conceptual framework, particularly for students. The framework will probably be modified as the psychiatrist develops his own way of thinking with continued study and practice.

### PROGNOSIS

A prognostic statement is a part of the evaluation of the patient. It is based on the psychiatrist's understanding of his patient's assets, strengths, and adaptive weaknesses and the reality of his life situation. It is modified by the history of the patient's previous patterns of adapting to situations of stress and relative normality. Proficiency in developing prognostic skills depends on the student's insistence on including a prognosis in every work-up he does and following it up by observing the course taken by each of his patients.

## RECOMMENDATIONS

These follow the systematic study of the patient. If the psychiatrist can understand the patient's development and the vicissitudes of his life experiences, he should be in a position to recommend an appropriate course of therapy. Alternately, there will be times when the recommendation may be for no psychiatric therapy. When psychiatric referral has been for the purpose of evaluating a patient, such a recommendation may be most helpful to the referring physician.

## REFERENCES

Barish, J., and Buchenholz, B. A teaching technique for inferring psychodynamics. Psychiat. Quart., 34: 103, 1960.

Deutsch, F. The associative anamnesis. Psychoanal. Quart., 8: 354, 1939.

Lewis, N. D. C. *Outlines for Psychiatric Examination*, ed. 3. State Hospitals Press, Utica, N. Y., 1943.

# CHAPTER THREE

---

# Psychological Testing of Intelligence and Personality

---

## ZYGMUNT A. PIOTROWSKI, Ph.D.

IT SEEMS BEST to view psychological tests as microscopes or X-rays if one wants to grasp their significance, advantages, and limitations. Performance on psychological tests, it is assumed, reflects certain selected performances in real life. Another assumption is that differences in test performance correspond to differences in life performances, other conditions being equal—be they differences among many individuals or differences among several test examinations of the same individual.

Different tests yield information about different psychological aspects. Tests of potential intellectual capacity differ from tests of intellectual efficiency. Tests of acquired mental skills differ from tests of ability to apply acquired skills to the solution of new tasks. Tests often give information not accessible in direct interviewing because it is not always possible to differentiate adequately between the level of highest potential capacity and the level of actual effective functioning. Thus, many ineffectual psychotics perform surprisingly well on some tests of abstract reasoning; less frequently, an apparently imaginative patient does poorly on tests of imagination as well as on tests of reasoning. Some patients, after brain concussion, appear clinically to reason logically and on a superior intellectual level but reveal a severely and consistently defective immediate memory on a variety of memory tests. A severe memory defect leads to confusion, even if the patient's verbal reasoning is superior. The norms of every standardized test enable the examiner to evaluate any individual's test performance and its implications for performance in life far more realistically than a nonstandardized interview can. However, the increased precision that testing provides is not always necessary for the understanding or treatment of diseases.

Reliability and validity are indispensable concepts in psychological testing. A test is reliable when repeated applications of the test yield the same results, provided the tested individual or mental function has not changed significantly between the testing periods. Reliability is the self-consistency of a test and depends primarily on the length of the test (longer tests tend to be more reliable) and the spread of test scores in the group of subjects measured (the greater the spread, the greater the reliability). Whereas reliability refers to how dependably a test measures what it measures, validity refers to how well the test measures what it is supposed to measure. A test can be reliable without being valid—that is, without having any useful application. It may have no significant correlation with any important empirical variable of emotions, conduct, reasoning, etc. A test cannot be valid unless it is reliable. It can have different degrees of validity when it is correlated in various degrees with different variables or personality aspects. For example, tests of emotional attitudes are more valid as indicators of internal emotional attitudes than of overt behavior in emotionally stimulating social situations; and verbal tests of intelligence reveal with higher validity potential reasoning power than effective handling of reasoning problems.

Microscopic or X-ray evidence is always limited, and this limitation applies to psychological tests. Sometimes a test is easily and validly interpreted, and at other times its relevance is doubtful or incomplete unless it is integrated with other data. The degree of reliability of different tests and of different uses of the same tests varies. The application and interpretation of some tests require long and difficult training; in other tests, they are relatively simple. The projective personality tests are among the most difficult to interpret; and consequently, in the present stage of development, it is still true that the skill of the interpreter of these tests is no less important than the tests themselves. The paper and pencil questionnaires (the personality inventories) eliminate the influence of the examiner almost completely, both in the administration and in the interpretation of the subject's responses, if norms are available. The application of intelligence tests requires sound training and care which is all the more true of projective tests.

## INTELLIGENCE TESTS

### GENERAL CONCEPTS

*Intelligence.*    Intelligence is a controversial concept. The most widely accepted definition of intelligence is: the capacity to solve new problems by means of reasoning. It involves an understanding of the relevant issues in new tasks and thinking of successful or satisfactory solutions to the tasks. The emphasis on novelty of the tasks serves the purpose of differentiating acts of intelligence from memory feats, although it is realized that memory has a role in reasoning. In tests of intelligence, reasoning is stressed, not concrete performances, because manual performances are easily influenced by transient emotional stress and by training. Moreover, it is useful to have a measure of potential intelligence in order to have an estimate of what kind of work the individual could be doing. This potential power cannot be measured directly, but it may be inferred from the results.

*Factors to be kept constant.* Since test results depend, at least in part, on training (including relevant experiences of any kind), interest, and effort as well as on intellectual capacity, it is important that training, interest, and effort be kept constant so that differences in intelligence can be measured in terms of differences in test scores. This requirement is met by (1) constructing tests measuring a great variety of mental tasks, (2) limiting the unqualified application of test norms to subjects who had at least the same educational opportunity as those whose test performance provided the norms, and (3) making certain that the subject was sufficiently motivated in answering the test questions.

The psychologist's role in ascertaining interest and effort is essential and can be difficult in the case of young children and withdrawn psychotics. Depression, which always affects test performance unfavorably, escapes detection easily. Test results should not be accepted as valid unless a qualified psychologist feels confident that all requirements of reliable testing have been met.

*Intellectual level.* The intellectual level, determined by a reliable examination with a sound test after the fourth year of life (provided there is no speech disorder and no disease of the central nervous system), is one of the most lasting and most important human traits. Individuals with adequate intelligence may not achieve what they are capable of for a variety of reasons, but no matter how hard a person with insufficient intelligence tries, he cannot achieve what is beyond his capacity. Time and again claims are made and alleged proofs are offered that intellectual capacity (the I.Q.) can be raised by proper training. But analysis shows that the improvement in the I.Q. on reexamination is spurious because motivation and cooperation greatly differed on both examinations.

*Individual versus group tests.* When an individually administered test differs from a group test, the result of the group test should be disregarded. Individual examinations are far more reliable than group tests because of the opportunity the examiner has during the individual test to estimate and control the degree of cooperation, a matter of particular importance in the study of mental patients.

*Emotional factors and brain disorders.* Intelligence tests measure reasoning about impersonal and rational mental problems, the solution of which may require prolonged and conscious concentration. Different types of tests differ in their resistance to emotional factors and are affected differently by different types of brain lesions. With the exception of patients with lesions in the speech areas of their dominant cerebral hemisphere, the ability to define words resists functional and organic brain disorders best, and vocabulary test scores can be accepted as approximate measures of premorbid intellectual ability.

As more and more is learned about specific test result patterns in different kinds of brain disorders, specific conclusions replace broad generalizations. In general, the effect of emotional stress or of functional and organic brain disorders on test results increase with the degree to which the test is an "open-eye test"—that is, the degree to which it involves visual-motor perception and coordination, speed, and adaptation to a new task, especially if the task is of no perceptible significance to the patient in his daily life. Words, speech, and communication are always important. "Closed-eye tests" that can be answered quickly and briefly on the basis of long-acquired and well-tested verbal knowledge without the use of the hands or the senses (except hearing) resist deterioration best. This is well illustrated by the significantly greater variability of scores on nonverbal tests, particularly in the case of very disturbed mental patients.

*Measuring and scoring I.Q.*    Modern psychological testing began in the last decade of the nineteenth century when Alfred Binet developed the first intelligence scale to separate the mentally defective (who were to be given special education) from the rest of the children (whose school progress was to be speeded up). Realizing that intellectual capacity cannot be measured directly and that test scores are a function of training and practical experience as well as of intellectual capacity, Binet eliminated the effect of differences in training and experience by constructing the first battery of diverse tests, assuming that training and experience would be approximately the same for all children on a test battery, even when they differed on the individual tests of the battery.

Binet also introduced the concept of the mental age (MA), which is the average intellectual level of a particular age. The intelligence quotient (I.Q.) is the ratio of MA over CA (chronological age) multiplied by 100 to do away with the decimal point. When chronological and mental ages are equal, the I.Q. is 100—that is, average. Since it is impossible to measure increments of intellectual power past the age of 15 by available intelligence tests, the highest divisor in the I.Q. formula is 15.

Another way of expressing the relative standing of an individual within his group is by percentile. The higher the percentile, the higher his rank within a group. For example, if an individual is at the 80th percentile level, he exceeds 80 per cent of the group in the trait measured and is exceeded by the remaining 20 per cent. An I.Q. of 100 corresponds to the 50th percentile in intellectual ability for the general population. The intellectually lowest per cent are usually classified as mentally defective.

*Purposes.*    The reason for intelligence testing is to ascertain the role the intellectual level may play in the difficulties the subject experiences or to make educational or occupational plans for the future. Nontest estimates of intellectual capacity can be difficult, especially if the patient's education has been irregular or if he is inhibited and tense. The level of intellectual capacity has a definite influence on symptoms and the psychotherapeutic process.

## INDIVIDUAL TESTS

The Binet test battery was revised and enlarged by Lewis Terman and published in this country in 1916. Two newly revised and greatly enlarged parallel batteries, L and M, of the 1916 tests were published by Terman and Merrill in 1937. The new revisions extend from the mental age of two years to the highest adult intellectual level.

These tests have been largely displaced in clinical practice by the Wechsler Adult Intelligence Scale (WAIS), published in 1939 and revised in 1955, and the Wechsler Intelligence Scale for Children (WISC), published in 1949. One reason for the displacement is the difference in the content of many of the tests. The WAIS consists of tests of interest to adults. The Binet is of primary interest to children. However, the chief reason for preferring the WAIS and the WISC over the Terman tests is that considerable time is saved in administering the WAIS and the WISC. This saving is made at some cost in accuracy. Both the WAIS and the WISC are less discriminating in the youngest and oldest subject groups, and even among the most and least intelligent at any age level, than are the 1937 Terman tests. The latter are more accurate as measures of mental deficiency.

The Terman revisions of the Binet, the WAIS, and the WISC are all individual intelligence tests—that is, they are administered to one person at a time, giving the examiner an opportunity to control cooperation and other behavioral patterns.

*Wechsler Adult Intelligence Scale* (*WAIS*). This is an intelligence test for adults and adolescents of both sexes from the age of 16 up. The scale is designed for individual administration and consists of six verbal and five nonverbal tests. Norms are provided for each of the tests, for the verbal test group, for the nonverbal test group, and for the entire scale. The order in which these single tests are given is not important.

Three of the eleven tests give results that correlate very highly with the entire scale. They are verbal and include the test of general information, the similarities test (a test of logical hierarchy), and comprehension questions (chiefly a test of social intelligence). The similarities test measures a basic function of abstract intelligence, subsuming two specific terms under their appropriate generic term; for example, orange and banana are fruit, praise and punishment are methods of correction. The comprehension questions call for answers regarding matters of social importance, such as, "Why should people pay taxes?" and "Why are people who are born deaf usually unable to talk?"

One of the verbal tests consists of arithmetical problems. Results on this test are influenced considerably by training and experience. The fifth verbal test is repeating digits forward and backward. Strictly speaking, this is not an intelligence test but one of immediate recall. Performance on this test is considerably affected by mood. People who are greatly worried by emotional problems are, as a rule, too preoccupied to do well on this test. On the other hand, some detached schizophrenics can do remarkably well and even some brain disorder patients without distinct memory defect can repeat long series of digits. The vocabulary test calls for defining single words. It is a good test, but it requires more time than the others. Schizophrenics who have primary thought disturbances often score poorly on the similarities or comprehension questions.

Three of the nonverbal tests—the digit symbol (placing geometric symbols in squares beneath digits according to a key), the object assembly (resembling jigsaw puzzles), and the colored block designs (imitating, with colored blocks, designs presented on a printed card) —are particularly sensitive to brain damage. The picture completion and picture arrangement tests complete the list of nonverbal tests.

Although David Wechsler, the originator of WAIS, suggested that the I.Q. computed on the entire scale be used as an indication of intellectual capacity, it seems advisable to use only the verbal test performance (excluding repeating digits) in the calculation of the I.Q. because performance on the verbal tests is much less variable than that on the nonverbal tests and because verbal tests resist the effects of emotional tension, psychosis, and brain disease more effectively than do nonverbal tests, unless there is damage to the speech areas of the dominant cerebral hemisphere. Performance on nonverbal tests varies noticeably with mood disturbances in schizophrenia, but performance on verbal tests is relatively stable. A subject rarely introduces idiosyncrasies into his intelligence test responses that would throw light on his emotional attitudes.

A subject's I.Q. score indicates the degree of deviation of his intellectual capacity from the average. In this lies its importance. By general agreement, an I.Q. of 100 has been selected to denote average intellectual capacity on all intelligence scales, but the tests differ somewhat in the probability of obtaining I.Q. scores differing from 100. Therefore, I.Q. scores are not directly comparable unless they are 100 or near 100. On the WAIS, the middle 50 per cent of the adult and adolescent population (there are no sex differences) obtain I.Q.s between 90 and 110. The lowest quarter obtain I.Q.s below 90, and the lowest 5 per cent obtain I.Q.s of 75 or less. Analogously, the upper quarter obtain I.Q.s over 110, and the highest 5 per cent obtain I.Q.s of 125 and over.

## GROUP TESTS

These tests are so named because they are given to many subjects at the same time, although they can also be administered individually. The greatest users of them are schools and the armed services. Being paper-and-pencil tests, they nearly always require good reading and thus are unreliable with poor readers. They are speed rather than power tests. They rely on questions where the answer is usually a choice among alternatives (multiple choice). They are economical and convenient but much less reliable and valid than individual tests. It is particularly inadvisable to attempt predictions in the case of emotional disturbance because transitory emotional upsets interfere with speed of reading and responding and with grasp of printed questions. Motivation during mass testing leaves much to be desired in many individuals. It is preferable to give an abbreviated individual test rather than a group test to the mentally disturbed.

Among the widely known group verbal tests are the American Council on Education Psychological Examination (ACE) for college freshmen, the Cooperative School and College Ability Tests (SCAT) for grades 4 to 14, the Lorge-Thorndike intelligence tests for grades 1 to 12, the Otis Quick-Scoring Mental Ability Tests for grades 1 to 16, and the Concept Mastery Test for undergraduate and graduate college students.

## PERSONALITY TESTS

### PERSONALITY

Definitions of personality are numerous. They rarely exclude one another logically, but they emphasize different aspects of the concept. The most frequent reason for their multitude is the inclusion in the definition of not only a description of human behavior but also references to causal factors, confirmed or hypothetical. Since similarity of behavior does not always imply similarity of motivation, internal psychological attitudes that escape direct visual inspection must be included in the concept of personality.

A purely psychological definition of personality—one that omits physical, physiological, sociocultural, biographical, and other factors (relevant as these are in shaping personality) but that is a good working definition and is accessible to clinical observation and psychological test measurements—is the following: Personality is the role the individual plays in interhuman relationships when he feels his vitally personal matters are involved, the term "role" connoting not only overt behavior (conscious and unconscious) but also internal attitudes, action tendencies, and inhibitions (conscious and unconscious).

### PROJECTIVE PERSONALITY TESTS

The word "projection" in the term "projective personality tests" should be taken in its basic psychological meaning. These tests are concerned with visual images, elicited by and externalized on the ambiguous test stimuli and thus made objects in space.

It is frequently thought that the word "projection" should be taken in its specific Freudian meaning, which limits the process of psychological projection to traits (action tendencies, emotional attitudes, instinctual drives, intellectual processes, etc.) that the projecting individual represses in himself because they cause him anxiety when he becomes aware of them and that he, denying them in himself, unconsciously ascribes to others when he cannot repress them completely. The fact that every examination with any projective test reveals traits of which the subject is aware, of which he approves, and which he does not hide as well as some which cause him anxiety and some others of which he is unaware proves that the Freudian concept of projection is too narrow a theoretical base for the modern projective tests of personality. Besides, there is room and need for a theory of the tests (for an explanation of how and why the tests reveal what they do) and for a theory of personality (for an explanation of how and why people become what they are). Freud's theory of projection is just one personality theory.

In projective personality tests, the subject projects himself by making something definite out of an indefinite sense datum or relatively ambiguous stimulus. Thus, everything that is definite in his responses reflects the subject's habitual ways of reacting. These modes of reaction are never the same in all details in any two people or in any two examinations of the same person. But no adult ever changes his personality completely except the relatively few who markedly deteriorate because of a severe organic brain disease. Two or more Rorschach test records of the same individual, taken even years apart, hardly ever differ enough to prevent correct matching in experiments that consist of selecting the record of an individual from among the records of twenty or more subjects, using another test record of that individual as a clue.

*Assumptions.* The following assumptions provide a partial basis for a theory of projective personality tests.

SELECTION. There is no perception without selection, and the process of selection is a function of personality. This is the broadest principle underlying the tests. Selection is not a superficial or accidental process; it reflects significant life interests, the intensity and quality of emotions, fears and anxiety, physical and mental strength, and degree of activity. The degree of spontaneous activity determines both perceptions and attitudes toward the world. It is through action that we verify the existence of an object and discover its full significance for us. The nervous system is active not only in receiving impressions but also in reacting to them, and selection plays a role in both reception and reaction. Selection is inevitable because of the inability to perceive and react to all potential stimuli. *What* matters and *how much* it matters are functions of personality. The primary function of selective perception is to facilitate action, sometimes to start action, but always to aid the acting organism.

VISUAL IMAGERY. Visual imagery aids our orientation in reality much more than does the imagery of any other sense. Rorschach postulated that even the form aspects of visual percepts (visual images projected on the stimulus cards) correspond to significant personality traits. Sight is the most active, most highly organized, and most informative of our senses. It is also the most important sense phylogenetically.

AMBIGUITY OF STIMULI. This is what makes genuine self-expression possible. The visual stimuli can be considered ambiguous when they meet the following requirements: (1) They elicit a great number of different percepts from different people looking at them. (2) Each individual produces a limited number of percepts. (3) The set of percepts produced by one individual differs from those of others to a maximal degree. (4) Each individual's set of percepts varies concomitantly with his personality changes. (5) The information contained in the percepts is of a satisfactory degree of validity no matter by whom produced. The freedom the subject has in the selection of the areas he interprets and in the manner he interprets assures freedom of self-expression.

CONSCIOUS EFFORT. The weaker the conscious effort, the greater the freedom of self-expression. The projective tests differ a great deal among themselves in the amount of conscious effort required to answer them. Drawing human figures and other objects, answering questions, and completing sentences in writing require more effort than freely associating to inkblots or even making up stories about pictures, although the latter limits the imagination far more than do the more indeterminate inkblots. The amount of useful and valid information obtained decreases as the amount of effort in answering the test increases. Any definite objective task that demands voluntary and conscious control, be it ever so small, places some limitation on spontaneous self-expression.

DIRECTIONS. Absence of specific directions facilitates self-expression. When the subject can determine the nature of his task as well as his response to a given task, his freedom of self-expression is greatest. The projective tests differ a great deal in this respect. The inkblot test permits the greatest freedom in this respect because it does not demand any consistency, objectivity, or rationality. The subject can produce successive responses of very different types, varying in significance, without feeling any tension or being aware of any internal inconsistency or irrationality. When making up stories about pictures, the demand for consistency is much greater, and the subject unwittingly follows the rules of rationality and objectivity, since the stimuli themselves, pictures of real people, suggest that the stories be in some relation to the world or to objective human relationships as they are known to the individual taking the test. This is still more the case with the Minnesota Multiphasic Personality Inventory. After all, the sense of reality works automatically except in psychotics severely handicapped by their illness.

IGNORANCE. Anxiety is alleviated through ignorance of what one discloses about himself. Unless the subject knows the projective techniques well and makes a successful effort to give responses that, interpreted according to standard test rules, create an impression deliberately intended by him, the test responses are reliable. The more the test stimuli and the interpretation of them by the subject absorb the subject's genuine involuntary attention, the freer and more reliable is his test performance. Nearly all people enjoy the free play of their visual associations and do not think about the significance these associations may have. This attitude of ignorance and unconcern, most easily sustained on the Rorschach and hardest to sustain on personality inventories, keeps the subject willing, consciously and unconsciously, to cooperate. Being unaware of what one discloses seems to be crucial for the validity of the tests if they are to give information not readily available through other sources. Awareness of what one reveals arouses anxiety and ambivalence easily; it alerts the mechanisms of disguise and displacement.

CREATIVE IMAGINATION. This faculty facilitates the expression of specific personality traits. At least some degree of creativeness is necessary to give meaning to inkblots and pictures of people, to draw, and to complete unfinished sentences. Very little, if any, creativeness is needed to answer questionnaires. When the subject does not know by what standards his responses will be evaluated, he is not restrained in his freedom of associations by self-criticism and is more creative than in a state of critical self-evaluation. The significance of this assumption is illustrated by the fact that original—that is, extremely rare—and particularly unique interpretations always disclose something very important about the creators of these interpretations, even when the examiner does not know what it is they reveal. The drive they reveal plays a great role and is usually conscious to the individual, even when he does not know he has revealed it in his response.

PERSISTENCE. The persistent and lasting test aspects reflect the persistent and lasting personality traits that constitute the basic structure of personality, assuring continuity and assimilation of experiences, stability, learning, and control over self and environment. When subjects are retested, a comparison of the easily changeable aspects of the test responses with those that change slowly or little is necessary before a decision can be made as to the nature and degree of personality change. This assumption implies that the degree and nature of the test changes correspond to the degree and nature of personality changes. This assumption, necessary for the validity of the tests, is confirmed best in the case of the revised Rorschach and least in the case of personality inventories.

ANXIETY AND DIFFICULTIES. These stimulate imagination more than do pleasure and contentment. All projective techniques seem to reveal trouble, inner conflicts, and tension much more readily than contentment, happiness, and success. This is not true of personality inventories, but these techniques are not projective tests. Among the reasons for the ease with which projective tests sample trouble and worry is their functioning like psychological microscopes: All surfaces look rougher under a microscope than when viewed with the naked eye. Sometimes the stimulus favors dysphoric reactions (for example, many Thematic Apperception Test pictures). Another relevant reason is that an important function of imagination and thinking about sense data is the function of warding off possible trouble and preparing for handling trouble. An attitude of carefree self-confidence seems to stimulate thinking and imagination much less than does anxiety. States of gratifying relaxation are states of diminished readiness for both mental and physical action. An unanxious, well-adjusted person does not linger in his own past because he does not have much unfinished psychological business that stirs unpleasant memories. This assumption explains, in part, why projective tests are valuable in psychopathology.

PARALLELISM. The handling of projective test stimuli parallels the handling of personally vital interhuman relationships; the latter includes not only overt behavior toward others but also internal attitudes, not accessible to direct observation, related to the handling of significant interhuman relationships. Unless the internal attitudes are considered, the assumed parallelism cannot be demonstrated. In fact, projective personality tests reveal the inner man more fully than the outer man. Moreover, only results of a full analysis of the tests can parallel the role the individual plays in personally vital interhuman relationships. When the analysis is limited to the verbal narrative or anecdotal content and the nontest psychosocial behavior of the individual is limited to overt and directly observable action, no parallelism can be expected because pertinent aspects of test responses and actual living are left out of the comparison. The Rorschach test does not even allow a direct comparison between verbal test content and overt psychosocial conduct; it would be absurd to view the subject's responses about animals, inanimate objects, and many other objects as literal descriptions of his own social behavior. It requires a special dictionary to translate the subject's manner of handling the test stimuli into ways in which he deals with others, internally and externally. The translation from test behavior to life behavior is almost direct and simple in the case of some test components, and it is indirect and complex in the case of other test reactions. Projective tests differ in the degrees to which they meet the requirements of the parallelism assumption. Their degrees of validity differ accordingly.

*Principles.*    Not all reactions to any psychobiological test, including projective personality tests, are of equal significance; they vary in degree of validity and importance. Some are of little if any significance, some may have an unknown meaning, and some are very valuable. There are two formal principles that aid in the sorting out of projective test responses and even of dream and interview material. They are named the verb versus noun principle and the same figure versus other figure principle.

VERB VERSUS NOUN PRINCIPLE. It is easier to deflect an action tendency toward another object or person than to suppress it. We love our desires more than the objects of our desires. People change the objects more readily than the desires themselves. Since drives are expressed in verbs and objects of drives are expressed in nouns, verbs are much more likely to be undisguised and valid at face value than are nouns, which frequently fail to indicate the primary or genuinely intended object. Changing of imaginary human figures is easy in dreams and in projective personality tests, especially in interpretations of inkblots. On the other hand, imagined drives need not be changed because the dreamer or tested subject can make them appear innocuous to himself in his own imagination: He can make the wishes come true and the dangers safe.

The easiest way to calm anxiety while engaging in spontaneous visual imagery is to have one's unacceptable, tension-producing drives carried out in imagination by characters unlike oneself or to direct them at characters unlike the real persons for whom they are actually intended, though the subject may not be aware of it. Nouns connoting human beings, then, are likely to be more frequently distorted than verbs connoting social interactions. The nature of the test stimuli (blots, pictures) facilitates this difference in distortion. The verbs can be classified into groups according to whether they indicate movement toward or away from others, movements overcoming or surrendering to the pull of gravity, free versus inhibited movement, active versus passive movement, successful versus failing actions, lonely versus social activities, etc. The difference in the degree to which drives and their objects are distorted must be remembered in studies of validity; otherwise, validation of projective tests misses its purpose.

SAME FIGURE (SF) VERSUS OTHER FIGURE (OF) PRINCIPLE. The SF is a test figure of the same sex, approximately the same age, etc., as the subject; the OF differs from the subject in all these traits. The principle states that drives ascribed to the OF are less likely to be manifested in overt behavior than those attributed to the SF. In other words, drives acceptable to the subject tend to be projected onto the SF, the unacceptable ones are projected onto the OF. The meaning of the differences between same sex and other sex test figures applies also, though in a lesser degree, to the difference between same age and other age, human and nonhuman test figures, and to the difference between statements made using the first person singular pronoun and the third person singular pronoun.

Since it is most difficult to say whether an action tendency elicited by a test is conscious or unconscious, the terms "acceptable" and "unacceptable" are preferred. The principle implies that drives and other attributes ascribed to the OF are at least partly inhibited and cause anxiety when the subject becomes conscious of them or tries to carry them out in action. Special favorable conditions (strong motivation, good rationalization) are needed to actuate the unacceptable drives.

What a subject says about the OF may also divulge his views of real people of the opposite sex, different age, etc. A subject who is anxious about his weakness may reveal his feeling by ascribing weakness to children in his test performance. Similarly, fear of old age and death can be expressed by creating old and sickly test figures. Knowledge of ourselves and knowledge of others are interdependent, and the greater the inhibitions (the unacceptability of one's own drives), the greater the likelihood of feeling uncomfortable with others. As inhibition increases, the likelihood of preconceived and distorted ideas about others as well as oneself also increases.

Inferences from the OF regarding the subject's unacceptable drives seem to be more frequently confirmed than those concerning the manner in which the subject thinks other people relate to him. The SF-OF principle can be applied to Rorschach human movements, Thematic Apperception Test characters, free drawings of males and females, and even dream figures.

## RORSCHACH PERCEPTANALYTIC TEST

The purpose of the Rorschach test is to deduce personality traits of individuals from an analysis of spontaneously produced visual images stimulated by indeterminate stimuli, a set of inkblots. A stimulus is called indeterminate when it can be interpreted in a variety of ways with equal plausibility.

Leonardo da Vinci was the first to use indeterminate forms to stimulate creative imagination and to test future painters. Alfred Binet, in 1895, revived the use of inkblots as a test of individual differences, but he limited their scope, calling them a test of passive imagination. George V. Dearborn, in 1898, was the first one to realize that inkblot responses can reveal complex traits reflecting social relationships and the degree of emotional stability.

It is doubtful that Rorschach knew about the work of his predecessors. His greatest achievement was the discovery that not only the verbal content of the responses but also the formal aspects of the visual images contribute important information about distinct personality traits. Although many diverse responses to the blots are obtained, the fact that each individual limits his personal reactions to relatively few responses contributes greatly to the reliability and validity of the technique. Rorschach records of the same individual are very similar, regardless of the number of examinations, unless the personality changed as a result of a psychosis or brain damage.

*Description.* The Rorschach test consists of ten symmetrical inkblots, printed on a white background and mounted on 6½- by 9½-inch cardboards. Five of the blots are in varying shades of gray, two are red and gray, and three are multicolored. The subject can view the blots in any position, but he is not allowed to hold them at a distance greater than arm's length. The examination consists of the performance proper, during which the free visual images are obtained, and a subsequent inquiry. The purpose of the inquiry is to remove any doubts the examiner may have concerning the images produced by the subject and thus to assure reliable scoring.

*Scoring.* The main scores are divided into four categories. The area scores indicate the portion of the blot interpreted: the whole blot, a frequently selected detail, a small and rare detail, or the white areas. The next category, the determinants, includes movement, color, shading, and form responses. The third covers content: humans, animals, anatomy, botany, inanimate objects, etc. The fourth category contains components indicating the degree of accuracy with which the images fit their respective blot areas. There are good, poor, and indeterminate fits. The subject is permitted freedom of association. Encouragement to elaborate on some of the responses does not invalidate the test, as long as the examiner makes no direct suggestions.

The scores or components help in the analysis of the test records by providing a summary. The W or whole responses cover whole blots and are positively associated with a genuine readiness to achieve something noteworthy through personal efforts: no W, no drive; many W, marked drive. However, the quality of the drive and the results depend on a number of other traits besides genuine readiness to achieve something difficult and constructive.

The D components stand for details or parts of blots that are often selected for interpretation. The D are the most frequent area components, and a marked reduction of their number suggests poor judgment. The D scores cover small and rarely selected blot details. When increased in number, they indicate a tendency to preoccupy oneself with tiny, disparate details that, put together, do not amount to much. The main implication of increased numbers of D is alleviation of anxiety through keeping one-self busy with small and unimportant tasks.

Increased white space responses or S (more than two) are associated with constitutional strength, habitual oppositional attitudes, and a tend-ency to change decisions, each time with a feeling of finality. Psychotics with S may be difficult to handle, but they resist the effects of psychoses better.

The M or human movement responses reveal deep-seated action tend-encies that press for outward manifestation whenever there is an opportu-nity. The FM components symbolize animal movement, and the m scores symbolize movement of inanimate objects. The m scores seem to reveal attitudes the subject considers desirable but beyond his psychological means. The FM responses tend to influence overt behavior in states of diminished consciousness, such as great fatigue, intoxication, and twilight states.

The color responses are divided into three components: FC or form-color, CF or color-form, and C or formless color. All these CR (color responses) disclose emotional attitudes regarding others. As the form ele-ment in the CR increases, the consideration for others increases also, but the intensity of emotions weakens. Being a late addition, the shading and dark color responses have been given a variety of symbols and meanings in Rorschach literature. The light shading responses or cR are related to alleviating anxiety through a decrease of motor activity (increased motor control); the dark or black color responses, the c'R, are associated with alleviation of anxiety through counterphobic increases of motor activity.

The F or form responses are, as a rule, the most frequent in an individ-ual test record. If not, the individual tends to take too many things per-sonally. The F scores represent action tendencies or attitudes that are least personal, relatively most socialized and rational. A separate component is the percentage of sharply perceived forms; when this drops below 70 per cent, the capacity for prolonged and conscious control over thought proc-esses is strikingly decreased. The rare people whose F + percentage is 100 are intellectually meticulous, if not rigid.

Content components are indicated with abbreviations: h, whole human being; hd, human body parts; sex, genitals; bt, botany; ntr, nature; bl, blood; obj, inanimate objects; etc.

Since the publication of Rorschach's book in 1921, many new compo-nents have been added but are not in universal use.

*Interpretation of basic life roles.* The realization that an individual can act as if driven toward a definite and persistent purpose even when unaware of it is a discovery that has radically changed psychology in recent decades. Drives that change least and, when they do, change gradually are revealed by the M (human movement responses) of the Rorschach ink-blot test. These potential behavior patterns press for overt manifestation insofar as internal and external conditions permit. They are stronger than the effects of pain and pleasure, and most of their driving power comes from the unconscious.

Three main types of M can be differentiated: assertive, compliant, and blocked. In the assertive, the movement overcomes the pull of gravity, and the M figures expand in space—for example, "two women dancing." If this kind of assertive movement is felt to be unhampered in any way, if it is free and spontaneous both physically and mentally, a person producing such M exclusively would be described as self-confident, ready to assume responsibility for himself and frequently for others as well, having initiative, and eager to leave a mark of his personality on others.

In the compliant M, the figures give in to the force of gravity or submit to the influence of another power, reducing movement or self-controlled expansion in space—for example, "falling down," "bowing." Persons who produce exclusively compliant M lack self-confidence, look for a benevolent guide who would take the ultimate responsibility for their thoughts and actions, and suffer from having their spontaneity curtailed. The great majority of people who seek psychotherapy have compliant M or essentially assertive M with serious restriction of spontaneity and freedom of action in their M figures. An example of the latter is: "Two men trying to lift something; it's heavy, and I doubt that they'll make it."

Patients with assertive M are easier to help psychotherapeutically than those with compliant M. Reexaminations show that the quality of the M is the last test component to change, if it changes at all. There is no more desirable M than an easily performed, spontaneous, countergravity activity. Patients undergoing a real character improvement move toward this ideal M in their posttreatment reexamination. Some patients undergo an apparently spontaneous movement in the opposite direction, toward compliant M or assertive M restricted in freedom and speed of expression. Such changes are usually a sign of an approaching psychotic breakdown.

The third type of M is blocked between assertion and compliance and thus discloses deep-seated and hard to change obsessive doubts whenever an important decision affecting significant human relationships must be made. The classical example is: "Two men pulling in opposite directions with equal strength." Much energy is spent, but no overt movement or change is made. Such individuals have lost much of their self-confidence but have not yet surrendered to the directing and domineering influence of others. They do not know whether to trust themselves or others, to take responsibility for themselves or depend on someone else for support and guidance.

The action tendencies or life roles revealed by the M go back to early childhood, and thus the M responses throw light on patient-parent relations. Even minor variations in the content of the M seem valid and should be analyzed. No single Rorschach plate elicits, always or exclusively, information about the subject's attitude toward father or mother. However, M components in which male figures appear indicate life roles developed in living with father; M components with female figures disclose life roles developed in living with mother. "Quarrelling women" suggests that the patient developed verbal aggressiveness while accommodating to mother. "Bowing men" points to father as responsible for the patient's compliance; it is expressed in an acceptable social form, but it is a handicap nevertheless.

People who produce M responses of different kinds are more complicated than those with but one type of M response. Since overt behavior is never a vector or average of all potential behavior patterns (we are never perfectly integrated), the presence of various types of M does not complicate life as much as might be expected, although it does cause strain. Effective doers usually have only one type of M, the assertive type as a rule. On the other hand, introspective individuals produce M scores of a large variety. The capacity for diversified M seems associated with psychological perceptiveness and intuitive understanding of others. Schizophrenics who produce many M responses do not deteriorate, and deterioration caused by brain damage results in the loss of the ability to produce M responses. Cerebral cases with M have a better insight into their condition than those without M, and thus they complain more of their handicaps. As M increases, pride appears. The main concern of the individual with many M responses is to be at peace with himself and to live up to his own standards rather than those set by others.

*Interpretation of emotions regarding others.* Clinical observations and projective personality test conclusions gain in clarity and meaning when emotional attitudes regarding mainly others are separated from those regarding primarily the subject himself. These two types of emotions can vary independently of each other, especially in mental patients.

Emotions concerning others can be defined as desires to associate with or dissociate from others with the intent of continuing or discontinuing the exchange of pleasures and pains. This definition divides emotions into positive (love, affection) and negative (hate, repulsion) and defines them as desires that can be accompanied by conscious feelings of varying intensity and awareness. The first impulse of a person motivated by a negative emotion is to avoid others; it may develop into open aggression if attempts at avoidance are frustrated, as in the case of children who cannot leave their parental home. Positive emotions prompt the seeking out of others to experience pleasure through them. These promptings fail if the other does not approve of the intention and refuses to be involved. It takes more tact, persistence, and effort to gratify positive emotions than negative ones, at least in the case of the great majority of adults. One has to be trained to love successfully; hating comes much more easily. Thus, sheer human inertia explains the prevalence of dislikes.

The Rorschach measure of positive emotions is a meaningful interpretation of chromatic color areas in which appear objects or processes indicative of a secure or attractive life—for example, "red apples," "canaries," "bouquet of flowers," "beautiful landscape." Negative emotions are indicated by meaningful interpretations of chromatic color areas that suggest a state of disintegration or destructive processes—for example, "blood," "ugly painting," "cross-section of a human body," "burning (destructive) fire." Successful psychotherapy increases the relative number of positive color responses.

Patients without any color responses are emotionally flat; those with many color responses are frequently stimulated to seek others for pleasure or avoid others to discontinue pain or fearful emotional relations. The negative color individual dreads emotional involvement with others because he expects to suffer as a result of such involvement. He is a frightened person who can be quiet in manner and is often mistaken for an indifferent and unemotional one. In both schizophrenic and organic deterioration, there is decrease in color responses. The emotionless diencephalon lesion cases do not produce Rorschach color responses.

*Signs of anxiety.* Projective tests reveal anxiety in so many different ways that it is necessary to specify the types of anxiety to be meaningful. Furthermore, every Rorschach sign of anxiety simultaneously indicates the life area causing anxiety and the manner in which anxiety is experienced and alleviated.

It is important, too, for best results to differentiate between anxiety and fear. Anxiety can be defined as a dread of an impending danger, the nature and probability of which is unknown and not calculable, accompanied by tense and physically exhausting alertness, an apprehensive self-absorption that interferes with an effective and advantageous solution of reality problems, an irresolvable doubt concerning the best means of counteracting the danger and one's own capacity to meet the emergency effectively when it arises. Though similar, fear differs from anxiety in that it is a dread of a known external danger, the probability of which is approximately calculable, and against which definite, objective, and effective defense measures can be taken. Fear, unless excessive in degree and thus changing into anxiety (the excess introducing the incalculable element), mobilizes mental and physical energy. Anxiety cuts down initiative, intensifies the feeling of weakness, and raises the probability of being overwhelmed and destroyed.

The classical sign of anxiety is a sudden and temporary paralysis of function. Its main Rorschach manifestation is an initial delay (measured in seconds) in the production of a meaningful interpretation of a new stimulus. Occasionally, subjects fail to give any response at all to a Rorschach plate, thus displaying the highest degree of shock. There can be other shock manifestations, such as exclamations and critical remarks. The Rorschach shocks indicate neurotic ambivalence regarding the advisability of acting in accordance with spontaneous and genuine action tendencies.

The color shock, nearly always red shock, elicited by Plate II or Plate VIII reveals neurotic ambivalence regarding emotional desires involving others. Color shock individuals tend to blame others for their frustrations. Dark color or dark shading shock, measured by delays in responding to Plate IV or Plate V, is associated with anxiety over experiencing anxious and depressive states, feelings of inferiority, and blaming oneself for one's frustrations.

The frequent sex shocks pertain primarily to male genitals (potency difficulties in males, anxiety over contact with male genitals in women) when triggered by Plate VI and to female genitals (castration fear in males, anxiety over possible injury or pregnancy in females) when elicited by Plate VII. Sex shocks can occur as early as the eighth year of life and apparently have the same meaning as in adults. They vary greatly in intensity and sometimes are the only shocks in the test record. Plate IX shock is a valid indicator of heterosexual intercourse anxiety. Plate III shock always means that the patient is neurotically ambivalent about being his true self and, in most cases, about whether to give in to homosexual tendencies. A Plate III shock in the absence of noticeable psychosexual difficulties may signal the onset of a manifest psychosis.

If not due to inadequate preparation of the subject for the test, Plate I shock (failure to see anything in it or longest initial reaction time in the record) suggests paranoid schizophrenia. Shock on Plate X is rare; when there is delay, it probably means anxiety regarding ability to tackle successfully the relevant problems of the future and severe criticism of past personal achievements.

Interpreting the Rorschach plates at a rapid and even pace—for example, with all reaction times below ten seconds—signifies absence of consciously felt anxiety. It is good and normal not to feel anxiety when there are no serious personality problems. Psychotics who react in this nonanxious way lack insight into their illness and cannot be helped psychotherapeutically. Absence of shock to a plate suggests absence of anxiety and acceptance by the subject of what he does and experiences in the area to which shock on this plate pertains. Thus absence of shock on Plates VI, VII, and IX (all three) means that the individual is not anxious over his psychosexual intentions, active doings, and passive experiences, regardless of what they are. Homosexuals without sex shock do not want to change, even if they give lip service to the idea of change. An analysis of the Rorschach shocks alone gives knowledge about areas that trouble the subject and in which therapeutic help is likely to be desired and areas that cause no trouble, at least at the time of testing, and where probing is likely to be resented, thereby jeopardizing the success of therapy.

One of the main ways of alleviating anxiety is a reduction of motor activity, partial withdrawal with attempts at making one's self inconspicuous. It is a prudent method in a tightly organized society in which records are kept on everyone and are consulted. Light shading responses—meaningful interpretations of the graduations of gray on the blots—are the most important Rorschach signs of this method. As these responses—such as "furry skin," "billowy clouds," "topographical map,"—increase in absolute numbers and relatively to the sum of chromatic color responses, so does the individual's ability to automatically (without conscious effort) suppress subjectively undesirable motor impulses concerning others.

The other method of alleviating anxiety consists of increasing motor activity, which results in performing an action designed to reduce anxiety by attacking the source of anxiety directly or indirectly or, less frequently, in escaping anxiety by flight (suicidal attempts). The belligerence that often characterizes dark color individuals exposes them to the danger of retaliation.

When a subject produces more than three responses each of light and dark shading, he is unpredictable in the handling of anxiety. Since he cannot alleviate anxiety in both ways at the same time, he alternates, to the bewilderment of others. The great majority of patients with many responses of both kinds are schizophrenic. Few adults (no more than one-fourth) produce dark shading responses. More than three-fourths of adults produce at least some light shading responses. Dark color responses can appear below the age of 3. The light shading type is very rare below the age of 7. The dark color responses are prominent in brain concussion and relatively frequent in epilepsy and delinquency. They are associated also with intermittent depressive moods that come and go and are not unwelcome; these moods differ greatly from chronic and deep depressions with psychomotor retardation.

Anxiety indicated by human movement responses appears when the subject actuates the life role contained in the response. "A man just run over by a steam roller" as a response to Plate IV expresses an expectation of being destroyed by inimical forces, not necessarily physical. "A contortionist with head between his legs and a grotesque mask" as a response to Plate IV suggests pathetic attempts at gaining attention and influence. Both M responses point to great inner anxiety and insecurity.

**Signs of depression.** Deep depressions are revealed on the Rorschach by a uniformly very slow pace of interpretation with long initial delays, lack of imagination, great reduction in movement and color responses, and sometimes even a significant drop in whole responses. Any frustration projected onto an indeterminant, ambivalent stimulus—one that could be interpreted with equal plausibility in several or more different ways—discloses depression. Handicapped or frustrated movements—such as, "trying hard to climb; I doubt that they'll make it"—or strenuous movements suggest persistent depression associated with attempts at self-assertion. Producing significantly smaller numbers of test components that express interest in the world and in spontaneous personal activities points to depression. It is much more difficult to lift the depression indicated by human movements than depression indicated by uniformly long initial reaction times.

Greatly reduced numbers of whole responses (covering entire blots) signify depression, with resignation and giving up of ambitions for personal and noteworthy achievement. When there are no other signs of depression, this reduction of drive is not associated with subjectively acute depressions but with chronic depressive underactivity. In general, there is a small and gradual increase in the signs of depression with increasing age after the fourth decade.

*Signs of drive for acting out.* An analysis of the verbal content alone on the Rorschach results in a list of potential behavior patterns, but content alone does not suffice to predict the chances of the behavior patterns being acted out. Evidence of well-controlled, goal-directed, and prolonged voluntary attention is revealed by clarity and completeness of thoughts adequately verbalized, respect for reality (making interpretations fit the test stimuli), and production of sharply conceived images. This is an important control factor, preventing overt manifestation of action tendencies that the individual may feel should be suppressed. This control, the Rorschach F + percentage, requires conscious effort and has the limitation of all consciously maintained attitudes. After a while, fatigue sets in, and the control may cease to function. The value of a high F + percentage (percentage of sharply perceived forms) is demonstrated by schizophrenics whose behavior in conventional social situations betrays nothing peculiar.

A better control is provided by the light shading responses, being at least equal in number to color responses. This control functions without the subject's conscious effort and is more reliable than the F + percentage. Shading responses vary more readily than color responses and can be more easily affected by psychotherapy.

There are also negative controls, which consist of a reduction of drive. Low whole responses show reduced ambitious striving; compliant, passive or qualified, inhibited movements ("trying hard to," "about to," "getting ready to") and other signs of obsessiveness point to inhibitions and delays that serve as controls. This must be said also of shocks, slow pace of interpretation, and low numbers of color and movement responses.

In schizophrenia there is an additional negative control, a lack of integration or depersonalization (extremely difficult to evaluate, if at all, on any psychological test). Highly inhibited individuals can afford to produce disapproved, antisocial, and even bizarre ideas because of the very small likelihood that these ideas will lead to actions.

*Interpretation of symbols.* Psychological symbols refer to those action tendencies affecting interhuman relationships and not to static objects. "Death," symbolizes emotional loneliness and depression; rarely does it symbolize physical destruction. "Food" means emotional hunger much more frequently than physical hunger. "Blood" symbolizes fear of close emotional ties with others and fear of mental pain rather than murderous intentions or fear of physical injury. "Eyes" always reveal great sensitivity to criticism by others and to self-criticism, but paranoia can be inferred only when the patient is a schizophrenic. High percentages of anatomy indicate fear of not having sufficiently good reasoning power and a wish for better intellectual functioning rather than symbolizing sexual activities.

It is advisable to divide content according to the formal Rorschach components with which it appears. Content in form responses is more ego-distant (further from the core of the acting personality) than content in human movements. Form content expresses fears of the environment or wishes that can be gratified by objects in the environment. Responses like "ragged edges," "torn wings," "crushed animal," disclose fears of being overwhelmed by external dangers. They are produced mainly by schizophrenics in their most anxious early phases of psychosis and also by cases of brain damage (especially head trauma) and occasionally even by very energetic and successful normal achievers who feel they have overextended themselves.

Such an unrealistic response as seeing color where none exists—for example, "a yellow butterfly" in the completely gray Plate V—is produced rarely but occurs in all diagnostic groups, even very mild neurotics. It is related to a good character trait: the deliberate and successful attempt to feel and appear serene when actually suffering from a depression. The depression of cases with color projection is frequently underestimated, which may be serious in very disturbed patients.

Content of human movement responses is very close to the ego, to the core of the acting person, and thus it is of great significance. "Knives," "scissors," "swords," and similar form responses are signs of fear of being attacked; but "two men fighting" is a sign that aggressive behavior, or at least the tendency to it, is an inherent part of the personality; the subject wants to attack.

When an activity is capable of causing intense excitement in the doer, and the repertory of overt movements necessary to carry it out is simple and limited, allowing little room for variety, responses that symbolize this activity are easily and usually validly read. This is true of physical sexual activity and acts of bodily aggression. However, the repertory of all aggressive acts is so large that even strong aggressive attitudes can escape detection in tests. It is possible to develop great skill in interpreting correctly (as proved by subsequent clinical observations) the symbolic meaning of many responses.

**Signs of sexual disturbance.** Many Rorschach signs of inadequate heterosexual attitudes in males have been suggested. The signs that indicate definite sexual aversion to women and clinically noticeable tendency to homosexuality are: (1) anal responses, human or animal, male or female; (2) bisexual figures endowed by the patient with both male and female primary or secondary sex characteristics; (3) spontaneously expressed inability to decide whether a figure seen in the blot is male or female; (4) figures reclining backwards with legs at least partially raised (this correlates highly with passive homosexual tendencies in males and with desire for heterosexual intercourse in females); (5) human movement responses that are frankly sexually exhibitionistic, such as fan dancers of either sex; (6) misinterpreting the usual female figure in the center of Plate I or the bottom center detail of Plate VII as men or male genitalia.

It is very difficult to infer overt homosexual practices correctly. Moreover, many homosexuals produce none of the above six signs. On the other hand, "two penises, side by side" and "two men touching each other with their backsides" are valid indicators of overt homosexuality. If an area frequently interpreted as a phallus (top center grays of Plate II, VI, or X) is perceived as black or as covered with dirt, guilt over homosexual activity can be inferred.

**Relation to symptoms.** When the human movements exceed the colors on the Rorschach, the symptoms are usually ideational, thoughts rather than actions. When the colors outnumber the movements, the symptoms are motor.

The classic obsessive-compulsive reaction on the Rorschach is to perceive the blot well, to suggest a sharply conceived form to fit the respective blot area, to note spontaneously the discrepancies between the blot shape or color and those of the imagined object, to be right about the discrepancies (which are real), and to steadfastly keep in mind both the sensation of the blot and the image of the object while comparing them with each other. The larger the absolute number of such responses, the more prominent the obsessive-compulsive symptoms. Limiting freedom of action in the human or animal movement responses indicates obsessiveness in making vital decisions. When movements and colors are about equal in number, and there is also color or dark shading shock, the character structure is likely to be obsessive-compulsive. The same uncertainty and tentativeness of responses, the same spontaneous explanation of causal and spatial relations that slow down the process of interpretation, the doubt and self-criticism, the same guarding against possibilities of misunderstanding and failure are apparent on the Thematic Apperception Test.

By contrast, the conversion hysterics are not intellectually uncertain, produce very few anatomy responses, are not concerned with the adequacy of their test responses; but their perceptiveness, both physical and psychosocial, is limited. Patients with dark color responses are counterphobic.

Significant group differences have been found between suicidal and nonsuicidal cases in several tests. However, the effort to find significant differences between attempted and completed suicides has failed, and prediction of fatal suicides is not feasible with any accuracy. Similarly frustrating has been the search for dependable criteria of alcoholism in individual cases, although some group differences have been noted.

Absence of psychosis, presence of inner stress and anxiety, inadequate capacity for a good, automatically functioning self-control (fewer Rorschach light shading than color responses) is a frequent finding in psychosomatic cases.

*Usefulness in diagnosis.* The Rorschach excels all other tests as an aid in making neuropsychiatric diagnoses, although there are cases in which it fails when the clinical examination and other tests provide relevant evidence. The diagnoses most frequently missed by the Rorschach are paranoid schizophrenia and brain damage with mild mental changes. An outstanding asset of this test is the information it contributes about the manner in which the patient reacts to his sickness and the curative steps he takes to minimize the effects of the illness on his thinking and acting.

There are four different diagnostic procedures, which are not mutually exclusive but complementary.

1. The pathognomonic procedure is limited by the relatively small number of patients with pathognomonic reactions and the small number of pathognomonic signs.

2. The most intensely studied procedure is the descriptive-statistical one, which consists of noticing the frequencies with which all scorable test components occur in various diagnostic groups. It is based on the assumption that an individual whose test record approaches the average test performance of a particular diagnostic group is likely to belong to this group. Experience shows that this approach is not very successful because the test scores obtained by members of different groups overlap too much to be helpful in individual cases and because the absolute and relative frequencies of the scored test components vary far more with the severity of the disease and the patient's reaction to it than with the specific nature of the mental illness.

3. The third diagnostic procedure is systematic. It depends both on a pattern analysis of test components (correlating them instead of taking them one at a time, noting only their frequencies) and on a theoretical assumption substantiated by decades of clinical observations and concerned with the behavior of patients struggling with mental illness. The best validated systematic approach pertains to schizophrenia. It resulted in a pattern of underactivity or withdrawal and characterizes about 30 per cent of mild or early schizophrenia. Patients who manifest this pattern fare relatively well, without appreciable deterioration, for three to five years and should not be given intensive, insight-giving psychotherapy because the removal of the defense (underactivity) intensifies the psychotic symptoms and undermines self-control. These patients are frequently misdiagnosed as obsessive or anxious neurotics.

4. The fourth diagnostic procedure is potentially the soundest but actually the most difficult one. It requires a thorough knowledge of clinical neuropsychiatry and psychopathology and an excellent mastery of the Rorschach and other tests. It consists of deducing the patient's main personality traits from the test results and using this information as a basis for

diagnostic conclusions.

The Rorschach method has a built-in test of the sense of reality that must always be evaluated in any differential diagnosis involving a possible psychosis. It is necessary to differentiate between the image produced by the patient in response to the blot and called a "percept" and the patient's elaboration, both perceptual and verbal, on the primary percept. The original percept reflects the basic condition of the patient's mind much better than does the secondary elaboration. The latter is influenced primarily by emotional attitudes and the patient's way of handling his illness. The original percept reveals the condition of the primary and basic thought processes. Thus, good images with bizarre elaborations bespeak a better mental condition and thus imply a better prognosis than do vague, limited, and confused images with normal-appearing, nonconspicuous verbal elaborations.

Only schizophrenics produce pathognomonic Rorschach signs. These signs must be defined in very exact terms to be truly pathognomonic. One of them, contamination, is relatively frequent and can be defined as the unknowing fusing of two or more visual images (of shapes of objects) that cover the same blot area into one unintelligible visual image, without the patient being able to disentangle the resulting confusion. The visual images must overlap at least partially. Often when a patient's attention is drawn to his contamination, he will deny having produced it. This denial does not invalidate the significance of the contamination but indicates a mild form of schizophrenia in which the patient is capable of intellectually rallying when given the opportunity. Contaminations retain their diagnostic significance, even if it is obvious that emotional strain is partly responsible for the content of the response. Children below the mental age of 8 years produce pseudocontaminations, a confusion of color and form (not several forms) with a pleasing content—for example, "flags in the sky" (blue in Plate VIII), the color of the area suggesting the sky, and the form suggesting the flags. The content of the pseudocontamination is part of normal experience, but the content of a genuine contamination is likely to be peculiar—for instance, "liver of a statesman," "female butterfly."

The second most frequent pathognomonic sign of schizophrenia is the inconstant percept of variable dimness. This consists of placing securely only part of the visual image on the blot and having difficulty in delineating the rest of it, leaving it in a dim and variable state. For example, a patient had no difficulty in locating an animal's head in the upper half of the right gray area of Plate II, but he was puzzled as to how much of the animal's body he saw—that is, how much of the blot area was included in his own response.

A third pathognomonic sign is the use of an indeterminate visual image. The patient is not sure what he imagines. His image is very vague, but his words sound definite. An extreme example is: "This is a prehistoric creature which never existed and of which nobody knows anything." The patient simultaneously affirmed and denied his image. A similar response, given earnestly, is "half of nothing." To be pathognomonic, the response must be given in earnest.

One type of response, almost pathognomonic, expresses the schizophrenic's emotional ambivalence—such as, "two friends, toasting each other and fighting; their heads are bloody." Here love and hate are entwined in one intimate relationship. The experience of emotional ambivalence is not limited to schizophrenics, but schizophrenics are almost the only subjects who express it in a clear visual image on the Rorschach.

There are no easy rules for diagnosing all patients with high degrees of accuracy (over 80 per cent), but some experienced clinical psychologists have developed very high diagnostic skills, based in part on subtle signs difficult to quantify. It is hoped that eventually knowledge will advance and diagnostic rules will result in conclusions of high validity though based on formalized rules.

## THEMATIC APPERCEPTION TEST

The TAT, as the Thematic Apperception Test is usually called, was introduced by Dr. Henry A. Murray in 1935 as a new way of interpreting stories made up about pictures representing, among other things, human beings of both sexes and different ages, appearing alone or in a group, in various surroundings, and in various types of interaction. The interpretive system is based on a psychoanalytical theory about defenses against anxiety feelings.

Originally, the chief usefulness was seen in revealing action tendencies or drives of which the subject himself was unaware. When it became obvious that some conscious as well as some unconscious tendencies were revealed by the test, its aim was enlarged to study many personality traits, including dominant drives, emotions, neurotic defenses against anxiety, conflicts, intellectual level, work habits, active ambition, attitudes toward parental figures, and psychopathology.

In administration of the TAT, the subject is shown one picture at a time and requested to tell a complete story—that is, to describe the interactions taking place, the events leading up to these interactions, the thoughts and feelings of the figures involved, and the outcome.

*Description.* Murray and his collaborators offered a set of ten pictures for males, another set for females, and a third set for both sexes, the last set to be administered at a later date. For a number of reasons, among which a lack of time seems to be paramount, the TAT is rarely given in more than one session, and the usual number of pictures shown is about ten.

The selection of the pictures is important, since every picture teases out some specific type of information. This results not only from the differences in pictorial content but also from differences in the degree of anxiety the pictures arouse, enabling the subject to change deliberately his spontaneous, freely associated stories in order to make the desired impression on the examiner and, through him, on others. The TAT stories are more easily and more frequently changed for this reason than are the inkblot interpretations. Many subjects feel that they can predict the meaning that the examiner will attach to their TAT stories.

The use of pictures specially prepared to study specific attitudes or drives—delinquency, social relations, special occupational activities, etc.—has been disappointing. The main reason seems to be the subject's ability to guess the aim of such special examinations, and this awareness arouses anxiety or fears that, in turn, curtail the freedom of association. Thus, paratroopers retested shortly before executing a jump did not express as much fear when interpreting pictures plainly related to the dangers of parachuting as they did when interpreting pictures not related to parachuting.

**Administration.** The administration of the TAT is important. It is permissible to encourage subjects to give meaningful stories if they say little or are evasive. However, the examiner should not suggest to the subject any specific interpretation of a picture because the value of the test rests on spontaneous free association. Some valuable conclusions can be drawn even from brief TAT stories. As a rule, mental patients who voluntarily seek help cooperate well. The problem of inadequate cooperation, evasion, and faking is more likely to occur with normal subjects made to participate in research projects or with patients involuntarily receiving psychiatric help. It is impossible to cover the same points in every examination; however, this does not lower validity; rather it raises validity.

Included in the Murray set of pictures is a blank card; the subject has to imagine a picture first and then tell a story about it. A meaningful interpretation of the blank card demands more of the subject than does interpretation of the regular picture cards. Dynamic self-expression is reduced in blank card stories. Nearly all subjects reveal wishes for happiness and relief from tension and responsibilities in their blank card stories, manifesting the universal human desire for personal security (physical, financial, emotional) and protective affection. It is a sign of severe mood disturbance and poor prognosis to produce stories of failure, violence, sickness, and fear in response to the blank card. Stories elicited by this blank card must be analyzed in a special and different manner from the other stories.

**Interpretation.** The regular TAT picture stories should be divided into two main parts for the purpose of teasing out information: the verbal narrative content (the events seen, in the picture) and the formal aspects (the manner of narrating). The latter include nonverbal as well as verbal reactions: pauses, doubts, qualifications, corrections, inconsistencies, remarks that do not directly bear on the story, external pictorial elements added to the visual sensations of the picture in the subject's story, and any other signs of hesitation and inhibition.

The verbal content reveals some of the subject's drives, and the formal aspects throw light on the chances of the subject expressing the drives in overt motor behavior. The neglect or misuse of the formal aspects is one of the main reasons for the unsuccessful prediction of overt behavior. By contrast, inner attitudes—drives inferred from the verbal content of the TAT regardless of the degree of inhibition—agree well with information obtained during psychotherapy, which provides the best independent information for validation of projective test results. Changes occurring during psychotherapy are also reflected in repeat TATs.

Pictures that strongly suggest ideas pertaining to a particular drive— aggressive, competitive, sexual, personal achievement, etc.—tend to elicit reaction formations and signs of inhibition; pictures weakly suggesting a particular drive elicit less distorted and more genuine attitudes toward the drive. One explanation for this finding is that nearly all the TAT pictures inspire, in almost all subjects, themes of frustration, conflict, delinquency, and other undesirable human relationships that most people prefer to avoid or, if they cannot avoid them, prefer to deny.

Age, sex, intellectual and educational level, social class membership, cultural and racial affiliation are among the socially relevant factors that to some degree determine the content of TAT stories. These factors contribute to the personality development, but they influence even more the frankness with which genuine drives are expressed in the test. The essential point is the degree to which an individual shares the values of his group. If he does not share its values, group norms do not help the examiner understand his TAT. One would expect women to mention nurturance and abasement more frequently, aggression and sex less frequently than men do; and indeed this is the case. With increasing age, the majority of people tend to become more depressed and more realistic about social relationships; these changes also are reflected in long-term reexaminations with the TAT. Autobiographies have been successfully matched with TAT stories. Many other studies, including evaluations of intellectual and educational levels, have been published demonstrating the value of TAT. There were also many failures.

**Value of the TAT.**   The reasons for disagreement regarding the value of the TAT are basically the same as those responsible for the difference in opinion regarding other projective tests. The foremost reason seems to be the failure of investigators to duplicate exactly the studies they set out to check. Another important reason is the lack of a sufficiently comprehensive, clear, and formalized basis for the interpretation of TAT results. A frequent error is predicting overt behavior solely from the verbal anecdotal content, overlooking the indices of inhibitions that must be considered in predictions of overt behavior. Among the causes of the disagreement is the ignorance of clinical psychopathology on the part of many critics of the

TAT. Any measure of potential behavior is clinically valuable. Experienced clinical psychologists are in far greater agreement on the value of this test and interpretive procedures than are other investigators. The difficulty in acquiring sufficient experience and skill for satisfactory interpretations of TAT results is considerable. It is easy to learn how to administer the test well but hard to interpret it well.

The TAT set of pictures was collected primarily for patients undergoing psychotherapy in order to enable the therapist to gain greater insight into repressed drives and not to infer from them overt behavior. The purpose was to discover what troubled the inner patient. No wonder the TAT reveals liabilities much more readily than assets. Health is less dramatic than sickness. This should be kept in mind when evaluating the degree of overall adjustment. The tendency is to underestimate the social adjustment and to overestimate inner tension.

The TAT cannot be subjected to trenchant validation until its conceptual framework is put in order. To cite an example, male undergraduates' TAT records were evaluated as to the degree of dependency. The same students were also shown slides of large and small breasts of equal degree of attractiveness as determined by preliminary studies. The dependent males showed preference for small breasts, and this was interpreted as contradicting a psychoanalytical theory that presumably demands that dependent males prefer large breasts. It could be argued with equal if not greater plausibility that, since dependent males are likely to have castration anxiety and be ambivalent about large maternal breasts, they may prefer small breasts and would be less defensive about them. Moreover, there is a great difference between an unconscious, or a conscious but unacceptable, wish to snuggle up with Mother and a frank admission of the wish. We cannot be sure of the genuineness of the choices, and the matter certainly requires a more thorough and subtle analysis before reaching final conclusions. Validation attempts of the TAT and other projective tests suffer from such theoretical oversimplifications and disregard of psychological complexities.

Man is not what he appears but what he has done and will do. He uses words to conceal as well as to reveal. The freedom of his activities is influenced by external reality conditions, which cannot be inferred from the test, and by inner inhibitions, some of which are disclosed by the test. The presence in the test of verbal or nonverbal indicators of inhibition and of reduced freedom of mental association or physical action means that the chance of a spontaneous and complete manifestation of a drive associated with those indicators of inhibition is reduced.

Although subjects can deliberately change their spontaneous associations to the TAT for various reasons, thus lowering its validity, the examiner can counteract these changes to a considerable degree, using his experience and the rapport to allay anxiety and encourage spontaneity. The proved sensitivity of the TAT to rapport can be an asset.

With increased knowledge about a patient and greater skill in meaningfully and validly relating information from a variety of sources, the examiner finds the TAT increasingly valuable. He can then make inferences that knowledge of the TAT alone does not make possible.

*Interpretation of drives.* A TAT record containing exclusively benign stories contains so many reaction formations of insignificant driving power that it obscures the genuine drives. Socially approved drives in the TAT are reaction formations because of the nature of the TAT pictures, which strongly favor depressive and socially disruptive themes. Drives disapproved by society and likely to lead to retaliation are much more likely to reflect genuine action tendencies. The probability of these expressed drives affecting overt social relations is high.

Drives ascribed to same sex and same age figures are apt to appear much more frequently in the subject's manifest behavior than drives ascribed to other sex and other age figures, with one apparent exception. Prepuberty children reveal as much valid information about themselves when giving stories about pictures of animals as about pictures of human figures. The Children's Apperception Test (CAT), a test analogous to the TAT but depicting animals, was especially designed for use with children. By comparison with adults, children are more frank and less inhibited, but they are also more dependent and protected. Consequently, their need for defenses is smaller.

Stories preceded by delay—a long initial reaction time and sometimes pauses within the stories—refer to drives about which the individual is ambivalent. Ambivalence leads to inconsistency of action regarding both the frequency and degree to which the drive is manifested. A sudden change in the process of interpretation, including the level of imagination, the mood of the stories, their complexity and inner consistency, discloses great suspiciousness of others, especially if this change persists to the end of the examination. The greater the diversity of the stories and the greater the incompatibility of drives described in different picture stories, the larger is the number of unresolved problems with which the subject struggles. This is striking when the subject is passive and underactive.

An optimistic attitude, not contradicted by references to obstacles or failure, indicates a desire to accomplish even in the face of difficulties. Emphasizing the contrasting dark and light areas of the pictures is related to alleviating states of oppressive anxiety by impulsive acting out, which is almost certain to increase the subject's difficulties in dealing with others. As a rule, any spontaneous mention of hesitation, physical weakness, mental irresolution, fear, guilt, or anxiety is a sign that the drives that are the objects of hesitation seldom affect motor behavior directly.

Proof of internalization of social norms; expressed respect for law, customs, and social order; and indications of consideration for others in the

TAT stories are highly correlated with refraining from antisocial behavior, even when antisocial drives appear in the TAT record. References to remorse, shame, and punishment justify the conclusion that chances of overt delinquent behavior are greatly reduced. By contrast, stories of aggression that remain unpunished and are not criticized directly or indirectly are usually produced by people who do not mind being overtly aggressive.

Drives occurring in a number of different picture stories are a result of cognitive and emotional weakness when the stories are unimaginative or neglect to account for the specific features of each picture. On the other hand, when the same basic drive is appropriately modified and elaborated on in the stories, with meaningful interpretations of the specific features of each picture in which the drive appears, and the stories are comprehensive and of good narrative quality and do not offend the requirements of consistency and respect for physical and logical laws, it means the subject is preoccupied with the drive. Such persistence presupposes strong pressure for appropriate overt behavior.

Confused and unclear thinking reduces the ability to implement drives. Spontaneous criticism of one's own process of making up the stories or of the pictures themselves is a sign of marked obsessiveness. Such criticism is much less frequent on the TAT than on the Rorschach.

The doer looks ahead. A long view into the future is associated with active ambition and self-confidence. The longer the prospective span in the TAT stories and the more successful the outcome of the activities described therein, the greater is the chance that the individual will openly pursue the drives of his TAT. On the other hand, looking backward and mentally living in the past is associated with retrospective TAT time spans and with limited driving power for achievement. Some schizophrenics extend the past into prehistoric periods.

*Interpretation of figures.* A TAT figure's sex or age is rarely misrecognized. Only several of them are vague enough to make identification difficult. A misidentification of a figure that is plain to nearly all is a sign of severe personality disturbance, associated almost always with conflict over homosexuality and with psychosis. Some Congolese as recently as thirty years ago mistook the TAT human figures for animals without being psychotic. This misinterpretation may be attributed to cultural rather than psychopathological factors.

*Interpretation of symbols.* There are those whose training, experience, and talent make them adept in unraveling meaning hidden in symbols. If such a skill is applied to the TAT, much more information can be extracted with all the uncertainties accompanying interpretation of symbols. As long as symbolic interpretations are treated as hypotheses and as statements alerting the observer to information from other sources that can either confirm or contradict the interpretations, there can be no serious objection to them. Information extracted from symbols should complement but not substitute for information deduced with the aid of more reliable and more valid principles.

Stories about Picture 1, showing a boy looking at a violin, may symbolize any pleasurable activity, including sexual activities, although the latter are not plainly stated. The same sex and other sex, same age and other age principles can be used to classify drives as ego-syntonic and ego-disturbing.

Male undergraduates were shown slides of nude women and were then retested by an attractive and affable female psychologist. The number of frank sexual ideas did not increase by comparison with a previous TAT, but the number of symbolic sexual responses did. There was a negative correlation between increase of frank and symbolic responses. When the repeat TAT was preceded by intake of alcohol, symbolic expressions decreased in favor of plain expressions. Symbolic communication implies hesitation and delay in thought and in action.

**Usefulness in diagnosis.** The TAT is not helpful in differential neuropsychiatric diagnosis. Patients who manifest specific psychotic signs in the TAT display even more diagnostically pertinent symptoms in clinical behavior. The TAT is less challenging to the subject's sense of reality than are the Rorschach inkblots. Consequently, the TAT rarely elicits schizophrenic and other psychotic responses, including mental changes concomitant with brain damage. The TAT indicators of psychosis do not differ from clinical signs, except that they occur more frequently in the patient's clinical behavior and with even greater frequency in the Rorschach.

These indicators of psychosis can be classified as follows: logical ambivalence (affirming and denying the same statement within the same story though in different sentences) and other indicators of incoherence and confusion; emotional ambivalence (describing the TAT figures as both hating and loving each other, as being both cruel and affectionate with each other); withdrawal from reality into a world of magical and bizarre events; stories of violence and persecution about pictures of relaxation and peace (8 GF, 9 BM, 16, 17 GF); obvious misidentification of the sex of a figure, especially if the figure is made into a mysterious person with possibly malevolent intentions; pseudogeneralizations, such as, "It shows the condition of the world, humanity struggling to get out of its misery" (18 GF, the squeezing of the throat scene); heartlessness and excessive revengefulness, such as, "This girl killed her small brother because he ate her candy" (3 BM). Paranoid schizophrenia can be recognized by references to spying and abrupt, marked changes in the process of interpretation.

Mild psychotics very rarely reveal anything plainly psychotic in the TAT. However, typical reaction patterns—such as depressive, obsessive, hysterical, and phobic—can be frequently inferred. As a general rule, the manner in which these patterns manifest themselves in the TAT is not basically different from that observed under other conditions.

Severe depressions are indicated by a slow pace of interpretation and long initial reaction times, minimal interpretive imagination going barely beyond mere description, no references to feelings, and either no thought of the future despite encouragement or disastrous future outcomes of described activities.

Suicidal themes are signs of a less severe depression. They seem to reflect a painful anticipation of perpetual loneliness rather than of personal death. "Death," like "suicide," should be treated as a symbol and not as a description of an anticipated real event. Suicidal attempts cannot be predicted from the TAT. Death or killing in the TAT usually means permanent separation (mainly emotional), loss of control over one's fate in life or over one's own mental processes (impulsiveness in severely inhibited individuals), and suicidal thoughts. Stories in which the characters cannot successfully communicate with each other, though they try, are also associated with suicidal thoughts and depression. When the stories are dramatic and frustration and sadness are expressed in strong emotional terms, the depression is not deep. Stories in which difficulties and obstacles are conquered and stories depicting happy endings suggest a mild depression.

The most characteristic aspect of obsessiveness is irrelevant meticulousness, arguing back and forth without being able to make a definite decision or judgment. Obsessives take excessive care not to be misunderstood. They repeat themselves and explain not only their themes but also how they happened to think of them in order to dispel any impression that they may have arrived at their interpretations of the pictures rapidly and spontaneously without preparation. The severest degrees of obsessiveness are indicated by spontaneous and plainly stated criticism of one's own test performance and its products. This happens rarely during the TAT; it occurs much more frequently during an inkblot examination.

The essential feature of hysteria is avoidance of an anxiety-producing idea or drive that presses for outward manifestation. The hysteric represses the subjective psychomotor reaction that would normally be stimulated by the idea or drive but unconsciously overreacts in inappropriate ways that attract the attention of others. He ineffectually tries to have intense emotional relationships beyond his capacity. The desire to avoid anxiety and disappointment is so strong that it leads to a degree of psychological blindness. Mention, in the test, of the inability to see or read points to hysteria. So do clearly stated sex drives that are frustrated and frank expressions of love and hate in a setting of intense but anxiety-free activity in the TAT story. Words or phrases that imply uncertainty or impossibility are rare (no obsessiveness). Feelings or actions of TAT figures engaged in a sexual or aggressive relationship are usually described clearly with the aid of many emotionally charged adjectives.

***Interpretation of child-parent relationships.*** One of the easiest, most highly valid, and most useful applications of the TAT concerns the subject's relations with his parents. Relations between the figures in Pictures 2, 6 BM, and 7 BM as they emerge from subjects' stories can be taken, in the majority of cases, as almost literal descriptions of the subjects' relationships with their parents. The relatively small degree of disguise is remarkable. It seems that, regardless of age, people never cease to feel the impact of their parents. Very old subjects, nearly all of them parents and grandparents, identify whenever possible with a TAT child figure and interpret an older figure as a parental authority. Pictures 1, 3, 5, and 12 F also contribute pertinent information but less frequently.

When the figures in 2, 6 BM, 7 BM, and 12 F are not interpreted as mothers or fathers or if they are identified as parents but described as emotionally indifferent in their relationships, the subject is seriously maladjusted. An aggressive, hostile TAT child-parent relationship reveals gross maladjustment. When TAT child-parent relations are described as affectionate, supportive, and free of conflict, the subject is likely to be emotionally stable. On the whole, psychosomatic cases express overt aggressive hostility in their TATs—but not against maternal figures.

**Signs of sexual disturbance.** Rather than speak of homosexuality, for better understanding it is preferable to speak of heterosexual inadequacy, including at least partial impotence. These remarks pertain only to males, since females are much more complex in this respect.

Inadequate heterosexuality in the adult male is indicated in the TAT by stories containing odious remarks about women and expression of affectionate attraction for men. Occasionally frank homosexual themes are produced; these disclose active homosexual experiences. In the great majority of cases it is impossible to infer overt homosexual behavior, but inadequate heterosexuality can be deduced frequently and with a high degree of validity. The general principles work well. The highly valid test signs are few and identify only a small percentage of cases. Among these themes are overt homosexual activity, men killing women, misidentification of the sex of TAT figures, definite rejection of marriage, expressions of close attachment to mother, and an obvious elaboration of feminine attitudes with a simultaneous neglect of masculine attitudes. Pictures 4, 6 BM, 7 BM, 10, 12 M, 13 MF, and 18 BM are most helpful, especially peculiarly imaginative stories about 18 BM, in which three hands are placed on a slumped man.

## FREE DRAWINGS

It takes little time to obtain spontaneous drawings of human figures and other objects. This is a great practical asset. The information conveyed by free drawings is limited but can be very important, especially in mental patients who have serious unresolved problems. Free drawings usually reveal attitudes that are important to the patient at the time. Enduring attitudes can also be revealed at times; this is the reason for obtaining free drawings.

The attitudes are expressed through the posture or movements of the drawn figures. The usefulness of the technique is increased when the same-figure and other-figure principles are applied to it. Much slips by the censor (superego) while drawing. Degrees of rigidity and cohesion are, as a rule, well reflected in human figures.

**Technique.**   The drawing technique is simple and can be used by both psychiatrists and psychologists. The free drawing technique consists of handing the subject a pencil and a blank sheet of paper with the request that he draw a person, a tree, a house, an animal, or any other object. The most informative free drawings, called free because they are not copies of models, are those of human figures. "All that is good or inferior in you will appear in the corresponding parts of your figures," said Leonardo da Vinci. Free drawings are created largely from unconscious motives. One cannot help but reveal through them more than one intends to. It is a common experience that it is most difficult to change them in a specifically desired manner. What the drawings reveal most clearly are body postures and body movements. Variations in these are associated with different inner attitudes.

After the subject has made a human figure drawing, the usual procedure is to ask him to draw one of the sex opposite that of the first drawn figure. Sometimes he is asked to draw also the "most unpleasant thing you can think of," his entire family, the family as animals as occurs in fables, two people (unspecified), a tree, or a house. There is also an incomplete drawing test by Wartegg-Kinget.

The free-drawing technique, except the drawing completion test, does not use external visual stimuli. As with the TAT blank card, the individual has to create a mental image and then place it on a blank surface. The free drawings seem to represent the wished for or feared object that preoccupies the subject at the time.

**Interpretation.**   Being a psychomotor test, the drawings involve more effort than does describing ideas that spontaneously appear in the mind. This effort limits freedom of self-expression but favors expression of certain habitual physical attitudes.

These attitudes may be transient or lasting, as is well illustrated by preoperative and postoperative drawings of patients who underwent successful surgical operations for seriously handicapping pathology. Preoperatively, the figures they drew were distorted; postoperatively, the figures were physically normal. The feeling of personality loss and lowered energy is frequently reflected in the difference between pre-operative and postoperative drawings of psychotics whose frontal lobes were operated on.

Hysterics frequently draw large eyelashes. Neurotics, worried about their reputations, pay attention to details of clothing. Psychotics and cerebral cases, having far more serious problems, show much less interest in socially important physical attributes; frequently, they even show less interest in clearly indicating the sex of the figures. These patients' interest in human relationships is weak, and their desire to live up to social standards is greatly decreased. The deindividualization of brain-damaged patients with habit deterioration is plainly shown by their crude and oversimplified drawings, with no indication of sex or age, except perhaps for more hair or high heels in the drawings of women.

Patients who feel the danger of impulsive acting out draw larger drawings than subjects who are controlled because of depression, lack of energy, or lack of maturity. As the danger of acting out increases, the drawings tend to grow in size. When the figures barely fit the paper on which they are drawn and appear bloated because of inadequate graphic differentiation of body periphery, suicidal attempts are highly probable.

Transparency—body contours showing through clothing—reveals marked personality disturbances. Dark, heavy, and irregular shading, creating the impression of a smudge, is associated with a tendency to alleviate anxiety through physical and sadistic aggression.

As a rule, free drawings give the impression of plainly divulging a great many psychological attitudes. Sound knowledge of the graphic arts and of sound graphological principles help the therapist to grasp the message of free drawings. As in the case of the other projective tests, one can evaluate drawings in two different but mutually not exclusive ways: (1) a formal attempt based on reliably identifiable graphic signs and (2) a global inspection aided by empathic insights. In experienced hands, the latter procedure works far better at the present time. It is possible to differentiate more than 100 objective graphic signs in human figure drawings, and most of the signs can be ascertained with a fair degree of reliability. Significant differences in the average number of signs between many different subject groups have been obtained. However, considerable overlap frustrates the use of signs for diagnostic purposes in borderline individual cases.

Long continuous strokes indicate perseverance at work, usually associated with obsessiveness and fear of failure and risk-taking. Long continuous lines are a good prognostic sign in psychosis. Broken lines in drawings made by children are associated with poor work habits; in children they are related to poor school achievement, but they are associated with inventiveness in adults who have high intelligence and other assets. Shaded areas consisting of short, broken, and parallel lines indicate anxiety and feelings of personal inferiority.

The stance of the figures is of paramount importance. A strong, stable stance indicates self-confidence, even if the drawings contain peculiarities. It bespeaks a good prognosis in psychosis. Some figures drawn by resigned and withdrawn schizophrenics appear to float in space, though presumably standing on the ground. The greater the deviation from the physically most stable posture—one that can be maintained with ease for a long time—the greater is the inner tension and emotional instability.

Instability is associated also with deviation from the central location of the figure on the paper. Inhibition seems to be correlated with increasing moving of the figure toward the right edge, and a tendency to impulsive acting out is correlated with moving it toward the left edge. Pushing it down is said to suggest respect for authority figures; pushing it up is said to reveal a lack of appreciation of differences in social influence.

Crude whole figures with only some facial features, absence of crotch, omissions and distortions of body are the most valid signs of great anxiety. Depression is suggested by small size, heavy lines, scarcity of details, and a dejected facial expression. Body rigidity and emotional rigidity in drawn figures are dependable signs of deep-seated rigidity in the subject, even if his conventional behavior does not show it.

When the male and female figures differ in an easily noticeable degree in nonsexual features, the other-sex figure practically always looks more anxious or disturbed in some other way. Marked differences in size indicate either depression or fear of impulsive acting out, according to whether the other-sex figure is smaller or larger. Depersonalization and emotional withdrawal are sometimes clearly revealed in the other-sex figures drawn by incipient schizophrenics. If different from the same-sex figure, the other-sex figure shows what the subject wishes not to be. When the other-sex figure looks normal and contented, while the same-sex figure looks odd and anxious, schizophrenia is most probable.

The condition of the drawn tree is believed to parallel roughly the subject's vivacity. A dead tree without leaves suggests emotional emptiness. A full-blown tree with many leafy branches reflects liveliness. A weeping willow suggests weakness and inability to resist others. A tree that looks like part of a defense palisade, with spearlike branches or trunk ends, points to a tendency toward sadistic physical aggression. Sometimes preoccupation with past psychological traumata can be inferred from holes or cuts in the tree trunk. The approximate period in which the trauma occurred can be deduced from the position of the deformity. The higher in the tree the deformity, the more recent is the trauma presumed to have been; and the lower the deformity, the older the trauma is believed to be.

Drawings of houses rarely add important information. They disclose, at times, how the subject would like to live, among whom, and on what scale. The feeling of security and sociability is reflected in the type of house drawn. The houses differ in friendliness, the extremes looking like barely accessible fortresses with small and high windows or like an inviting open house in which many people engage in diverse activities.

***Value of free drawings.*** Although free drawings of human figures and other objects do not reveal as many personality aspects or as many lasting traits as the inkblots or the TAT pictures, they are very helpful as indicators of problems nearer the surface of consciousness that trouble the subject at the time. This renders them invaluable as an adjunct in psychotherapy. The hand usually speaks sooner than the tongue. The value of the drawings can be raised by having the subjects tell stories about their creations.

## BENDER-GESTALT DESIGNS

Clinical psychologists often use these easily administered designs to aid in the diagnosis of brain damage. Sometimes the designs are also used as a personality test, but the results of such an application are of low validity or, when valid, of limited scope. They can be of value in estimating the chances of impulsive acting out.

*Description.* Nine of Max Wertheimer's geometric designs, greatly differing from one another, constitute the Bender-Gestalt test. The designs are presented one at a time to the subject, who is instructed to copy them on a sheet of paper. Frequently, the subject is immediately asked to copy the designs from memory after he has finished copying them from models. Thus, the Bender designs can be used as a test of both visual-motor coordination and immediate visual memory.

*Value.* The value of these designs as a personality test is doubtful at best. Objective scores based on measurement of deviations of the copied designs from the models do not provide more or better information about personality dynamics than a global inspection, but they decidedly are important in the detection of brain disorders.

Although not all patients with brain damage make conspicuously deviant designs, certain identifiable peculiarities—such as rotation by 45°, marked distortion, perseveration, straight lines for dots or curves, inability to reproduce the angle between two figures constituting one design, conspicuous fragmentation—indicate brain damage with a satisfactory degree of validity, with the following qualifications. In the case of children, it is important to differentiate between a lack of skill due to immaturity and a lack of skill due to brain damage. Chronic schizophrenics with personality damage and poor prognosis sometimes copy the drawings in a strikingly deviant manner. It is necessary to guard against interpreting tremulous lines and other graphic defects caused by a transient examination fear or peripheral neurological or muscular impairment as signs of central organicity. Norms, helpful in detecting brain damage, are available. The Bender-Gestalt rarely aids in other differential diagnostic problems.

## WORD ASSOCIATION AND SENTENCE COMPLETION TESTS

The word association is the oldest standardized personality test. C. G. Jung was the first to use this test for the discovery of neurotic conflicts. The test is easy to administer and score and takes little time, but its results are usually meager.

*Description.* A number of these tests require the subject to name, sometimes to write down, the first word that enters his mind when he hears the stimulus word. For several of these tests, norms are available that consist of lists of the most frequently obtained associated words. Kent and Rosanoff provided frequency tables of responses given by various neuropsychiatric patient groups to a list of 100 words. Special lists of stimulus words can be made up for special purposes: to identify tension in special areas, severe physical illness, chronic defects, sexual frustration, etc. It is relatively easy to collect normative data.

The examiner records not only the verbal reponse but also the time and any signs of blocking or tension. An immediate repetition of the test, which can vary from 50 to 100 words, sometimes provides additional clues when the response words differ from those obtained during the first administration. Original responses are always worth investigating.

The sentence completion test is an elaboration of the word association technique. It consists of incomplete sentences, one word or more, which the subject is requested to complete with the first words spontaneously occurring to him as he reads the unfinished sentence. These tests can be given orally, which gives the examiner an opportunity to observe the patient, or they can be given in writing to save time. The number of test items varies greatly from one form of the test to another. All these forms share many aspects, but they differ in their attempt to tap certain psychological areas—pathology, occupational problems, political and social views, leadership qualifications, etc.

**Interpretation.** Many sentence completion tests have few reliable norms or none at all. The interpretation is left to the skill of the examiner. Therefore, the value of these tests depends very much on the psychological acumen of the evaluator of the tests.

Other forms do have norms. The A. R. Rohde sentence completion method provides carefully collected norms for different age and sex groups. The J. B. Rotter incomplete sentence blank was designed to get an overall picture of emotional stability. The Veterans Administration incomplete sentences test was designed to assist in therapy planning.

The sentence completion tests provide little information if one uses only the available norms for their interpretation. They provide some useful information if interpreted by very experienced clinicians who have sound knowledge of the correlations of clinical symptoms and verbal expressions. Easy to administer and evaluate, the sentence completion test is sometimes given in the hope of getting original deviant responses.

One has to know how to read well between the lines to deduce from the word association and sentence completion tests new and valuable information. Both tests are projective tests because of the indeterminateness of the stimulus. However, the indeterminateness of these stimuli is very restricted when compared with the unstructured inkblots, which elicit a much greater variety of responses than words and unfinished sentences.

## Minnesota Multiphasic Personality Inventory

Known as MMPI, the Minnesota Multiphasic Personality Inventory was introduced by Starke R. Hathaway and J. Charnley McKinley in 1942. It is the most carefully constructed and investigated inventory in use today.

The projective tests, like the Rorschach and the TAT, were prompted by a desire to penetrate deeply into the personality of the individual and were created in peacetime. The questionnaires were constructed to meet the need for quick mass examinations. The first one, Robert S. Woodworth's of 1917, and the best one, Hathaway's of 1942, originated during wartime to meet the pressing needs of the military. Questionnaires are easy to administer and require little time and effort on the part of the examiner, since the subject evaluates himself. Only the scoring of the complete MMPI takes a good deal of time, unless it is done by a computer. Much of the popularity of the test can be explained by the psychology of the examiner. He does not have to make any decisions and thus has no responsibility for the results.

*Description.* In its present revised form the MMPI is a paper-and-pencil questionnaire used more widely with mental patients than any other paper-and-pencil personality test. It consists of 550 questions in the form of positive and negative statements pertaining to a great many personality aspects, including general health, neurology, motility, physiological functions, habits, family, sexual attitudes, religion, political attitudes, and many psychopathological items relevant to psychiatric diagnosis and treatment. There may soon be available a shorter form of the MMPI, consisting of about 100 of the most discriminating items.

The MMPI can be administered in groups, but it is usually given individually. The subject is asked to answer each item in one of three ways: "true" if he thinks the item applies to him; "false" if he thinks it does not; or, when he cannot say whether an item is true or false, by writing the appropriate answer on the test blank.

It has been discovered that some questions that did not appear to have any relation to important psychological syndromes are actually subtle and indirect signs of pathology. Most of the items are taken from clinical psychiatry (chiefly Kraepelinian). A deliberate attempt has been made to use descriptive items. No question was included for purely theoretical reasons.

The items are combined in scales. Each scale was validated by studying various psychiatric diagnostic groups to see whether the scale items truly differentiated them. The inclusion of an item in a scale depended on the results of such an investigation. There are nine psychopathological MMPI scales: hypochondriasis, depression, hysteria, psychopathic deviation, masculinity-femininity, paranoia, psychasthenia, schizophrenia, and mania.

*Usefulness in diagnosis.* Since the test pertains to intimate personal matters and since in many instances the subject can predict what interpretation is likely to be placed on his response, answers to the MMPI (or any questionnaire) are seldom completely frank, either because of conscious fear or unconscious defense against anxiety. The directness of the questions violates the principle of anxiety alleviation, which seems to be a condition of a frank and valid psychological self-evaluation. For this reason, the MMPI is not a dependable aid in neuropsychiatric diagnoses, especially in borderline cases, when a diagnostic aid is most helpful.

In general, the MMPI profiles formed by the scores of the nine scales agree more or less satisfactorily with clinical conclusions concerning the kind and degree of mental symptoms in about two out of three individual cases. In about one out of five cases the MMPI significantly exaggerates the psychopathology of an individual, if information from other sources serves as a criterion for judgment. Admissions of difficulties are not necessarily more valid than assertions of well-being.

*Validity of the test.* The assumption of the MMPI is that the accuracy of the subject's self-ratings is not a condition of the test's validity. The authors believe that the test rests on what the patient says, not on the truth value of what he says. For example, it is clinically true that hysterics exaggerate their troubles to gain sympathy, but rating the MMPI statement, "I think a great many people exaggerate their troubles in order to gain the sympathy and help of others," as true is scored as evidence of health, since most subjects who are not mental patients do not deny it. By contrast, when the statement about exaggeration of troubles is rated as false, points are added to the hysterical scale because most hysterics rate it that way, denying the statement. What the patient does and what he thinks he does do not always coincide.

Statements are made in the first person singular in the belief that this encourages self-identification and self-references. However, this use of the first person instead of the third person is incompatible with the anxiety-alleviating principle.

Auxiliary scales have been introduced in order to permit identification of unreliable MMPI test records. One of them is the lie scale. It consists of items that, when answered candidly, imply a socially undesirable attitude. "Do you ever tell a lie?" is a lie scale item. The vast majority of people do tell some lies. Denying this by answering the question with "no" results in adding some points to the overly virtuous individual's lie scale. Another question of this type inquires whether the subject's table manners are as good when he eats in the privacy of his house as when he eats with others. If someone gives incredible responses to too many such questions, his MMPI is suspect. He is too good to be true; he tries too hard to make a good impression.

Another auxiliary scale consists of the number of "no" responses.

A large number of denials tends to invalidate the test; it reveals an attitude of extreme guardedness. On the other hand, too small a number of "no" answers may indicate too great a suggestibility or lack of judgment, which also renders the test undependable.

The third scale, the K scale, was designed to discriminate between faking good at one pole and faking bad at the other pole of the bipolar scale. The chief aim of the K scale is to clarify the meaning of a borderline scale result by ascertaining whether the subject tended to exaggerate his strength or his weakness.

Many mental patients manage to produce normal MMPI profiles; that is, the peaks of all scales are within the middle range of T scores, between 30 and 70. But only 10 to 15 per cent of mental patients can *deliberately* simulate a normal profile. Those who fail in this attempt succeed only in making their MMPI look more abnormal. This shows that the lack of frankness and the pseudonormality can be a function of unconscious defenses against anxiety as well as a deliberate effort of self-concealment. The test gives better results when the subject feels it is to his advantage to be frank and to admit weaknesses; it is usually unreliable when he feels it is not to his advantage to be trustful and guileless.

As the subject's understanding of the content and intent of the MMPI questions increases, his capacity to modify his spontaneous answers to the questions in anticipation of the conclusions the examiner will draw from them also increases. This is true even of psychotics. Mild and intellectually average or superior schizophrenics evaluate themselves, as a rule, more normal than the normals. One difficulty of the test is that the number of deviant responses is relatively small, and, as a rule, subjects appear more stable in the MMPI than they actually are.

It may be that the MMPI has reached its highest level of perfection and cannot be improved upon. The paper-and-pencil personality inventories have definite limitations even when they are as sophisticated in structure as the MMPI.

*Interpretation.*    The majority of all mental patients produce MMPI profiles in which the D (depression) and Pt (psychasthenia) scales have the highest peaks and the T scores exceed 70 on both of them. This is to be expected, since anxiety and depression are the most frequent mental symptoms and since the existence of both tends to be associated with obsessive-compulsive tendencies; without the latter, symptoms would not persist. Phobias, forms of obsessiveness, are suggested by the Pt being the highest peak scale, provided it scores above 70. Profiles with Pt and Hy (hysteria) as the highest peaks point to psychoneurosis.

When both Pa (paranoia) and Sc (schizophrenia) score highest and when the T scores are above 70, the probability of schizophrenia is high. However, when only Sc scores above 70, the diagnosis is not certain. This is not surprising, since early or mild schizophrenics have all kinds of symp-

toms; schizoid withdrawal and reserve need not be their outstanding feature. There are schizophrenics with well-developed hysterias, depressions,
or marked anxiety states. This explains, in part, why the MMPI is a poor
diagnostic aid but a better tool for the detection and measurement of
psychopathological reaction patterns.

Although relatively little is known about the Ma (mania) scale, studies
have shown that there is some positive correlation between Ma scores on
the one hand and sociability and activity on the other. T scores of over 70
on both Sc and Ma may signify catatonia. High scores on both Ma and Pd
(psychopathic deviation) are associated with delinquent behavior, impulsiveness, immaturity, rebelliousness, hostile aggressiveness, and low frustration tolerance.

Patients with high scores on the three scales of D, Hy, and Hs (hypochondriasis) are conspicuously ill with various psychosomatic symptoms.
They are inclined to be resigned and passive. They lack assertiveness. They
are irritable but dependent, tense, timid, and worrisome. When there is a
high score on Pt as well as on D, Hy, and Hs, the patient is likely to be a
severe alcoholic, especially a male subject. Such patients are very demanding and very frustrated in the pursuit of gratification of their demands.

Pt is the anxiety and tension scale that modifies the other scales because
it is associated with alertness to potential, overwhelming, and unknown
danger. Though disturbing, anxiety intensifies interest in reality. Patients
with high scores on Sc and Pa alone are, on the whole, sicker than those
who, in addition to these two, have a high score also on the Pt scale. Many
patients with high Pt and D scores have good work records on routine jobs
that do not call for initiative, self-expression, courage, or sense of responsibility for others. When the scores on Pt, D, and Mf (masculinity-
femininity) are all high, the individual is likely to be inhibited, nondelin-
quent, effeminate, and neurotic.

Patients with high scores on Pa and Pd are very different. They tend to
be moody, assaultive, and heavily alcoholic. They make more frequent
suicidal attempts as a group than patients with other MMPI profiles. The
MMPI discriminates rather well between depressed and nondepressed psychotics, which is important in the case of potential suicides.

## FACTOR ANALYSIS OF PERSONALITY

Although the statistical procedure known as factor analysis can be applied
to any matrix of correlational coefficients, by far the greatest majority of
factor analytic studies in psychology are done with personality questionnaires. Raymond Cattell has made the most extensive, systematic use of
factor analysis and produced the 16 Personality Factors questionnaire in
1950.

Factor analysis has as its aim the discovery of the minimal number
of statistical factors with the lowest possible correlations among them

that would account for the obtained correlational coefficients. Factors, then, are a mathematical summary, the content of which depends on the summarized data. When the correlated tests, the subjects, or the complexity of the tests varies, the factors change. Some of the correlations are not high enough to trust the system of the questionnaire factors.

*Drawbacks.* A questionable assumption of psychological factor analysis is that positive correlations between test variables are due to a common source trait (factor) in the subjects' personalities. Another assumption is that traits correlated in one individual are correlated also in other persons. Because of the diversity of personality structures, this is frequently not the case, thus destroying the universality of factors. If they are not universal, the prerequisites of their applicability must be determined. The acquisition of such knowledge would be a formidable task. Lack of universality greatly decreases the usefulness of the factors and dampens the desire to go through the lengthy procedures of factor analysis.

The allure of factor analysis is the promise of objectivity and precision. This promise is spurious. For, once the factors are mathematically derived, they must be assigned a meaning; otherwise, they would remain meaningless. The meaning given is at best the result of a calculated guess regarding the common significance of the test items that mathematically constitute the factor. Without wild guessing, one cannot extract from factor analysis more than one puts into it; Catell's factors suffer from all the weaknesses of personality questionnaires. In the process of assigning meaning to factors, the gate is opened to unreliable subjectivity, which the laborious and copious statistical calculations were designed to remove. Examples of the two-dimensional factors are "enthusiasm versus melancholia," "cyclothymia versus schizothymia," and "will control versus character stability."

The same arguments apply a fortiori to other factor analytic studies based on personality questionnaires, whether they pertain to inner mental attitudes, overt conduct, neuropsychiatric diagnoses, prognosis, or other aspects of normal and abnormal personality.

## REFERENCES

Baker, G. Diagnosis of organic brain damage in the adult. In *Developments in the Rorschach Technique*, B. Klopfer, editor, vol. 2, p. 318. World Book Company, New York, 1956.

Bohm, E. A *Textbook in Rorschach Test Diagnosis*. Grune & Stratton, New York, 1958.

Brown, F. The Bender Gestalt and acting out. In *Acting Out*, L. E. Abt and S. L. Weissman, editors, p. 320. Grune & Stratton, New York, 1965.

Buck, J. N. The house-tree-person technique: a qualitative and quantitative scoring manual. J. Clin. Psychol., 4: 319, 1948.

Carr, A. C., Forer, B. R., Hooker, E., Henry, W. E., Hunt, M. L., and Piotrowski, Z. A. *The Prediction of Overt Behavior through the Use of Projective Techniques*. Charles C. Thomas, Springfield, Ill., 1960.

Gilberstadt, H., and Ducker, J. *A Handbook for Clinical and Actuarial MMPI Interpretation*. W. B. Saunders, Philadelphia, 1965.

Henry, W. E. *The Analysis of Fantasy: The Thematic Apperception Technique in the Study of Personality*. Wiley, New York, 1956.

Kent, G., and Rosanoff, A. J. A study of (word) association in insanity. Amer. J. Insanity, 67: 37, and 67: 317, 1910.

Machover, K. *Personality Projection in the Drawing of the Human Figure*. Charles C. Thomas, Springfield, Ill., 1949.

Murray, H. A. *Explorations in Personality*. Oxford University Press, New York, 1938.

Piotrowski, Z. A. *Perceptanalysis: A Fundamentally Reworked, Expanded and Systematized Rorschach Method*. Ex-Libris, Philadelphia, 1965.

Rorschach, H. *Psychodiagnostics: A Diagnostic Test Based on Perception*. H. Huber, Berne, 1921.

Shneidman, E. S., Joel, W., and Little, K. B., editors. *Thematic Test Analysis*. Grune & Stratton, New York, 1951.

Wechsler, D. *The Measurement of Adult Intelligence*, ed. 4. Williams & Wilkins, Baltimore, 1958.

Wolman, B. B., editor. *Handbook of Clinical Psychology*. McGraw-Hill, New York, 1965.

# CHAPTER FOUR

---

# *Psychological Tests for Brain Damage*

---

## *ARTHUR L. BENTON, Ph.D.*

As the primary integrative mechanism of the total human organism, the central nervous system (CNS) mediates mental processes, complex behavioral reactions, and somatic and vegetative responses. Consequently, disease or injury at the higher levels of the CNS is likely to be reflected in disturbances in mentation, feeling, and conduct. It is this fundamental fact that makes behavioral assessment a necessary part of clinical neurological evaluation, particularly when the question of disease involving the cerebral hemispheres has been raised. Such behavioral assessment can be accomplished in various ways: by direct observation of the patient's behavior in a natural setting, from the description by informants of aspects of the patient's present and past conduct, by questioning and observation during the interview, and by tests. All these approaches have proved to be useful in aiding diagnostic inference.

The method of tests differs from the other approaches in a number of respects. A test is essentially an attempt to elicit a specific type of behavior under relatively controlled stimulus conditions. This control is achieved by presenting a defined task or stimulus complex (for example, arithmetic problems, material for memorization, inkblots) in a defined manner to every patient. Moreover, the task or stimulus complex is of such a nature as to evoke behavior that is relatively easy to describe in objective or quantitative terms. Because of their relatively objective and quantitative nature, psychological tests are often conceived of as laboratory procedures, comparable to serology, electroencephalography, and radiology procedures, with respect to their role in neuropsychiatric diagnosis. This perspective emphasizes the distinctive contribution these methods can make, as contrasted with the more global forms of behavioral evaluation; that is, they provide findings characterized by a degree of precision and objectivity that cannot be obtained through the use of the other methods.

Furthermore, psychological tests, when considered as laboratory procedures, are seen in their proper role as aids to or components of the total clinicodiagnostic process. Nevertheless, it is important for the clinician to appreciate the fundamental difference between serology or electroencephalography procedures and neuropsychological tests. The former deal with infrabehavioral events, the latter with behavioral events. Classes of phenomena not otherwise open to analysis are disclosed through the use of the infrabehavioral methods. In contrast, neuropsychological tests deal with overt behavior, a class of phenomena already available, actually or potentially, for global clinical evaluation. It should be noted that the majority of psychological tests represent attempts to objectify and quantify impressions already gained from general clinical observation.

Thus, to a considerable degree, the aspects of behavior sampled by clinical observation and by neuropsychological tests are the same (for example, speed of response, level of comprehension, use of language), but the tests assess these aspects of behavior with greater reliability and precision. The tests go on to sample other aspects of behavior, such as visual memory and psychomotor skill, that are not readily elicitable in the general examination. Hence, the employment of neuropsychological tests serves both to validate the impressionistic findings of the general clinical examination and to provide additional information about other aspects of intellect and personality.

It is a truism that behavior has multiple determinants and that the same behavioral deviation may be produced by factors of a diverse nature. Hence, when behavioral deficits that raise the question of cerebral dysfunction are observed in a patient, it is necessary to consider other possible determinants of defective performance before the inference of cerebral disease is made. Among these are: (1) lack of adequate cooperation and effort on the part of hostile, asocial, or paranoid patients; (2) lack of mental energy in patients who are depressed or seriously depleted by systemic extracerebral disease; (3) inattention and concentration difficulty associated with preoccupation or intense anxiety; (4) simulation or exaggeration of mental incompetence, particularly when questions of compensation for injuries received or a pension are involved; and (5) poor comprehension and task adjustment on the part of culturally handicapped patients.

## SURVEY OF NEUROPSYCHOLOGICAL TESTS

### GENERAL INTELLIGENCE

The clinical observation that patients with cerebral disease may show an overall behavioral inefficiency and be unable to meet the diverse intellectual demands associated with the responsibilities of daily life dates back many centuries. The observation is expressed in the global concepts of dementia and deterioration. The normal counterpart of these pathological concepts is the concept of general intelligence, which is equally global in nature. The application of this concept in clinical practice assumes that there is a sufficient degree of positive correlation among various intellectual abilities to warrant the conclusion that a single general ability is a significant component in performance on diverse intellectual tasks—verbal skills, mathematical abilities, abstract reasoning, and the like. Granted this assumption, it is justifiable to derive a single score from a battery of mental tests and to use this score as an index of general intelligence. This is what is done when an intelligence test battery such as the Wechsler Adult Intelligence Scale (WAIS), which consists of ten subtests, is administered and the patient's scores on the various subtests are combined into a total score, which yields an I.Q. (See Table I.)

*Obtained I.Q. versus expected I.Q.*    In the United States, the WAIS is by far the most widely used test battery for assessing general intelligence in adult subjects. In its clinical application, a number of procedures have been used to evaluate the possibility of a decline in general intelligence that may be ascribed to the presence of cerebral disease. The most direct approach is to compare a patient's obtained age-corrected I.Q. score with the age-corrected I.Q. score that may be expected in view of his educational background, cultural level, and occupational history. A negative discrepancy—that is, obtained I.Q. below expected I.Q.—beyond empirically established normal limits may be interpreted as indicating a possibility of the presence of cerebral disease. This procedure has been shown to have considerable clinical utility. However, it also has serious limitations since, as is well known, many patients with unquestionable cerebral disease do not show an overall decline in general intelligence of sufficient severity to be reflected in a significant lowering of the WAIS I.Q. score. Consequently, this procedure may be expected to yield a fair proportion of false negative results.

A variant of this procedure is to compare obtained and expected I.Q. scores on the WAIS performance scale, which consists, for the most part, of nonverbal and relatively novel tasks. This has proved to be fully as useful as the comparison of full-scale I.Q. scores.

*Sensitive versus insensitive tasks.*    Since it has been found, at least in nonaphasic patients, that certain types of performance tend to be more seriously affected by cerebral damage than others, a second approach consists of comparing performance level on presumably less sensitive tasks with that on more sensitive tasks. Thus, verbal scale I.Q. is compared with performance scale I.Q., or performance on a set of insensitive tests (for example, information, picture completion) is compared with performance on a set of sensitive tests (for example, arithmetic, block designs). Although widely employed by clinical psychologists, these procedures, which rely on a discrepancy score or a deterioration ratio within the test battery

TABLE I

*Tests for Assessing Brain Damage*

| Category | Subcategories | Remarks |
|---|---|---|
| General scales | Wechsler Adult Intelligence Scale (WAIS)<br>Stanford-Binet<br>Wechsler Intelligence Scale for Children (WISC) | Given the availability of adequate normative standards in relation to the patient's educational and cultural background, a performance significantly below expectations should raise the question of cerebral damage. This generalization applies to both adults and children. |
| Reasoning and problem-solving | Abstractions (Shipley)<br>Progressive matrices (Raven)<br>Proverbs (Gorham)<br>Perceptual mazes (Elithorn)<br>Object and color-sorting tests (Goldstein and Scheerer) | Performance level is closely related to educational background and premorbid intellectual level. In general, the clinical application of these tests is more useful in the case of educated patients. If specific language and perceptual defect can be ruled out as determinants of defective performance, failure suggests frontal lobe involvement or diffuse cerebral disease. |
| Memory and orientation | Immediate auditory memory—repetition of digits<br>Immediate auditory memory—reversal of digits<br>Immediate visual memory (Benton, Graham-Kendall)<br>Recent auditory memory—words or stories<br>Recent visual memory—words or pictures<br>Temporal orientation (Benton, Van Allen and Fogel) | For complete assessment, a number of memory tasks (auditory versus visual, verbal versus nonverbal, immediate versus recent) should be given. Minor defects in temporal orientation may be elicited and suggest weakness in recent memory. |

TABLE I (*continued*)
Tests for Assessing Brain Damage

| Category | Subcategories | Remarks |
|---|---|---|
| Visuoperceptive and visuoconstructive | Identification of hidden figures (Teuber-Weinstein-Rudel) <br> Identification of fragmented figures (Street-Gestalt) <br> Block design construction (Kohs, Goldstein-Scheerer, Wechsler) <br> Stick-arranging (Goldstein-Scheerer) <br> Copying designs (L. Bender, Benton visual retention) <br> Three dimensional block construction (Benton-Fogel) <br> Inkblot interpretation (Rorschach, Holtzman) <br> Perceptual mazes (Elithorn) <br> Responsiveness to double visual stimulation (M. B. Bender) | These types of task are relatively sensitive indicators of the presence of cerebral disease. Analysis of qualitative features of performance and comparison of performance level with the status of language and reasoning abilities often provide indications with regard to locus of the lesion. |
| Somatoperceptual | Tactile recognition (Parker, Ross) <br> Finger recognition (Benton) <br> Right-left orientation (Benton) <br> Responsiveness to double tactile stimulation (M. B. Bender) | Frequently useful indicators of the presence and locus of cerebral disease. |
| Language | Token test (De Renzi-Vignolo) <br> Abstractions (Shipley) <br> Proverbs (Gorham) <br> Word fluency (Benton-Spreen-Fogel) | Test performance is dependent on educational background, and it is essential that clinical interpretation allow for this and other possibly significant factors. In adult patients, defective |

TABLE I (*continued*)
*Tests for Assessing Brain Damage*

| Category | Subcategories | Remarks |
|---|---|---|
| | Illinois test of psycholinguistic abilities (Kirk-McCarthy) | performance (particularly in relation to other abilities) suggests dysfunction of the cerebral hemisphere that is dominant for language. In children, defective performance does not have this localizing significance but does raise the question of the presence of cerebral damage. |
| Attention, concentration, and motor abilities | Continuous performance test (Rosvold) Visual vigilance (McDonald-Burns) Reaction time (Blackburn-Benton-Joynt) Motor impersistence (Garfield) Imitations of actions (Bergès-Lézine) | Valuable behavioral indicators of the presence (and sometimes locus) of cerebral disease that deserve more extensive clinical application. |

itself, have been found to possess only relatively modest clinical utility.

*Impaired performances.* A third approach would be to focus attention on those subtest performances (block designs, arithmetic, digit symbol) that clinical experience indicates are most frequently and severely impaired in patients with cerebral disease. This is a rational procedure, but full exploitation of its clinical value depends on the availability of valid and precise normative standards of performance in relation to age, educational background, and sex. In a given clinical setting, the establishment of such standards may require the development of local norms, since test performance patterns may vary in different parts of the country and among different cultural groups.

## REASONING AND PROBLEM-SOLVING

Impairment in the capacity for abstract reasoning and reduction in behavioral flexibility when confronted with an unfamiliar situation are well-known behavioral characteristics of the brain-damaged patient. Both types of deficit are important components of Kurt Goldstein's concept that the fundamental behavioral change resulting from cerebral disease is "impairment of the abstract attitude."

A relatively large number of special tests designed to measure each of these capacities have been devised. Among those that have shown clinical usefulness are the Shipley abstractions, Raven's progressive matrices, the Gorham proverbs test, the Porteus mazes, the Elithorn perceptual mazes, and the Goldstein-Scheerer sorting tests.

Defective performance by brain-damaged patients on such tests is frequent enough, but it is important to determine the *basis* for a given patient's failure. Language skills play a role in performance on some tests, and other tests make demands on visuoperceptive capacity. Hence, it is essential to rule out language and perceptual handicaps as determinants of a defective performance before making the inference that it indicates impaired reasoning or problem-solving ability.

The tests mentioned have proved to be particularly valuable for disclosing behavioral deficit in the neurologically negative patient with frontal lobe or beginning diffuse cerebral disease who shows no specific sensory, perceptual, language, or motor impairments and who, on initial encounter, may appear to have a functional psychiatric disorder. Conversely, these tests are practically useless for the specific purpose of inferring brain disease when applied to unintelligent or uneducated subjects or to individuals suffering from psychosis.

## MEMORY AND ORIENTATION

Impairment in certain types of memory, most notably short-term and recent memory, is a prominent behavioral deficit in brain-damaged patients and is often the first sign of beginning cerebral disease and of old age. For this reason, procedures for the assessment of memory functions have always found a prominent place in the mental status examination and in psychological test batteries.

**Memory.** This catch-all term covers the retention of all types of material over different periods of time, involving diverse forms of response. Empirical studies have shown that a subject's performance may vary significantly as a function of a number of factors, such as the sensory modality involved (auditory versus visual), the type of material to be remembered (verbal versus nonverbal), or the form of response required (recognition versus reproduction). For this reason, the neuropsychological examiner is more inclined to give specific memory tests and to evaluate them separately than to utilize an omnibus battery, such as the Wechsler Memory Scale, which provides for a brief assessment of a large variety of performances and which yields a single score in the form of a memory quotient. However, this type of instrument has some usefulness as a screening device, despite the fact that it does not adequately measure such memory functions as visual retention and also despite the fact that combining the separate scores into a single total score is a dubious procedure.

IMMEDIATE MEMORY. A differentiation between immediate memory, recent memory, and remote memory is often made, and this distinction proves meaningful from a clinical standpoint. For example, it is a common observation that patients with a Korsakoff syndrome, showing a pervasive and severe impairment in recent memory, may be able to perform well within normal limits on tasks involving the immediate repetition of digits or sentences and may show preserved memory for events in the remote past.

Immediate memory may be defined as the reproduction, recognition, or recall of perceived material within a period of not more than 10 seconds after presentation. It is most often assessed by digit repetition and reversal (auditory) tests and memory for designs (visual) tests. Both have been found to discriminate significantly between brain-damaged and control subjects, but the visual task is the more sensitive indicator.

The precise reason for this difference in discriminating power is not known. The relatively novel nature of the task of drawing designs from memory may be an important factor here, or perhaps the difference in sensory modality is the crucial factor. A comparative study of the discriminative efficiency of auditory and visual digit span tasks would be of interest in this regard and might provide information of clinical utility.

In any case, both an auditory-verbal task such as digit span (or memory for words or sentences) and a nonverbal visual task such as memory for designs (or faces) should be given to assess a patient's immediate memory. Despite the fact that group studies show a significant positive correlation between performances on the two types of tasks, dissociation (that is, adequate performance on the one and defective performance on the other) is not rare and may be of clinical interest. Patients with lesions of the right hemisphere are likely to show significant defect on visual nonverbal tasks while performing on a normal level on auditory verbal tasks. Conversely, patients with left hemisphere disease, including those who are not aphasic, are likely to show deficit on the auditory verbal tests with variable performance on the visual nonverbal tasks.

RECENT MEMORY. This refers to the reproduction, recognition, or recall of perceived material after a given period of time (10 seconds or longer) has elapsed following the initial presentation. It is typically assessed by measuring the patient's memory for a story read to him, for items in a display of words or pictures or abstract forms, or for such learned material as lists of words or pictures. This type of task provides one of the more sensitive indicators of the presence of cerebral disease. However, since quality of performance is closely dependent on level of effort and attention, the examiner must carefully consider other possible determinants before interpreting failure on these tasks as a sign of brain damage.

MEMORY FOR REMOTE EVENTS AND ORIENTATION FOR PERSON OR PLACE. These are rarely disturbed in the brain-damaged patient who is not psychotic or severely demented.

TEMPORAL ORIENTATION. Minor defects in temporal orientation are not at all rare. These are often overlooked by the clinical examiner because of his tendency to regard slight inaccuracy in giving the day of the week or of the month as being inconsequential. But, in point of fact, objective assessment based on empirically derived normative standards has shown that 20 to 25 per cent of nonpsychotic patients with cerebral disease are likely to show significant inferiority with respect to precision of temporal orientation.

## PERCEPTUAL AND PERCEPTUOMOTOR PERFORMANCES

Many brain-damaged patients, when examined by means of appropriate techniques, show defective analysis of complex perceptual situations and/or inability to translate their perceptions into appropriate motor action. Unless the impairment is of a gross nature (as in visual-object agnosia or dressing dyspraxia) or interferes with a specific occupational skill (such as typesetting or assembling a machine), these deficits are not likely to be the subject of spontaneous complaints. Nevertheless, objective testing discloses a remarkably high incidence of impaired performance on visuoanalytic, visuospatial, and visuoconstructive tasks in brain-damaged patients, particularly in those with disease involving the right hemisphere. The impairment also extends to tactile and auditory perceptual task performances.

Many tests have been devised to measure these capacities; only a few of them can be mentioned here. Higher level visuoperceptive capacity may be assessed by means of tests involving the recognition of hidden figures and fragmented figures. Visuoconstructive capacity may be assessed by tests calling for block design construction, stick-arranging, copying designs (for example, Bender-Gestalt, and three-dimensional block model construction. Defective capacity for visual and synthesis is also brought out in performance on the Rorschach test by poor percepts (F-), failure to see movement (low M), and paucity of response (low R).

Performance on the Elithorn perceptual mazes often discloses the same type of impairment. Patients with apparently intact stereognostic capacity, as evidenced by their accurate recognition of palpated objects in the neurological examination, often show defects in tactile recognition when subjected to more demanding test procedures. Defects in auditory discrimination and recognition may also be manifested. Somatoperceptual defects, such as impairment in finger localization or in the identification of the right and left side of one's body, are sometimes revealed by appropriate testing. Elementary perceptual integration within the visual and tactile modalities can be assessed by application of the method of double simultaneous sensory stimulation.

The application of these perceptual and perceptuomotor tests in the detection of the presence of cerebral disease has proved quite rewarding and possesses certain advantages. Although not culture-free (no behavioral performances are), these tests are generally less dependent on educational level and cultural background than many of the more intellectual tasks. Many of the tests are relatively sensitive indicators of the presence of cerebral disease. Finally, they often provide suggestions with regard to the probable *locus* of the cerebral lesion and thus may help to offer a focus for further neurological exploration.

## LANGUAGE FUNCTIONS

Gross impairment in language functions in the form of frank aphasia can scarcely be overlooked by the psychiatrist, although the less experienced examiner may sometimes misinterpret some types of defect as signs of dementia or psychosis. On the other hand, it is quite likely that less severe disturbances of language expression and comprehension may go unrecognized for the simple reason that the interview or the application of a few simple tests for aphasia fails to bring them out.

Relatively minor defects in the use of the instrument of language may be valid indicators of the presence of disease of the dominant hemisphere. These defects are often the first signs of a developing aphasic disorder. Higher level language tests have been successfully used to indicate the presence of such a subclinical or latent aphasia. A number of instruments can be used for this purpose. The token test of DeRenzi and Vignolo brings subtle as well as gross disturbances in the comprehension of oral language into sharp relief. The Shipley abstractions make demands on verbal reasoning that the patient with latent aphasia is unable to meet; understanding of the meaning of proverbs is likely to be poor. Verbal-ideational impoverishment is shown by defective performance on word fluency tests.

Performance on all these tests is heavily dependent on educational background, and clinical interpretation must allow for this variable, and for other possibly significant factors, such as age and sex. When these corrections are made, these tests provide valuable information that can aid in diagnosis. The sensitivity of performance level to the presence of disease of the dominant hemisphere negates the assumption that verbal abilities remain intact in nonaphasic patients with brain damage while nonverbal skills decline. The seeming disparity is a question of what tests are used to assess verbal abilities.

## Speed and Flexibility of Response

It is a common clinical observation that some brain-damaged patients are quite slow in responding to diverse stimuli and have notable difficulty in modifying their behavior to meet the changing demands of a shifting situation. Objective quantitative methods of assessment not only confirm these observations in such patients but also disclose the same response retardation and behavioral rigidity in many others who may appear, on clinical ground, to be unremarkable in these respects.

Reaction time studies have shown that both simple and choice visual reactions are significantly retarded in 40 to 45 per cent of nonpsychotic, brain-damaged patients. Moreover, patients with unilateral cerebral disease show clear retardation, even when the ipsilateral hand (on the unaffected side of the body) is used to effect the response. These results indicate that reaction time is a fairly sensitive indicator of over-all cerebral integrity and that retardation in reaction time reflects the presence of a cerebral lesion *regardless* of its locus. It may be noted that comparison of the reaction times of the right and left hands often provides an indication of the probable hemispheric locus of a focal lesion. This method deserves more extensive application as a diagnostic procedure, particularly when the question of differentiation between neurosis and cerebral disease is involved.

A variant of the simple reaction time experiment, in which the patient must react to successive presentations of different stimuli instead of to successive presentations of the same stimulus, provides an opportunity to measure behavioral flexibility on a basic sensorimotor level. Excessive slowness in response to a stimulus that has been preceded by a stimulus in another sense modality (cross-modal retardation effect) is exhibited by both schizophrenic and nonpsychotic brain-damaged patients. Neurotic patients do not show this marked susceptibility to the cross-modal retardation effect.

Other measures of behavioral flexibility are provided by tasks in which the patient must modify his approach to a problem in accordance with changing requirements—color-form sorting, object sorting, and concept formation tests. The last type of test has been found to be particularly valuable in identifying patients with frontal lobe disease.

## ATTENTION AND CONCENTRATION

The capacity to sustain a maximal level of attention over a period of time is sometimes impaired in brain-damaged patients and is reflected by oscillation in performance level on a continuous or repeated activity. There is some evidence that this instability in performance is related to electroencephalographic abnormality and that the occurrence of inexplicable declines in performance is related temporally to the appearance of certain types of abnormal electrical activity. For example, Prechtl and associates were able to show that episodes of response retardation in a continuous performance task in epileptic patients coincided with the occurrence of diffuse flattening of the EEG.

A variety of tests have been devised to assess vigilance and capacity for sustained attention. Simple reaction time provides a convenient measure of variability and speed of simple responses and is possibly as discriminative and informative as assessments of performance on more complex and lengthy tasks. While the patient's median reaction time can be utilized as an index of speed, the standard deviation of his reaction times provides an index of variability that can be conceptualized as reflecting limitations in capacity for sustaining maximal attention. Intraindividual variability in both simple and choice reaction time has been shown to be significantly higher in brain-damaged patients than in matched controls. Among the more recent tests that have been developed for measuring attention and concentration is the continuous performance test of Rosvold et al., which has been shown to discriminate reasonably well between brain-damaged patients (both adults and children) and controls. Another test is a vigilance task, involving the detection of visual signals, developed by McDonald and Burns; it also discriminates significantly between brain-damaged patients and controls.

The clinical utility of these tests of attention and vigilance has not been adequately determined, and whether they deserve a place in the armamentarium of the clinical examiner is still an open question. Study along these lines will have to take into account the possible effects of drugs and of deviations in mood. Tests in this area seem to warrant further exploration, particularly since they furnish a type of task that includes the possibility of establishing a temporal correlation between performance and specified neural events.

## BEHAVIORAL INDICES OF BRAIN DAMAGE IN CHILDREN

For various reasons, it is very popular today to make the diagnostic inference of brain damage to explain entirely or in part the deviant behavior of many children. In the majority of cases, the inference is made on the basis of behavioral observation (for example, hyperactivity, distractibility, motor awkwardness, destructiveness) and is *not* substantiated by infrabehavioral clinical or laboratory findings. The clinical psychologist is then called on to validate the diagnostic impression by means of tests. Since, to a considerable degree, his tests assess the same behavior as that on which the clinical diagnosis was based, the chances of confirming the diagnosis are rather high. The circular nature of this process and the fact that at no point has an independent, infrabehavioral criterion of brain damage played a role are obvious.

The clinical impression of brain damage most often rests on observation of the symptom complex of overactivity, restlessness, impulsivity, irritability, and unpredictability. Although the reality of this symptom complex with its significant relation to the presence of brain damage is undeniable, this is by no means *the* characteristic behavioral picture of brain damage in children. The behavioral consequences, if any, of early brain damage may take many forms, of which the hyperkinetic impulse disorder is only one. In fact, the latter is not a particularly frequent behavioral picture among children with unquestionable cerebral disease (tumor, trauma, degenerative disease). Furthermore, one must be prepared for the possibility, clearly indicated by animal studies, that early brain damage may result in very little or no behavioral deficit and that, when such deficit does appear, it is always less severe than that caused by a comparable cerebral lesion in adults. Thus, there is reason to believe that there are many brain-damaged children who are not identified by current methods of behavioral assessment.

These preliminary remarks are not intended to foster an attitude of nihilistic skepticism. They are made because they bear directly on the judicious use of test results by the psychiatrist when the question of brain damage in a child has been raised. The clinical psychologist may report (indeed, is likely to report) signs of brain damage in various test performances. Or he may report a normal profile of test performances. Whichever the case may be, it is important for the referring physician to be aware of the complexities of the situation so that he is in a position to place the test results in proper perspective.

In the following survey, emphasis is focused on the use of tests to infer brain damage in the nondefective child (that is, a child with an I.Q. of 80 or higher) of school age.

## General Intelligence

As in adults, general intelligence in children is measured by overall performance level on an omnibus test battery. The most frequently used batteries are the Wechsler Intelligence Scale for Children (WISC) and the revised Stanford-Binet. A low level of general intelligence is probably the most constant behavioral result of brain damage in children. The failure in intellectual development may, or may not, be severe enough to place the child in the category of mental retardation. When the child is not retarded, his intelligence level still tends to be below expectations, based on the intelligence levels of his parents and siblings and taking into account his socioeconomic status. The identified nondefective, brain-damaged child from an average family is likely to have an I.Q. in the 80's, instead of the expected 100 to 110. The identified nondefective brain-damaged child from a superior family may have a higher I.Q., perhaps even as high as 120, but an appreciable difference in level between him and his siblings is usually found.

In contrast to the findings in nonaphasic adults with cerebral disease, the performance scale of the WISC does not seem to be more sensitive than the verbal scale to the effects of brain damage. This is understandable when one considers that in the adult such tests as information, vocabulary, and comprehension measure knowledge and skills acquired in the remote past, whereas in the child they are indices of the rate of acquisition of these skills.

As with all tests, the procedure of comparing observed with expected I.Q. in the nondefective child suspected of suffering from brain damage no doubt produces its share of false negatives, and special test methods should be utilized. With respect to the problem of possible false positives, if the clinician is not willing to accept a significant discrepancy between observed and expected I.Q. as evidence of brain damage, he should be prepared to explain the discrepancy on other grounds. This simple, straightforward approach to the behavioral diagnosis of brain damage in children deserves more widespread clinical application than is now accorded it.

## PERCEPTUAL AND PERCEPTUOMOTOR PERFORMANCES

These tasks constitute the favored procedure among clinical psychologists for disclosing behavioral deficit related to brain damage. Their application is based on the long-standing observation that many brain-damaged children with adequate verbal skills show strikingly defective visuoperceptive and visuomotor performances.

The test most frequently employed is copying of designs, either from a model or from memory. Typically, about 25 per cent of brain-damaged school children of adequate verbal intelligence are found to perform defectively—that is, on a level exceeded by 95 per cent of normal children of comparable verbal intelligence. The task discriminates between brain-damaged children and those suffering from presumably psychogenic emotional disturbance. Another type of perceptuomotor task that has been investigated is path-tracing, as in the trail-making test.

Tasks involving the recognition of hidden figures—that is, figures imbedded in masking background—and the detection of patterns have also been utilized to probe visuoperceptive capacity and have disclosed inferior performance in brain-damaged children as compared with normal controls. Capacity for elementary perceptual integration within and across sensory modalities can be evaluated by double simultaneous stimulation and intersensory matching techniques; their application has yielded results of clinical interest.

Defective finger recognition and right-left orientation, often conceptualized as reflecting a disturbance in the body schema, are shown by some nondefective children with brain damage. Tests for these capacities deserve a place in any detailed examination directed toward the question of brain damage in a child of school age.

## LANGUAGE FUNCTIONS

Diagnostic evaluation of the child suspected of having brain damage has typically depended largely on assessment of his perceptual and perceptuomotor performances, but there is reason to believe that the status of his language abilities may be an equally sensitive indicator. It is not uncommon to find very poor development of language functions as compared with nonverbal skills in high grade mental retardates, and there remains the question as to whether this particular pattern of performance may not be the reason why many of these children are labeled retarded rather than brain-damaged. There is considerable evidence that aphasic children, those who show a gross maldevelopment of oral language abilities as compared with general mental level, suffer from brain damage. Moreover, a number of studies have raised the question of whether prenatal brain injury may not be a causative factor in at least some cases of developmental dyslexia. The finding of an excessively high incidence of electroencephalographic abnormality in dyslexic children points to the same conclusion.

All these considerations suggest that a careful analysis of language skills should be a part of the psychodiagnostic work-up in children suspected of having brain damage. The Illinois test for psycholinguistic abilities is an appropriate instrument for this purpose. Unless explainable in terms of cultural handicap, sensory deficit, or personality disturbance, observed deficit in this area should raise the question of brain damage.

## ATTENTION AND CONCENTRATION

It is commonly reported by parents and teachers that a brain-damaged child will show inexplicable inconsistency in behavior, now performing at one level, then at another. This everyday observation has been amply confirmed by analyses of performance on a variety of tests that require, either deliberately or incidentally, sustained attention and concentration. For diagnostic purposes, the Continuous Performance Test can be utilized with older school children as well as adults to probe this capacity. Variability in simple reaction time provides a rational measure in younger children that can be applied clinically if appropriate normative standards are available as a basis for evaluating performance.

## MOTOR PERFORMANCES

Motor awkwardness and inability to carry out movement sequences on command or by imitation are not uncommonly seen in brain-damaged children. Some of them show a virtual ideomotor apraxia and/or dressing dyspraxia. A variety of tests are available for the assessment of manual dexterity—for example, manipulations with tweezers, paper-cutting, and peg-placing. The new imitation of actions tests of Bergès and Lézine promise to be useful for the evaluation of higher-level praxis and would have even greater utility if an American standardization and revision were undertaken.

Motor impersistence—inability to sustain an action initiated on command, such as keeping the eyes closed or maintaining central fixation during confrontation testing of visual fields—is seen in a small proportion of adult patients with cerebral disease. However, it is shown with remarkably high frequency by nondefective, brain-damaged children. Many mental defectives also show excessive motor impersistence. Clinical studies of this rather singular disability suggest that it may well prove to be an extremely valuable symptom of brain damage in the younger school age child.

## REFERENCES

Bender, M. B. *Disorders in Perception.* Charles C Thomas, Springfield, Ill., 1952.

Benton, A. L. The visual retention test as a constructional praxis task. Conf. Neurol. (Basel), 22: 141, 1962.

Benton, A. L. *The Revised Visual Retention Test: Clinical and Experimental Applications,* ed. 3. Psychological Corporation, New York, 1963.

Benton, A. L., Elithorn, A., Fogel, M. L., and Kerr, M. A perceptual maze test sensitive to brain damage. J. Neurol. Neurosurg. Psychiat., 26: 540, 1963.

Benton, A. L., and Fogel, M. L. Three-dimensional constructional praxis: a clinical test. Arch. Neurol., 7: 347, 1962.

Benton, A. L., and Joynt, R. J. Reaction time in unilateral cerebral disease. Conf. Neurol. (Basel), 19: 247, 1959.

Benton, A. L., Sutton, S., Kennedy, J. A., and Brokaw, J. R. The cross-modal retardation in reaction times of patients with cerebral disease. J. Nerv. Ment. Dis., 135: 413, 1962.

Benton, A. L., Van Allen, M. W., and Fogel, M. L. Temporal orientation in cerebral disease. J. Nerv. Ment. Dis., 139: 110, 1964.

Bergès, J., and Lézine, L. *Test d'Imitation de Gestes.* Masson, Paris, 1963.

Birch, H. G., and Lefford, A. Intersensory development in children. Monogr. Soc. Res. Child Develop., 28, No. 5, 1963.

Blackburn, H. L., and Benton, A. L. Simple and choice reaction time in cerebral disease. Conf. Neurol. (Basel), 15: 327, 1955.

Davids, A., Goldenberg, L., and Laufer, M. W. The relationship of the Archimedes spiral aftereffect and the Trail Making Test to brain damage in children. J. Consult. Pyschol., 21: 429, 1957.

DeRenzi, A., and Vignolo, L. A. The token test: a sensitive test to detect receptive disturbances in aphasics. Brain, 85: 665, 1962.

Fogel, M. L. The intelligence quotient as an index of brain damage. Amer. J. Orthopyschiat., 34: 555, 1964.

Garfield, J. C. Motor impersistence in normal and brain-damaged children. Neurology, 14: 623, 1964.

Gorham, D. R. Verbal abstraction in psychiatric illness: assay of impairment utilizing proverbs. J. Ment. Sci., 107: 52, 1961.

Kirk, S. A., and McCarthy, J. J. The Illinois Test of Psycholinguistic Abilities: an approach to differential diagnosis. Amer. J. Ment. Defic., 66: 399, 1961.

Porteus, S. D. *The Maze Test and Clinical Psychology*. Pacific Books, Palo Alto, Calif., 1959.

Prechtl, H. F. R., Boeke, P. E., and Schut, T. The electroencephalogram and performance in epileptic patients. Neurology, 11: 296, 1961.

Raven, J. C. *Guide to Using the Mill Hill Vocabulary Scale with the Progressive Matrices Scales*. H. K. Lewis, London, 1958.

Rowley, V. N. Analysis of the WISC performance of brain damaged and emotionally disturbed children. J. Consult. Psychol., 25: 553, 1961.

Rowley, V. N., and Baer, P. E. Visual Retention Test performance in emotionally disturbed and brain-damaged children. Amer. J. Orthopsychiat., 31: 579, 1961.

Shipley, W. C., and Burlingame, C. C. A convenient self-administering scale for measuring intellectual impairment in psychotics. Amer. J. Psychiat., 97: 1313, 1941.

Teuber, H. L., and Rudel, R. G. Behavior after cerebral lesions in children and adults. Develop. Med. Child Neurol., 4: 3, 1962.

Teuber, H. L., and Weinstein, S. A. Ability to discover hidden figures after cerebral lesions. Arch. Neurol. Psychiat., 76: 369, 1956.

# CHAPTER FIVE

---

# Social Service Information

---

## C. KNIGHT ALDRICH, M.D.

A SATISFACTORY psychiatric diagnosis usually requires more information than can be obtained from the direct psychiatric, psychological, or physical evaluation of the patient. It requires an evaluation, to the extent possible, of the total setting of the illness, including the environment and the people who are and have been significant in the patient's life. Family members are the usual sources of this kind of information. They can also provide an alternative, if not necessarily a more objective, view of the symptoms and the course of the illness, of the patient's personality and its development, and of the character of his interpersonal relationships and his adaptation. The social worker's contacts are not limited to relatives but may include other community resources when indicated, such as social agencies, clergy, and, usually in collaboration with the psychiatrist, the family physician or other medical resources.

## ROLE OF SOCIAL WORKER

Although in most cases the psychiatrist can interview the relatives, the social worker's participation has distinct advantages. He offers the relatives a professional member of the psychiatric team who is primarily concerned with them and with whatever problems have developed in their lives as a result of the patient's illness; the psychiatrist, on the other hand, is primarily concerned with the patient and his problems. Furthermore, and particularly important with adolescent patients, the social worker's participation makes it unnecessary for the psychiatrist to communicate directly with the relatives; therefore, he does not appear to be relaying the patient's confidences back home. However, this advantage is lost if the psychiatrist uses the social worker as an intermediary for the transmission of information the patient has considered confidential, for the patient usually finds out what has transpired.

The social worker participates in the diagnostic assessment in most psychiatric training centers, and the psychiatric resident learns to rely on the social worker for several aspects of the work-up. He may be unprepared, therefore, for the situation that prevails in private practice. There, particularly in outpatient practice, he must usually do his own intake and secure his own social history. It is important, therefore, for the resident to learn about the technique as well as about the results of social work interviewing in his training years.

## PARTICIPATION OF SOCIAL WORKER

### GOALS

The social worker was originally concerned primarily with the mechanics of disposition—whether the discharged patient would have a place to live and enough to live on. To obtain this information usually required a knowledge of the family relationships, and, as the usefulness of this knowledge in diagnosis became apparent, the social worker began to interview relatives at the beginning of the patient's clinic or hospital experience.

Some of the information obtained from interviews with family members simply supplements information provided by the patient, and some—the history of a child's early development, for example—is inaccessible to the patient. If the family provides material the patient could have provided but has withheld because of fear or mistrust of the psychiatrist, it must be managed with considerable care. If the patient discovers that his relatives have revealed material he wishes to withhold, he will resent what he considers their betrayal, regardless of their benevolent motivation. If he discovers that the psychiatrist has secured from other sources evidence he was trying to conceal, his fear or mistrust of the psychiatrist will be increased. The psychiatrist may even decide, after weighing the advantages and disadvantages of filling in the information gap, that more is to be gained by waiting until the patient has developed enough trust to vouchsafe the information on his own. The goal of the social worker's interview, therefore, is not primarily to ferret out every possible fact in a patient's background but to take the kind of history that will contribute to the collaborative effort of the professional team in the way best calculated to strengthen diagnosis, treatment, and eventual disposition.

### VALUE

In child guidance clinics, particularly in cases of young children, most of the preliminary information necessary for a tentative diagnosis is obtained from parents, and the social worker's intake interview is usually the first contact between the clinic and the family. Information obtained at intake may also be valuable for purposes of screening, to determine whether clinic treatment is appropriate for the patient and family or whether a referral to another type of care is indicated. The intake process has been so successful in children's clinics that it has been adapted to adult psychiatric clinics for purposes of screening, preliminary history-taking, and explanation of the purpose and mechanics of treatment.

Although a social history is helpful in the understanding of almost any psychiatric illness, it is perhaps more essential in the understanding of childhood conditions, psychoses, character disorders, and marital problems than it is in the understanding of psychoneuroses or psychophysiological disorders.

When hospitalization is a possible plan, a home visit in advance provides valuable information concerning family dynamics and helps the patient make the transition from home to hospital. The social worker customarily makes visits of this kind, although in some settings one of the psychiatric nurses who will be closely involved in the care of the patient is assigned this responsibility.

The psychiatric diagnosis may not be finally established before treatment begins. In some cases it is an on-going process, subject to constant modification and refinement as treatment progresses and new information becomes available. The social worker usually continues to see the relatives at intervals throughout the period of the patient's treatment.

## GROUP INTERVIEWS

As psychiatrists have become more concerned with understanding the patterns of interaction among family members as well as the histories of individual family members, they have become more interested in observing families in action. Interviews with the patient and his spouse or with the patient and his parents can give valuable clues about family interaction that are helpful not only in diagnosis but in treatment. When a reluctant family sees that both psychiatrist and social worker participate in the diagnostic interview, they may be more easily persuaded to participate later in active treatment. Furthermore, the casework material that is elicited in a family interview can be more effectively understood by the social worker if he has directly observed the interaction than if he hears about it later from the psychiatrist.

### REFERENCES

Group for the Advancement of Psychiatry. *The Psychiatric Social Worker in the Psychiatric Hospital.* Report No. 2. Group for the Advancement of Psychiatry, New York, 1948.

Group for the Advancement of Psychiatry. *The Psychiatric Social Worker in the Psychiatric Clinic.* Report No. 16. Group for the Advancement of Psychiatry, New York, 1950.

# CHAPTER SIX

# The Medical Examination in Psychiatric Assessment

## VICTOR F. LIEF, M.D.

WHEN DR. ROBERT FELIX retired from the office of president of the American Psychiatric Association in May 1962, he asked psychiatrists to remember how to use a stethoscope. The then director of the National Institute of Mental Health was evidently making a plea to his colleagues in psychiatry to remember that they are physicians first and psychiatrists later. His remarks might also be taken to imply that the medical aspects of psychiatry are of major importance.

The well-trained psychiatrist is always aware of the possibility of structural illness in his patient. Any good psychiatric service includes a medical examination as a routine procedure. The same need is present in office practice if the patient is seen before a medical examination has been done.

In dealing with any patient, the psychiatrist can observe him in two ways: (1) the objective way—measuring his blood pressure—and (2) the subjective way—noting what he reports from introspection and trying to understand his display of emotion. The person who asks for help has the need to be understood both subjectively and objectively. The medical examination simply stresses the objective part of the psychiatrist's effort to arrive at a comprehensive diagnosis.

## THE MEDICAL EXAMINATION

Several basic points regarding the medical examination itself are important: (1) Who should do it? (2) When should it be done? (3) How thorough should it be?

## WHO SHOULD DO IT?

Many feel that the psychiatrist should avoid doing the examination if he intends to establish a psychotherapeutic relationship with the patient. They believe that the examination may introduce problems that could disturb this relationship. For example, the neurotic or psychotic patient may well misinterpret a rectal or vaginal examination as a sexual attack. For this reason and because the psychiatrist may have lost some of his medical skills in the process of his specialization, he may well decide to refer the patient routinely to a competent internist. After explaining the need for such expert help, it may be best to leave the choice of physician to the patient.

Of course, if the patient has been referred by a physician or a medical institution, the psychiatrist ought to inquire about the previous findings. This gives him the opportunity to establish a working relationship with the referring doctors, if one has not already been established, and to assess the medical examination in the light of his own findings.

## WHEN SHOULD IT BE DONE?

The timing of the medical examination is important. It should be done as soon as possible after the initial psychiatric interview. In the case of the severely depressed patient, it is important to adopt appropriate and effective treatment as soon as possible in order to prevent the possible tragic consequences of delay. With the threat of suicide, treatment in most cases should not be delayed because of possible physical disease.

## HOW THOROUGH SHOULD IT BE?

Occasionally, there may be strenuous objections to the medical examination on the part of the patient due to an irrational fear of physicians or prejudice against them. These feelings must be understood and respected. The presenting emotional symptom may be due to a disease that the patient is unconsciously attempting to hide from himself by denying its existence. After the psychiatrist establishes an empathic relationship with his patient, this reluctance can be tactfully discussed and cooperation for the examination secured. Exhaustive physical tests and special investigations should be performed only when strong indications are present, since they are in themselves a cause of doubt and despondency.

## DIFFERENTIAL DIAGNOSIS

The accomplished physician in every field is aware that the central nervous system can react to either emotional stress or physical stress by producing similar symptoms. These symptoms can be physiological, psychological, or both. The difficulties in diagnosis arise when a systemic disease in its early stages produces predominant emotional symptoms. Such symptoms may be anxiety, depression, fatigue, lethargy, headache, irritability, dizziness, poor or excessive appetite, drowsiness, or insomnia. The psychiatrist, with his basic medical background as well as his psychiatric skills, is in a unique position to evaluate the findings of the medical examination and to formulate an integrated assessment of the patient.

Behavioral symptoms are often attributed to a psychogenic disorder when in fact they are due to an unrecognized systemic disease. Such a mistaken diagnosis is actually more apt to happen in these days, when the term "psychosomatic" is so popular and comes so readily to the mind of both doctors and laymen. It must be remembered that these same behavioral signs and symptoms are manifested or elicited in infectious, toxic, metabolic, degenerative, neoplastic, and nutritional disorders and in some of the anemias.

Any illness that is difficult to identify or understand has a good chance of being labeled as solely psychiatric, particularly if the patient has some obvious emotional disturbance. However, diagnosis in both physical and mental disorders should be made not by exclusion but by positive findings. Trouble in differential diagnosis can result from an "either or" concept: Is the psyche at fault or the soma? In every case, both are involved in varying degrees, and psychopathology and tissue pathology may be present in the same individual. As an example, we note the high incidence of tuberculosis in alcoholism and in schizophrenia.

## EXAGGERATION OF PERSONALITY TRAITS

Personality traits that were present before are often exaggerated in the presence of somatic illness, and the choice of presenting symptom by the patient may be a clue to the underlying personality as well as to the illness. The following case illustrates this.

A 22-year-old single girl, a senior in a well-known women's college, was seen first by her family physician and then by a psychiatrist. She had an attentive, quick, eager appearance. She had very labile emotions, given to laughing and crying easily. She had been a good student but lately had found it hard to concentrate. At times she seemed anxious and depressed, but at other times she appeared gay and energetic, attending parties and dancing into the early hours. Her appetite was good at all times and often ravenous.

The doctor who saw her initially made the diagnosis of emotional instability and suggested the possibility of the onset of a manic-depressive state. In taking her history, he had not inquired into her sensitivity to heat or cold or about any recent weight loss. He recorded a heart rate of 110 and a blood pressure of 140/70 but attributed this to nervousness. No mention was made of the size of her thyroid. The therapist to whom she was referred saw her three times weekly for four months.

After her weight had gone down from 112 pounds to 94 pounds, the psychiatrist's basic medical training asserted itself, and he became suspicious of an underlying thyrotoxicosis. He voiced his suspicion to the referring physician, who then sent her to an internist for a diagnosis. She was found to have an enlarged thyroid, and tests confirmed the presence of thyrotoxicosis.

The psychiatrist's dynamic formulation was that the patient had a conflict; she feared losing her mother and her mother's approval, and then she rebelled against these fears by acting out. It was postulated that she herself was afraid of becoming a mother and accepting a female role.

In order for this correct dynamic formulation to be complete and lead to rational treatment, it had to account for the physiological intervening variable, which was crucial in determining the clinical picture: the overactive thyroid. The key to the complete diagnosis was the discovery of enlargement of the thyroid by careful medical examination and confirmation by laboratory tests. Treatment by radioactive iodine eventually restored the patient to her former state of health and enabled her to complete her college career. Perhaps further psychotherapy was needed, but she did not seek it.

## DEPRESSION-PRODUCING DISEASES

The insidious onset of malignant, metabolic, or degenerative diseases often results in depression. This has been noted as an early manifestation in a variety of illnesses, particularly those involving the liver. Clinicians have often seen depression in hepatitis and early cirrhosis of the liver. Carcinoma of the pancreas has, on occasion, been particularly hard to diagnose, for psychiatric manifestations tend to cloud the picture in a condition that is so often difficult to diagnose anyway because of the lack of objective signs early in the illness. Adding to the difficulty is the fact that a patient often tends to relate his vague symptoms to psychological factors, especially if he has a prior history of depression.

A 62-year-old married dentist with a good practice became depressed after the death of a favorite child, a married daughter, from carcinoma of the breast. His period of mourning seemed endless. He lost interest in his practice, seemed to lose interest in his wife and remaining daughter, and complained of severe headaches and back pain of gradually increasing severity.

He was examined over the course of two years by his family physician, two neurologists, and an orthopedist and was finally referred to a psychiatrist after a thorough work-up in a reputable hospital failed to reveal any structural lesions to account for his symptoms.

His wife was very unhappy because of the change in her husband from an energetic, happy man to a sad, pain-ridden, apathetic invalid. She was not satisfied with the treatment he had received and finally had him see another internist. The new physician had treated a patient who had depression, backache in the lower dorsal region, and a complete change in personality; that patient had turned out to have a nonobstructing carcinoma of the head of the pancreas.

As a result, the dentist was again admitted to a hospital. The correct diagnosis all too soon became evident. He had lost 30 pounds. He had both abdominal and back pain plus jaundice. An exploratory laparotomy revealed carcinoma of the head of the pancreas with widespread metastases to the liver.

Tests directed toward pancreatic function, examination of duodenal content, and liver scanning for metastases might have made for earlier diagnosis if the possibility of carcinoma of the pancreas had been entertained, thus sparing the patient much unnecessary expenditure of time and money and the shame of regarding himself as a neurotic. The errors made in diagnosis in this case were excusable. Severe depressions in this age group are common, especially in reaction to an object loss. Depressions with somatic symptoms frequently occur. It is the combination of depression plus persistent back pain in the lower dorsal or upper lumbar region that might have aroused the suspicion that there was a lesion in the pancreas and led to its diagnosis.

It may be noted that, in many instances involving disease in an early stage, a routine physical check-up will fail to reveal the pathology. The psychiatrist must remain alert to the possibility of underlying organic illness, especially if psychiatric considerations make an exclusive psychogenic diagnosis unlikely.

## PSYCHOSIS-PRODUCING DISEASE

Toxic psychosis associated with pancreatitis has been studied in alcoholics by Schuster and Iber. The question was whether the symptoms of delirium tremens were due to alcohol withdrawal or to an accompanying illness. Inasmuch as the clinical syndrome of acute hallucinatory psychosis exhibited by 53 per cent of a group of thirty patients with pancreatitis was indistinguishable from delirium tremens, this group was compared with a second group of alcoholics with pneumonia. Only 4 per cent of this group evidenced psychosis, in spite of the fact that fever was higher and the acute illness more severe. The results not only emphasize the frequent occurrence of psychosis in connection with pancreatitis but also suggest that the psychosis is not the result of a nonspecific stress coupled with a background of alcoholism but rather arises from a specific somatic (probably biochemical) disorder in the pancreas. It is postulated that depression may arise from a similar, as yet undetermined, biochemical change in that organ.

# FATIGUE-PRODUCING DISEASES

Fatigue, which is so often due to psychogenic factors, merits thorough medical investigation. A frequent complaint, fatigue is best defined as a sense of weariness or a lack of feeling of well-being. Other terms with similar connotations are listlessness, lack of energy, lassitude, and weakness. An attempt should be made to distinguish between fatigue and true muscle weakness or asthenia.

The majority of patients who complain of fatigue have no demonstrable abnormality on physical or laboratory examination. There are frequently associated symptoms of nervousness, irritability, and depression. The fatigue accompanying depression is usually present in the morning and represents a lack of motivation to get going for the day. There is often emotional conflict present in the home or place of employment. These patients are often classified as having reactive depressions or anxiety reactions. Some are called hysterical.

Chronic infectious diseases are the most frequent somatic causes of fatigue. Fatigue is a common complaint early in tuberculosis, subacute bacterial endocarditis, disseminated lupus erythematosus, infectious mononucleosis, infectious hepatitis, chronic pyelonephritis, and brucellosis. Early recognition may be difficult; it is helpful to remember that in these diseases the weariness appears after exertion and usually in the afternoon or evening.

Anemic states are also common causes of fatigue, and the hemoglobin level correlates with the severity of the symptom.

Metabolic causes include hypopituitarism due to the secondary effect on the thyroid and adrenal. Addison's disease and primary hypothyroidism are also causes. Less commonly, hyperfunction of the adrenal, as in Cushing's disease, will cause the feeling. Diabetes mellitus may present fatigue as one of the complaints.

Toxic causes of fatigue are associated with psychological and physical dependency on alcohol, barbiturates, opium and its derivatives, and the large variety of sedatives now widely misused and abused. Bromism, now rare, was once a common cause. Uremic states may also present themselves as fatigue.

The following case, in which fatigue was a prominent symptom, illustrates how a psychiatrist dealt correctly with this problem.

A 26-year-old married secretary came to a psychiatrist because of complaints of fatigue, nervousness, insomnia, depression, and a loss of sexual interest, which plagued her husband more than it did the patient. The psychiatrist referred her to an internist for a thorough medical examination, which involved a painstaking medical history, physical examination, and routine laboratory tests, including a red blood count, hemoglobin, and hematocrit.

The internist determined that she was suffering from an anemia due to intermittent blood loss from bleeding hemorrhoids. For some reason, the patient had paid scant attention to her bowel movements and the occasional discoloration by bright blood. She recalled these symptoms only when specifically questioned about them. Her hemoglobin was found to be 7 gm., and her hematocrit was 30. Surgery and administration of iron for several months renewed her vitality and her interest in work and love.

## REFERENCES

Lief, H. I. Some diagnostic errors in patients with a psychiatric label. J. Southern Med. Ass., 47: 8, 1954.

Lief, H. I., Lief, V. F., and Lief, N. R., editors. *The Psychological Basis of Medical Practice*. Hoeber Medical Division, Harper & Row, New York, 1963.

Perlas, A. P., and Faillace, L. A. Psychiatric manifestations of carcinoma of the pancreas. Amer. J. Psychiat., 121: 182, 1964.

Psychosis with pancreatitis (editorial). JAMA, 193: 9, 1965.

Soniat, T. L. L. Common neurologic complaints encountered in general practice. J. Louisiana Med. Soc., 117: 6, 1965.

# CHAPTER SEVEN

# Clinical Manifestations of Psychiatric Disorders

## LOUIS LINN, M.D.

THE SIGNS AND SYMPTOMS of illness, properly collated, form a basis for diagnosis, prognosis, prevention, and treatment.

It used to be said that the best diagnosis is one based on knowledge of etiology. The cure of malaria, for example, depends on chemical destruction of the causative protozoa, and prevention of the disease depends on the elimination of the vector, the anopheles mosquito. On closer scrutiny, even this simple example reveals complexities. South American Indians cured malaria with cinchona bark long before they knew what caused it. To complicate this matter, patients with sickle cell anemia develop immunity to malaria.

Or consider another example. The tubercle bacillus is surely the cause of active tuberculosis in some, and yet, with the formation of a harmless fibrotic nodule, it can provide lasting immunity in others. Thus, the boundary line between active disease on the one hand and healthy adaptations on the other is not always easily identified. There is, in effect, a continuum between the patient with active disease on the one hand and the healthy, though infected, individual on the other.

The life process in health *and* disease consists of an ongoing series of adaptations. Depending on their effectiveness, an individual may be healthy and functioning with unimpaired efficiency, or he may be mortally affected by stress, or he may display a number of intermediate reactive patterns representing disease states that are, in effect, the continuations of life in the face of handicaps. Thus, a symptom or even a complex disease process in its entirety may be viewed as a reaction pattern having adaptational significance.

The clinical manifestations of psychiatric disorder are the outcome of complex interacting forces—biological, sociocultural, and psychological (see Figure 1).

Clinical manifestations of psychiatric disorder are essentially expressions of a breakdown in adaptational process. Adaptation from a psychiatric point of view refers to a series of changes that occur within the individual, as a result of which he fulfills his wishes and needs in relation to his personal satisfactions and the realities of his environment. Breakdowns in this process are expressed primarily as abnormalities of thought, feeling, and behavior.

The fact that these abnormalities are the outgrowth of several factors acting in concert has been expressed in the past by such concepts as psychosocial and psychobiological. To express the thesis embodied in Figure 1, one should say that the clinical manifestations of psychiatric disorders are in all instances biopsychosocial. The weight of the biological, psychological, and sociological factors differs from case to case and may vary from day to day in the same case. An accurate prognosis and a rational treatment plan depend on a consideration of all these factors.

This multifactorial point of view is not embodied in the fixed nosological entities of traditional clinical psychiatry. This section, however, is concerned with each symptom as an adaptation, from essentially normal behavior through a variety of abnormal behavior patterns. It will explore how the patient thinks, feels, and acts; the degree to which he is alert and oriented; how well he observes and remembers. It will discuss his personal eccentricities and the ways he relates to other people in his family, at work, at play, and in the community.

For an understanding of symptom formation, certain additional concepts are useful. For example, there are primary symptoms and secondary symptoms. In schizophrenia, a primary symptom is an irrational fear of others, with withdrawal of interest and activity from the outer world. To reduce his fear further, the patient elaborates a series of rationalizations about the surrounding world; these rationalizations constitute the secondary symptoms of schizophrenia. These become his delusions and hallucinations. As a result of secondary symptom formation, the patient becomes less fearful of the world, albeit a world that is delusionally distorted.

There are also principal symptoms and accessory symptoms. In a depressed patient, a principal symptom is sadness, with loss of appetite. The accessory symptom may be a peripheral neuropathy based on nutritional deficiency.

There are deficit symptoms and release symptoms. For example, cortical injury may result in a circumscribed aphasic language disorder, which is a deficit symptom. However, if the cortical injury is severe enough, there may be widespread personality changes, which may be interpreted as release phenomena.

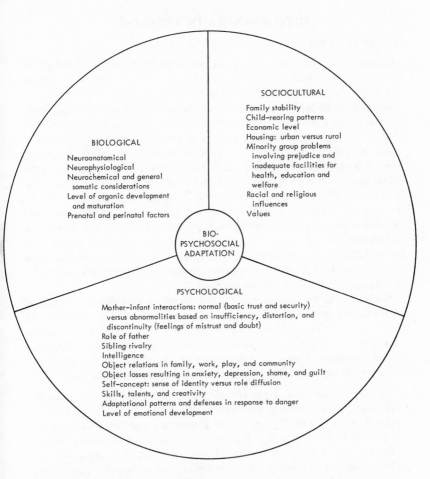

FIGURE 1. *Biological, sociocultural, and psychological forces. All these forces interact and affect the psychiatric health of the individual. (Modified after Richmond, J. B., and Lustman, S. L. J. Med. Educ., 29: 23, 1954).*

# DISTURBANCES IN THINKING

## Normal Thought

Thought, or the cognitive experience, includes the processes of judgment, comprehension, memory, and reasoning. It is to be distinguished from conation, which reflects the will or the basic strivings of an individual, as demonstrated by his motoric action and behavior. Norman rational thinking consists of a goal-directed flow of ideas, symbols, and associations initiated by a problem or task and leading to a reality-oriented conclusion.

An individual's flow of ideas becomes available for clinical scrutiny when it is verbalized in speech or writing. When, in the verbal communication of one's thoughts, a logical sequence of words, sentences, and ideas is followed, the associations are normal. Progression of thought involves the rate and manner of associations and is described as the stream of thought or stream of talk. In thinking, the communicator may be reacting to specific external stimuli or to his physical state, which is a source of internal stimuli. His reaction, in turn, modifies the effect of external stimuli. Or he may be reacting to certain conceptual goals that influence what he says and what he consciously omits.

Normally, the attentive listener is able to follow logically the verbal and ideational sequences of speech. In actuality, a perfectly logical associative flow is rarely observed. Much more commonly, speech sequences are interrupted by the forgetting of a familiar name or fact, a slip of the tongue, a period of relative incoherence during which the thread of the thought is momentarily lost, or a digression that is irrelevant to the main topic.

These lapses from logic (*parapraxes*), which are part of normal thinking, were described by Freud in the *Psychopathology of Everyday Life* as follows: "Slips of the tongue are the best examples of conflicts between strivings for discharge and opposing forces. Some tendency that has been warded off either definitely by repression or by a wish not to express it here and now finds a distorted expression counter to the opposing conscious will." The essence of the parapraxis, then, is that it constitutes a compromise or the solution of a problem arising from conflicting psychological drives.

A slip of the tongue (*lapsus linguae*) as an expression of intrapsychic conflict is illustrated by the following. A newspaper editor involved in a feud with the local law enforcement agency stated in an article that "Mr. X is a *defective* in the police force." An outraged response from Mr. X called forth a brief apology in the next day's paper with the statement, "What I meant to say was that Mr. X is a detective in our police *farce*."

Dreaming represents another normal setting in which lapses from logical thought and expression occur. Although dreams often seem bizarre, meaningless, and illogical, Freud demonstrated that a characteristic organization or pattern of thinking can be identified within the dream. He used the term primary process to signify that this pattern of thinking is primary, in the chronological sense that it occurs first in the developmental process. In the primary process, there is a tendency to concreteness, condensation of separate psychological items into one, displacement of feelings from one item to another, and a disregard for time sequences, so that items that are past and items that are present are treated as if they were occurring simultaneously. There is also a considerable use of metaphor and symbolism—that is, one object or idea unconsciously comes to stand for another. According to psychoanalytic theory, all these departures from logical thinking avoid painful feelings and fulfill forbidden pleasures.

Free association may be cited as an example of an artificially induced disturbance in association. In psychoanalytic psychotherapy the patient is requested to express spontaneously every thought that enters his mind without selection. In effect, he is encouraged to suspend the demands of logic and reality, at least on a purely verbal level, for the duration of the psychotherapeutic session. By this device the normal associative stream is deliberately disrupted and the flow of associations assumes qualities of unpredictability, strangeness, and disconnection with reality.

## DISTURBANCES OF THOUGHT OR ASSOCIATION

The flow of thought may become seemingly haphazard, purposeless, illogical, confused, incorrect, abrupt, and bizarre. This phenomenon is most conspicuous in schizophrenia. In fact, Bleuler regarded disturbance in association as one of the fundamental symptoms of that disease.

*Disturbances in form of thinking.* Under this category are included all deviations from rational, logical, goal-directed thinking. Many terms have been used to describe mental activity that deviates from the laws of logic and experience and that fails to take the facts of reality into consideration.

The term dereism, or dereistic thinking, emphasizes the disconnections that have taken place between the patient's mental processes and his ongoing actual experiences. The mental processes do not follow reality, logic, or experience.

The term autism connotes that the forces that distort the flow of associations are derived from within the patient and are in the nature of daydreams, fantasies, delusions, and hallucinations. Bleuler first coined the term autism and later dereism, and he used them interchangeably. Autism can occur as a character trait, referring to individuals who are bashful, shy, retiring, shut in, inaccessible, or introverted. In its extreme form, autism constitutes one of the primary symptoms of schizophrenia. There are two main characteristics of autistic thinking. First, it is less subject to correction by reality than is normal thinking; second, it is much less likely to be followed by action than is normal thinking because it gratifies pathological needs having no relationship to reality.

Early infantile autism is related to autism in general by its prevailing quality of extreme withdrawal and absorption with inner thoughts. More specifically, it refers to a form of childhood schizophrenia that is characterized by profound withdrawal and lack of contact from the first years of life, an obsessive demand for sameness in the environment, personalized use of language that is ineffective for communication, and a preference for relationships with inanimate objects. Kanner, who introduced the term, regarded it as a form of behavior resulting from the mother's inability to create a climate of emotional warmth.

**Disturbances in stream of thought.** Certain abnormalities may be observed in the manner and rate of associative processes.

Neologism refers to the coinage of new words, usually by condensing several other words, each of which have special meaning for the patient. These may occur within the limits of normal conversation. When used with great frequency in an essentially humorless context, they are characteristic of schizophrenia.

Word salad is a type of speech in which neologisms or incoherent words or phrases that lack logical meaning are used exclusively and in sequence. It is heard most frequently in severe forms of schizophrenia.

Blocking consists of sudden cessations in the flow of thought or speech in the midst of a sentence. Commonly, the patient is unable to explain the reason for the interruption, which is usually due to unconscious emotional factors. When, with conscious effort, the patient endeavors to continue the thought, new ideas may crop up, which neither the patient nor the observer can bring into any connection with the previous stream of thought. The blanking out of the flow of thought, the effort to renew it, and the inability to account for the interruption create an unpleasant feeling within the patient. Blocking is also known as thought deprivation. Although the phenomenon occurs intermittently in normal individuals and in a variety of diagnostic categories, it occurs most often among schizophrenic patients.

The withdrawal from object relations is the first step in the schizophrenic process. As a consequence of withdrawal, the flow of speech may be slowed up or interrupted intermittently in response to inner thoughts and feelings that the patient does not or cannot reveal to the examiner. As he recedes psychologically ever more deeply from the real world, he loses his capacity for abstraction, and his language becomes more concrete. Its logical structure assumes increasingly the patterns of thinking characteristic of childhood or hypothesized for primitive man (archaic speech). He is apt to speak in highly personal symbolism, unintelligible to the examiner or perhaps recognizable only because he uses universal symbols that are understandable cross-culturally. The logical lapses in the associative stream encountered in normal speech as a transient phenomenon may occur more frequently or even constantly in the speech of the schizophrenic patient.

The retreat from the real world is presumed to take place because the world has become objectionable and painful to the patient. As he withdraws his interest (cathexis, libido) from the real world, he may express feelings of emptiness, meaninglessness, and boredom. Having, in a sense, lost the world, he may feel that the world no longer exists (world destruction fantasies), and these ideas may contribute to the flow of his associations.

Alongside the primary drive to withdraw from the real world, there is present in every schizophrenic patient some degree of drive to recontact the world. The latter forms the basis for the secondary or restitutional symptoms of schizophrenia, for example, delusions and hallucinations. The patient now speaks rapidly and animatedly, even though the flow of his speech remains essentially unintelligible to the untrained listener. Thus, the speed of the association stream tends to be reduced during the preliminary stage of withdrawal in schizophrenia and to be speeded up during the restitutional phase, when the schizophrenic is making efforts to recontact the world. However, even in this phase, the intrusion of auditory and visual hallucinations may be abrupt and intermittent. These hallucinations are responsible for the seemingly haphazard and unpredictable nature of the thought disturbance.

Magical thinking, in psychiatry, refers to the belief that specific thoughts, verbalizations, associations, gestures, or postures can in some mystical manner lead to the fulfillment of certain unreal wishes or to the warding off of certain evils. This type of thinking may occur normally in dreams and in superstitions that are appropriate to a given sociocultural setting. Very young children are particularly prone to this form of thinking as a consequence of their limited understanding of causality. It is a prominent feature in the thinking of obsessive-compulsive patients. It achieves its most extreme expression in the schizophrenic patient.

In his attempt to mollify a threatening world, the schizophrenic patient may use certain words or gestures to control the evil forces. For example, schizophrenic patients may at times believe they are carrying out the most significant work in the universe when actually they are standing rigidly in catatonic stupor.

Intellectualization may be described as a state of brooding or anxious pondering about abstract, theoretical, or philosophical issues. It is a flight into intellectual concepts and words that are emotionally neutral in order to avoid objectionable feelings or impulses. It is commonly used by adolescents in reaction to the powerful sexual impulses that characteristically emerge at this time. It is also seen in obsessive-compulsive neurosis and as a trait of character in certain individuals.

A patient may torment himself with questions like: "What existed before the creation of the world?" "Why is God a man?" "How is immaculate conception possible?" Such questions, couched in religious terms, often conceal thinly disguised sexual issues.

Circumstantiality is a disorder of associations in which too many associated ideas come into consciousness because of too little selective suppression. The circumstantial patient eventually reaches his goal after many digressions. Circumstantiality is to be distinguished from tangential thinking, in which the goal is never reached. In circumstantiality, excessive detail is employed to describe simple events, at times to an absurd or bizarre degree. It may occur as a character trait. Its extreme forms occur in schizophrenia and organic brain disease. Like intellectualization, it often represents a way of avoiding objectionable impulses and feelings.

In response to the question, "Why did you come to the clinic?" a patient responded: "When I got up this morning, I showered and dressed. I was angry at my landlord for not fixing the faucet in my bathroom. I tried to get him on the phone. He wouldn't talk to me. I'll call my lawyer. You see, my rent is supposed to be paid by the Department of Welfare, but they're so nasty. [But why did you come to the clinic?] I'm coming to that, Doctor. You see, they don't care about an upright citizen. I did so much for my community. No one can say I wasn't a hard worker, etc." After repeated questioning, she finally stated she was worried about being constipated.

For the psychiatrist whose task it is to collect much data in little time, the circumstantial patient presents a special problem. A direct verbal assault on this mechanism of defense is apt to be frustrating and futile. It is more fruitful to recognize the underlying anxiety and to relieve it with appropriate psychotherapeutic measures.

A cardiologist complained that many patients exhausted him with trivial details about minor noncardiac complaints whenever he queried them about their heart conditions. He found this behavior particularly exasperating, since he was unable to influence it by cajolery or stern remonstrations. It was explained to him that these patients are fearful and are seeking to postpone as long as possible confronting what they fear most, namely, the possibility of cardiac invalidism or death. By prefacing his crisp inquiry about the patient's cardiac symptoms with a few words of reassurance, he found that such patients very quickly became more cooperative.

Stereotypy is the constant repetition of any speech or action. When this expresses itself as the continuous reiteration of a specific phrase, it is called verbigeration. It may also occur in the form of writing a given word or phrase over and over again, and it is most often seen in schizophrenia.

Perseveration is the involuntary and morbid repetition of a specific word or idea, which persists in spite of the patient's efforts to move on to a new idea. It occurs particularly after injury to the speech centers of the brain.

A patient with a left hemiplegia following a stroke named a key correctly but then called every other object presented to her during that period of examination a key.

When a patient gives an answer that is in harmony with and appropriate to the question, his answer is said to be relevant. If it is out of harmony, it is said to be irrelevant.

Incoherence is the result of disorderly thinking; thoughts do not follow in logical sequence. Under such circumstances the patient's verbalizations cannot be understood by the listener. A milder manifestation of incoherence is known as scattering.

The rate or speed of verbal production may be accelerated or slowed down. Volubility, or logorrhea, is copious speech that may occur more or less within the limits of normal conversation and that is coherent and logical.

Pressure of speech is voluble speech that is difficult for the listener to interrupt. It usually occurs in the context of psychoneurosis as a device for warding off anxiety-provoking questions or as a device for clinging in settings of depression. It may also be a precursor of flight of ideas.

Flight of ideas is a nearly continuous, high-speed flow of speech; the patient leaps rapidly from one topic to another, each topic being more or less meaningfully related to the preceding topic or to adventitious environmental stimuli, but progression of thought is illogical, and the goal is never reached. It is characteristic of acute manic states; hence it is most common in the manic phase of manic-depressive psychosis. The speed and cleverness with which the manic patient leaps from one idea to another can be dazzling. From a qualitative point of view, the manic patient's associations are not strange or absurd. In fact, the connections with identifiable events in the environment are often understandable and even amusing. Puns and witticisms are common.

Clang associations represent a pattern of associative disturbance in which the mere sound of a word rather than its meaning touches off a new train of thought. It occurs most often in the course of flight of ideas. It may result in a series of punning and rhyming nonsensical associations.

The flight of ideas of a manic patient must be differentiated from the disturbance of association displayed in the rapid speech of a schizophrenic patient in a state of catatonic excitement. The shifts in schizophrenic talk are confused by the indiscriminate overinclusion of material belonging to both shared social contexts and private fantasy contexts. It is the fact that the schizophrenic patient draws largely on an autistic reservoir for his ideas and verbal symbols that makes his productions so strange, as contrasted to those of the manic patient.

In spite of these qualitative differences between the associative stream of the manic patient and the catatonic-excited schizophrenic patient, the absence of a direction or goal for the associative stream is apparent and outstanding in both instances. Both represent a form of flight from the pain of some intolerable external reality, even though one draws on an inner and essentially inaccessible reservoir and the other on an outer and socially evident reservoir for the specific words and ideas that make up the associative flow.

For example, for all the appearance of joy and inner freedom that the manic patient displays, the careful observer can detect the sham. With firm reality-testing intervention, he can break through the mask, even if only for a moment, and reduce the manic patient to sobriety and even to tears.

Furthermore, in almost all clinical instances the differentiation between dependence on so-called inner versus outer resources for the associative flow is not a sharp one. More frequently, the sources of material are mixed, and a differential diagnosis is impossible. Such disorders are called schizo-affective.

In depressed states the flow of association is slowed up, not intermittently in response to hallucinatory or delusional intrusions, as in blocking, but as an on-going consequence of sadness. The patient thinks and speaks slowly and with great effort. In contrast to the manic patient, he is relatively unresponsive to his environment, and the range of his thoughts is sharply limited. Patients in whom the stream of associations is slowed up or shows retardation may complain of difficulty in thinking. This may be due to difficulty in concentrating on one topic because attention is obsessively pre-empted by another topic or because the actual flow of associations is sluggish. This difficulty is to be differentiated from mutism, where for conscious or unconscious reasons there is a *refusal* to speak.

Foreign language patients who are depressed or frightened fall back on their mother tongue and seem incapable of speaking English. As such patients improve, they often surprise their physicians with the amount that they do understand and with the degree to which they can make themselves understood.

It is not enough simply to know a foreign patient's language to establish contact with him. It is also necessary to help him overcome his distrust of the foreign examiner. As this is achieved psychotherapeutically, the patient usually prefers to communicate in the prevailing language of the community.

Brain-injured patients characteristically display slowing of speech and difficulty with speech, as in aphasia.

Aphasia is a general term for all disturbances of language and communication due to brain lesions but not as the result of faulty innervation of the speech muscles, involvement of the organs of articulation, or general mental or intellectual deficiency. Aphasia results in an inability to pronounce words and names and to indicate the use of common objects. The aphasic disorder occurs after lesions that are essentially localized in the speech centers in the dominant temporal lobe. Aphasias can be divided into motor (or expressive) forms and sensory (or receptive) forms. In the former, understanding is intact, but speech is lost; in the latter, comprehension and object use are lost. Speech impairments due to aphasia typically combine both motor and sensory elements. The difficulties may be on a purely verbal level and involve a disability in the formulation of individual words.

Nominal (amnestic) aphasia represents a difficulty in finding the right name for an object, even though the patient retains the ability to use the object and to describe what it is used for, often through various circumlocutions. It is closely related to the familiar experience within the limits of normal behavior of not being able to recall the name of a person or object at a time when one is able to describe many details concerning the object or person in question. In its mildest forms it may be seen in fatigue, anxiety, and alcoholic intoxication. It is more marked in senile dementia and in brain lesions involving the temporal lobe of the dominant hemisphere.

Syntactical aphasia is the inability to arrange words in proper sequence. The subject is usually aware that the word arrangement is wrong, even though he is helpless to correct it.

Semantic aphasia is the inability to recognize the full significance of words. It is related to a loss in the capacity for abstract thinking.

Jargon aphasia is a type of aphasia in which speech is reduced to a limited group of unintelligible neologisms, which the subject uses in a stereotyped fashion.

In aphasic disorders, the patient is usually alert. He is self-conscious about his errors and for this reason is often reluctant to speak. This is particularly true of patients whose premorbid personality included a great concern for orderliness and an inability to tolerate imperfections. Such aphasic patients tend to be depressed and withdrawn.

Catastrophic behavior is the term used by Goldstein to characterize the acute reactions of agitation, panic, and intensification of neurological defect that brain-injured patients show when they are pushed into performing simple tasks they can no longer do. Perseveration, mentioned earlier, is a device for warding off catastrophic behavior by clinging to a specific response with which the patient feels comfortable.

**Disturbances in content of thought.** Here again, the flow of ideas becomes available for clinical scrutiny only when verbalized in speech or in writing. And yet, certain types of thought content are essentially nonverbal.

Nonverbal thought content is encountered primarily in certain states of ecstasy or mysticism. In otherwise normal individuals, these feelings may occur fleetingly during the induction phase of general anesthesia. They may be chemically induced in addicts. They may also occur transiently in schizophrenia. In each instance the patient emphasizes that his thoughts are essentially inexpressible.

With the appearance of language in the developmental process, thought content of increasing complexity makes its appearance.

From a developmental point of view, concrete thinking—which involves specific objects or creatures, things, and phenomena, as distinguished from qualities or other attributes one can ascribe only to classes of objects, creatures, etc.—appears first in early childhood. The capacity for abstract thinking, characterized by symbols that cannot be directly perceived through the senses, develops later but probably earlier than was previously suspected. However, considerable verbal skill is needed to communicate abstract ideas; therefore, in their overt expressions at least, abstract thinking does not appear definitely until adolescence; it appears increasingly thereafter as verbal skills are developed.

In schizophrenia, verbal production often tends toward concreteness. Psychological tests devised to measure abstract thinking, such as the ability to interpret standard proverbs, show impairment in many schizophrenic patients. Goldstein emphasized the role of impaired abstract thinking in the language impairments of brain-injured patients.

A fantasy is a mental representation of a scene or occurrence that is recognized as unreal but is either expected or hoped for. There are two types of fantasy: creative fantasy, which prepares for some later action, and daydreaming fantasy, which is the refuge for wishes that cannot be fulfilled.

Creative fantasy may start in inspirational moments that are deeply rooted in unconscious factors. However, it is then elaborated systematically and is translated into a realistic program of action.

The daydream as a refuge for wishes that cannot be fulfilled is an almost self-explanatory category. It tends to be diminished with psychological and biological maturation. Increasingly, daydreaming is replaced by direct sexual satisfaction with an appropriate love object and by sublimation at work and at play. Sublimation is the substitution of satisfying guilt-free and anxiety-free activities for those that previously generated guilt and anxiety.

To some extent daydreaming persists within normal limits throughout life. However, in autistic characters and in borderline psychotic states, daydreaming may preempt so much time and energy that it seriously impairs the individual's capacity for normal relationships and responsibilities.

Pseudologia fantastica differs from normal daydreaming in that the subject believes in the reality of his fantasies intermittently and for long enough intervals of time to act on them.

Patients displaying this symptom are often referred to as pathological liars. They often outrage the moral sensibilities of the victims of their fantasies and commonly provoke punitive responses. These responses are reinforced by the fact that the patient acknowledges the falsehood of his statements when confronted with conflicting evidence. However, these patients have a compulsive need to act out these fantasies repeatedly. This is apparently a response to a pathological need for self-deception, with a resistance to correction. It is often difficult to ascertain whether the untruths are expressed with unconscious intent to deceive or as part of a pathological and even delusional distortion of reality.

The imposter is a type of pathological liar who seeks to gain some advantage by imposing on others various lies about his attainments, social position, or worldly possessions.

The imposter is obviously suffering from a severe identity problem. He is attempting to foist a false identity on society, but perhaps of greater significance is his need to reject his real identity for unconscious neurotic reasons. Such individuals are often quite gifted and are often capable of success in the real world, but an unconscious fear of success causes them to misspend their talents. They tend to be self-defeating in their dramatizations and usually end up with humiliation and punishment.

A phobia is an exaggerated and invariably pathological dread of some specific type of stimulus or situation. Table I presents a list of the most common types. Many other phobias have been described, and they are probably limitless in number.

The basic mechanism involved in a phobia is a reaction of anxiety in a setting in which a person would normally experience sexual excitement or rage. Various disturbances in thought content represent efforts to diminish this anxiety. At times the associative connections seem relatively direct. A forbidden wish to suck, bite, or devour, for example, may result in a fear of eating specific foods or a fear of eating in specific places. A fear of loss of control of violent impulses may lead to a fear of all scenes of violence. A fear of being cut or stabbed may lead to a fear of contact with sharp instruments. In other instances the associative connections have become obscured. A fear of walking on the street (agoraphobia), for example, may be based on unconscious prostitution fantasies. The sexual excitement and the fear of punishment connected with the latter may result in palpitation and breathlessness, which then presents clinically as a cardiac neurosis. Most often, the phobia for which the patient seeks treatment is like the manifest content of a dream. Behind the expressed fear is a chain of other fears. And entwined in the very fears supposed to guard against forbidden impulses are thoughts, feelings, and actions that secretly fulfill those very forbidden impulses (return of the repressed).

For example, a pretty young married woman, mother of a daughter aged five, became pregnant. She was aborted illegally at her husband's behest. When the abortionist let her see the bottle containing the curetted fetal tissue, she experienced a sharp pain in her eyes. Thereafter, she was afraid to go out into the street because of a fear that a foreign body would fly into her eyes. Psychoanalysis showed that this was a displacement from below upward. That is, her eye fear concealed a fear that she would be impregnated as a result of prostitution fantasies. The latter were the result of rage against her husband (whom, incidentally, she identified with her punitive mother) for not permitting her to have a baby. When she did venture out into the street (and she did so very often), she would experience a foreign body sensation in her eye, which would send her flying in a panic to her family doctor, who lived nearby. The family doctor's search for the foreign body was regularly associated with much fluttering of eyelashes, fearful breathing, and struggling, all of which resulted in her

TABLE I

*Phobias* [a]

| Phobia | Dread of | Phobia | Dread of |
|--------|----------|--------|----------|
| Acro- | High places | Nycto- | Darkness, night |
| Agora- | Open places | Patho- (noso-) | Disease, suffering |
| Algo- | Pain | Peccato- | Sinning |
| Astra- (astrapo-) | Thunder and lightning | Phono- | Speaking aloud |
| Claustro- | Closed (confined) places | Photo- | Strong light |
| Copro- | Excreta | Sito- | Eating |
| Hemato- | Sight of blood | Tapho- | Being buried alive |
| Hydro- | Water | Thanato- | Death |
| Lalo- (glosso-) | Speaking | Toxo- | Being poisoned |
| Myso- | Dirt, contamination | Xeno- | Strangers |
| Necro- | Dead bodies | Zoo- | Animals |

[a] Modified from Warren, H. C. *Dictionary of Psychology.* Houghton Mifflin, New York, 1934.

seducing her doctor into sexual play, consisting mostly of kissing and caressing. Since she unconsciously identified her family doctor with her father, this sex play represented a revival of her childhood attachment to her overly demonstrative father. As a result, it aroused much guilt and anxiety as well as sexual excitement.

An obsession is the pathological presence of a persistent and irresistible thought, feeling, or impulse that cannot be eliminated from consciousness by any logical effort. Obsessions may be experienced within normal limits as transitory thoughts that do not interfere substantially with the adequate performance of one's mental functions and that can be minimized or eliminated by actively concentrating on other objects. Obsessions as symptoms of obsessive-compulsive neurosis, on the other hand, control and plague the individual more or less constantly, compelling him to carry out specific ritualized or stereotyped acts, known as compulsions, in order to minimize their distressing effects. There are intellectual obsessions, in which the individual is constantly preoccupied with one or more pseudo-philosophical questions. There are also obsessive fears and doubts that overlap the phobias.

Whereas the phobic or hysteric patient dramatizes fantasies in the form of relatively simple fears and bodily sensations, the fantasies of the obsessional neurotic are converted into defenses that are largely verbal, intellectual, and complex. Words and thoughts are invested with unrealistic power. An inadvertent thought or comment, it is imagined, may cause great harm to a loved one or punishment to one's self. By the same token, a given verbal formula may ward off danger to self and to others. Since words are so powerful, it becomes necessary to choose one's words carefully. And for the obsessional neurotic, no matter how carefully he chooses his words, he is never sure that he chose carefully enough, and so he repeats himself with verbal formulae of ever-increasing complexity. Behind this preoccupation with seemingly magical but actually trivial words is concealed an intrapsychic struggle involving erotic and aggressive impulses in every conceivable combination of activity and passivity, of masculinity and femininity, of piety and blasphemy, of obedience and rebellion. Such verbal gymnastics demand a great mastery of language. The latter, in turn, requires considerable intelligence. Conversely, whenever verbal skills are limited because of limitations of intelligence or education, obsessional defenses usually do not appear.

It is not at all rare for patients with phobias and obsessions to function in an outwardly normal fashion and to maintain full awareness of the irrational nature of their thoughts—that is, the symptoms are ego-alien or ego-dystonic (repugnant to the ego of the patient), and he has insight into the irrational nature of his thoughts. The ego-alien attitude toward symptoms combined with the capacity to maintain a fairly full range of real object relations are characteristic of the psychoneuroses. However, ego-syntonic symptoms—that is, symptoms acceptable to the ego—can occur within the framework of psychoneurosis, particularly in the types in which the differential diagnosis between psychoneurosis and psychosis is difficult to make. Whether one measures the degree to which real object relations are retained or the degree to which symptoms are ego-alien, there is a continuum between normal, psychoneurosis, and psychosis.

A patient may seem to retain a completely ego-alien attitude toward phobic or obsessive symptoms but be so withdrawn from the world of real objects that a psychotic diagnosis is warranted. The fact that such psychotic patients present essentially psychoneurotic symptoms has led to the diagnostic description pseudoneurotic schizophrenia. Similarly, there is a continuum in the degree to which symptoms are experienced as ego-alien. Daydreams and phobias within the limits of psychoneurosis may shift over into the category of psychosis, with hallucinations and delusions, by a simple increase in the intensity of the experience.

When thought content centers around a particular idea and is associated with a strong affective tone, it is said to be dominated by a trend or preoccupation. Such excessively charged ideas are said to be overdetermined in that they are caused by the confluence of multiple conflicts and drives, all of which carry great affective weight and meaning.

A preoccupation or an overdetermined idea may lead to an obsession. At other times it may become the basis for an idea of reference if projection occurs, as when a person attributes to neutral remarks and incidents direct references to himself. Projections form the basis of paranoid or oversuspicious thinking. This form of thinking may occur more or less within normal limits in early childhood, when the youngster is self-centered and insecure. When a shy but essentially normal person enters into a social situation, he may experience a series of self-observing, self-criticizing thoughts, which he succeeds in brushing aside in favor of the social satisfactions open to him. Such thoughts, if intensified to the point of paralyzing discomfort but recognized as ego-alien, may then be described as neurotic hypersensitivity. The latter expresses itself as extreme shyness and in autistic tendencies.

A delusion is a false belief that arises without appropriate external stimulation and that is maintained more or less unshakably and fixedly in the face of reason. Furthermore, the belief held is not one ordinarily shared by other members of the patient's sociocultural and educational group. For example, it is not a commonly believed superstition or a religious or political conviction. Delusions are pathognomonic of the psychoses. They occur most frequently in schizophrenia, but they can be observed in all psychotic states, including those of organic origin. A delusion represents an autoplastic response, whereby one adapts by altering the intrapsychic milieu, as opposed to the alloplastic response of the reality-oriented individual, who adapts by altering his environment.

Freud's well known Schreber case is an example of projection. Freud observed that homosexual impulses, which were unacceptable to Schreber, underwent a series of transformations. Schreber first declared that he did not really love his homosexual object but hated him. In a still further development of his thought disturbance, Schreber declared that he did not hate his love object but rather that he himself was the object of that hatred. Thus, the unconsciously loved homosexual object emerged finally into consciousness as Schreber's persecutor.

The following case illustrates ideas of reference and paranoid delusions. A married man, aged 58, with a life history of dependable, conscientious work as a bookkeeper, became sleepless, anxious, and unable to concentrate. He developed the belief that his vision was failing because of poisons secretly placed in his food by former neighbors. He found a misprint in a newspaper that he felt was placed there by the editor to shame him publicly. Admitted to the psychiatric service of a general hospital, he said that cars passing up and down the street contained agents who were spying on him. He believed that the electric light bulbs in his room were emanating a purifying radiation to counteract syphilitic germs, which he was supposedly breathing into the atmosphere, although a physical examination was negative for syphilis. He was diagnosed as having involutional psychosis with paranoid and depressive features.

In some delusional states, persecutory feelings arise within the patient's body, as intestinal movements or the sensation of the stool in the rectum. Preoccupation with body feelings may result in a variety of somatic delusions that, in the schizophrenic, are characterized by a quality of strangeness. They differ in this respect from the localized somatic symptoms of hysterics and the generalized physical complaints of hypochondriacs.

In other delusional states, sexual feelings are attributed to a distantly located influencing machine operated by a persecutor. The patient may claim that this machine compels him to see pictures, forces certain thoughts and feelings on him, or abruptly drains off all thoughts and feelings. He may attribute to the machine erections, cutaneous eruptions, etc. The delusion of the influencing machine appears as a relatively late elaboration in schizophrenic thinking and seems to originate in the patient's need for causality. The description of the influencing machine by psychotic patients necessarily draws on the cultural and technological sophistication of the patient.

Pathological jealousy may occur in marital settings in which a spouse has unconscious extramarital sexual impulses, either heterosexual or homosexual, which are then projected onto the marital partner and emerge clinically as delusions of infidelity.

Litigiousness is a pathological tendency to take legal action because of suspected and imagined persecution. When these imagined persecutions reach delusional proportions, we speak of delusions of persecution. Legal action may be brought against a surgeon, for example, because of delusional misconceptions the patient harbors about a surgical procedure. Relatives of a hospitalized patient may have litigious attitudes toward the professional staff of the hospital because of their own hostility toward the patient, which is then projected onto the staff. ("It is not I who wants to be rid of this patient. The doctors and nurses have these feelings.")

The thought content encountered clinically is determined, among other things, by the patient's mood. The ecstatic states referred to earlier may be associated with delusions of grandeur, which means a delusional exaggerated idea of one's importance. The male patient may express the idea that he is the Saviour or a latter-day saint; the female patient may believe she is the Virgin Mary and is about to give birth to the Baby Jesus. The delusions of grandeur may result in identifications with political or military figures of great power. The salvation of the world is the basic delusional goal. Often this grandiose goal is to compensate for feelings of inadequacy. In manic states there may be inappropriate delusions of great wealth that result in crippling financial expenditures.

A shift of mood from elation to depression may result in the delusion of having committed an unpardonable sin. This is usually associated with guilt and may result in a delusion of self-accusation, characterized by intense remorse. In place of the delusions of saving the world, there may appear the end-of-the-world fantasy. The patient may believe that the salvation of the world depends on his own death, and he may destroy himself or seriously mutilate himself to save the world. In less bizarre terms, the depressed patient may feel that the world would be better off without him and have suicidal impulses or ideation on an altruistic basis. In contrast to the delusion of great wealth, there may be, in the depressed state, a delusion of poverty. The complaint, "I am poor," is characteristic of depression, almost independently of the patient's true economic condition. In addition to feelings of guilt, worthlessness, and poverty, the patient may express a loss of interest in all previously satisfying spheres of activity. He may lose his appetite for food, family, sex, work, and play. Loss of appetite for food may be the result of delusions of poisoning, as a result of which he doesn't eat, to the point of losing much weight. Paradoxically, some patients invest the process of *not* eating with intense emotional satisfaction, as a result of which they lapse into an anorexia nervosa which, on occasion, may lead to death by starvation in spite of an apparent continued interest in other aspects of life.

In considering the disorders of thought content, one must take into account the *intent* of the verbal production as well as the content. As a result primarily of depression and anxiety, many patients have a desperate need for the company and attention of the therapist. In return for his attention, these patients are motivated to say almost anything calculated to engage his interest. Is the therapist interested in dreams? Then the patient will dwell on dreams. Is he interested in infantile sexuality, in orality, in the castration complex? In each instance, the patient tunes in on the therapist's special interest. He responds to subtle cues almost telepathically. Such patients often seem to prove almost any theory that the therapist cherishes (doctrinal compliance). For the beginner in psychotherapy, the flood of associations provided by such patients can be an endless source of interest and yet prove, in the long run, to be of questionable psychotherapeutic value. It often takes great clinical skill to differentiate between content offered essentially for purposes of clinging and content that can be used to increase self-understanding and motivate clinical change.

Just as the content of associations may be rendered interesting by a patient who wished to please the therapist, so may the content be rendered boring or irritating by a fearful patient who wishes to keep the therapist at a safe distance. The beginner in psychotherapy may fail to understand the unpleasant feelings that such a patient arouses in him and may reject him, erroneously, as an "uninteresting" case. Whether the intent is to draw the therapist closer or to repel him, the actual content of the verbal productions in such instances is of secondary importance.

A patient who has withdrawn from normal object relations will often express this withdrawal by an unusual choice of words in his conversation. The flow of associations may be coherent and relevant, and the actual word choice correct from the point of view of dictionary meaning, yet an overtone of stiltedness, based on too personalized a vocabulary, may provide a subtle clue to clinically significant psychopathology. For example, when asked the function of the heart, a schizophrenic patient answered, "It invigorates the blood by putting red and white corpuscles in the blood stream." When asked how yeast causes dough to rise, another schizophrenic patient answered: "Something takes place in the bacteriological context. When heat is applied, molecules become active and cause it to rise."

When a patient seems slow-witted and dull, there may be an emptiness of content based on mental deficiency. Where this is suspected, confirmation by formal psychological testing is mandatory.

### Disturbance in thought content in brain-injured patients.

To understand the disturbances of association and thought content seen in patients with widespread (as contrasted to focal) organic brain disease, one must turn to certain theoretical considerations.

Most hospitalized patients suffering from a serious physical impairment of any kind wish to be well and wish to go home. Most such patients accept the realities of the illness and the necessity for hospitalization and make an adaptation based on premorbid personality.

The patient with widespread brain injury presents a different picture. In many ways he acts like a person in a waking dream. Is there a wish to be out of the hospital? Then the patient speaks and acts as if he were not in a hospital. Is there a wish to be well? Then, for these brain-injured patients, wishing makes it so, and they display the syndrome of anosognosia, the denial that physical illness is present. A blind person insists that he can see, and a paralyzed patient says that he can walk. Some patients deny the major illness and ascribe the need for hospitalization to a trivial illness or to a previous illness from which the patient has long since recovered. A patient who has just had a craniotomy, for example, may insist that all he had was a tonsillectomy or an appendectomy. On occasion, a patient admits that he cannot move a paralyzed leg but rationalizes this as a result of fatigue or laziness. A patient with a paralyzed limb may disown the incapacitated extremity by saying that it belongs to someone else or that a paralyzed arm is lying on a bedside table "like a set of false teeth." When questioned about their own illness, some anosognosic patients respond by discussing the illness of some other member of the family; others (still paralyzed) agree that they had a hemiplegia in the past but are fully recovered at this time. Blind patients give detailed descriptions of objects they are "looking" at; others alter the name of the hospital in a way to deny its medical function or to move it closer to home or business. They fill in memory gaps with extensive confabulations, the common denominator of which is the absence of physical disability.

In reduplication the patient acknowledges that he is in a hospital but insists that it is a good hospital compared with one with the identical name nearby. A patient may acknowledge that a right arm is paralyzed but insist that there is an extra right arm that is not paralyzed. The anosognosic patient may be mute and unresponsive when questioned by a physician and yet speak freely to a relative.

Anosognosic patients may show a language disorder called paraphasia, the use of word substitutes. In paraphasia, responses to questions are not particularly slowed up as they are in aphasia. The paraphasic abnormality occurs much more frequently in relation to hospital (or disease-connected) words. When a word is produced, it is usually a neologism or an inappropriate word that tends to deny illness. For example, a clinical thermometer is called a "gradient"; a wheelchair is a "chaise." At times, anosognosic patients speak of themselves in the third person. In response to a query about surgery already performed, a patient answered, "He did not have an operation." A paralyzed limb may be referred to as "he," "she," or "it," as if to disclaim possession of the sick part. A question about a personal disability may be followed by a detailed discussion of an illness suffered by some other member of the family. The patient may launch willingly into a discussion of some minor ailment while steadfastly refusing to discuss the major reason for hospitalization.

Other language patterns seen in anosognosic patients include intellectualization and the liberal use of cliches as facile platitudes available to the patient with the expenditure of little thought or energy. Characteristic of anosognosic patients is the fact that they do not alter their basic errors in spite of repeated corrections by the examiner.

In purely quantitative terms, the success with which the brain-damaged patient succeeds in denying his illness is determined to some degree by the extent of the brain disease. In acute reversible brain disease, the period of maximal brain damage is associated with equanimity or euphoria. In the euphoric stage, even the patient's speech may resemble that of a mild hypomanic reaction. However, the humor (*Witzelsucht*) is characteristically shallow, and the range of ideas is sharply circumscribed. It is a type of facetiousness with a tendency to punning. In intermediate stages of brain damage, the flow of associations tends to show a paranoid trend, although again with a relatively limited ideational content. With further improvement in brain function, the entire capacity for denial of illness may dissolve. At this point a depressive reaction, not entirely inappropriate to the clinical realities, may emerge. The slowed up flow of associations then reflects this affective state.

When a barbiturate, such as Amobarbital sodium, is injected intravenously into a depressed and no longer anosognosic brain-injured patient so that he shows nystagmus and slurring of speech, all the previously noted association patterns characteristic of denial of illness can be temporarily reestablished. This fact has formed the basis for a presumptive test of organic brain disease.

The manic and paranoid states seen in brain-injured patients have a certain stability that resist correction. However, during the transitions from one level of somatopsychic organization to another, there are intervening stages during which terror predominates and the flow of associations is maximally disorganized. The picture seen then is one of delirium and in many ways is comparable to the withdrawal reaction seen whenever a patient who has maintained some form of psychosocial adaptation with the help of a drug is suddenly called upon to readapt to his environment without the help of the drug.

It is thus possible to see in a single patient all the clinical manifestations that at one time or another have been associated with organic brain disease. The basic and fixed element in the clinical picture is the premorbid personality of the patient. The variables derive from the location, extent, and severity of the brain lesion.

Since the fact of brain damage impairs the availability of language and ideas, anosognosic patients tend to lack verbal and ideational complexity in their associations. Nevertheless, the delusional fulfillment of the wish to be well draws into its train wishful fulfillments from other layers in the emotional development, exactly as take place in a dream. The content of the clinical picture becomes more complicated as a consequence, but the wish to be well remains.

**Disturbances in judgment.**   Judgment, from a psychiatric point of view, is the mental act of comparing or evaluating alternatives within the framework of a given set of values for the purpose of deciding on a course of action. The comparison may be in terms of magnitude, rightness, goodness, beauty, or economic worth. If the course of action decided on is consonant with reality as measured by mature adult standards, the judgment is intact, good, or normal. If, on the other hand, the course of action is inconsistent with reality, the judgment is impaired, poor, or abnormal.

The capacity to decide whether or not to take action depends on the capacity to think—that is, to anticipate the future in the imagination. This, in turn, depends on the capacity to bring before the mind once again something that has been previously perceived, to reproduce an object in the imagination without requiring the actual presence of the object. The imagined or internalized representation of an object is not always a faithful one. It may be modified by omissions or changed as a result of merging elements. Reality-testing determines how far such distortions have gone.

The thought process involved in reality-testing takes time. Freud described thinking as "experimental action." It begins with a tentative sampling of data from the outer world; these data are then compared with data from the reservoir of stored memories. This process culminates in a decision, which puts an end to the postponement of action. *Thus, the controlled postponement of action is the essence of judgment.* The person with good judgment looks before he leaps. But judgment leads from thought to action. Reality-testing makes it possible to try out actively and in small dosage an experience that may be traumatic if permitted to happen passively and in unknown dosage.

The ability to recognize, love, and fear reality begins long before speech is learned. The infant becomes aware of reality as represented by the human face at approximately three months of age. The infant reacts reflexively to the sight of the human face with a smile. At about eight months of age, the infant begins to compare and evaluate human faces. He learns to differentiate the face of the mother from all others. The infant reacts with love to her face and with fear and anger to others. Psychoanalytically, it is hypothesized that the infant takes in her face with its eyes and eagerly swallows her food. It turns away from others and expels the food offered by these strangers as bad objects. These simple nonverbal relationships provide the model for the process of judgment—paying attention, comparing, evaluating, decision-making, and action.

Speech initiates a decisive step in the development of reality-testing and judgment. Words permit more precise communication and more precise anticipations of trial actions.

Thus far, the issues are quite clear. The function of judgment then depends on maturation of the mental apparatus. Intelligence and education are required for the inculcation of values.

Intelligence has been defined as the capacity to meet a novel situation by improvising a novel adaptive response. This capacity is composed of three factors: abstract intelligence, which is the capacity to understand and manage abstract ideas and symbols; mechanical intelligence, which is the capacity to understand, invent, and manage mechanisms; and social intelligence, which is the capacity to act reasonably and wisely in human relations and social affairs.

For good judgment to prevail, the sensory apparatus must be capable of accurate perception and discrimination. Memory must provide a reservoir of data as a basis for comparison. The motor apparatus must have the skills to carry out decisions and the inhibitory mechanisms for postponing action. Thus, a developmental process is automatically implied in the very concept of judgment. Although rudimentary manifestations of judgment can be found in infancy and early childhood, judgment develops steadily with biopsychosocial maturation. It is maximal in the fully alert, emotionally mature adult. It is impaired in all circumstances associated with regression.

If judgment is a mental function calculated to insure reality-oriented action, then mental states that avoid painful reality are inevitably associated with impairment of judgment. These may occur transitorily in relation to parapraxes. A suspension of logical judgment is characteristic of dreams. Impaired judgment is a regular accompaniment of all psychotic states.

Adolescents display impaired judgment for many reasons. Through lack of education and experience, they may fail to recognize which situations or ideas merit attention. Adolescence, with its characteristic intensification of intrapsychic conflict, may be associated one moment with excellent reality-testing based on adult goals and aspirations and a moment later with impaired reality-testing based on persistent, unmastered infantile longings. Undeveloped values and self-discipline may precipitate ill-advised actions. Thus, judgment in the adolescent is notoriously uneven and unpredictable.

Estimates of judgment may be based on responses to test questions or standard hypothetical situations. For example, a mentally defective subject with a long history of delinquency and fire-setting was asked, "What would you do if you found a stamped, addressed, and sealed envelope in the street?" He answered, "I would put it in the mailbox if it didn't have anything in it for me." Wechsler has observed that a significantly higher score in the performance scale over that in the verbal scale of the Wechsler Adult Intelligence Scale is suggestive of the character disorders associated with impairment of judgment.

## DISORDERS OF CONSCIOUSNESS

Consciousness has been defined as the distinguishing feature of mental life. It is synonymous with the quality of being aware and of having knowledge. Thus, it is a faculty of perception that draws on information from the outer world directly through the sense organs and indirectly through stored memory traces. Implicit in the concept of full consciousness is the capacity to understand this information and to use it effectively to influence the relationship of the self to the environment. Consciousness may be said to have a sensory component or degree of receptive awareness, which is measured as cognitive intensity, and a motor component or degree of kinesthetic readiness to initiate and execute a voluntary act, which is conative intensity.

### LEVELS OF CONSCIOUSNESS

Consciousness exists on a continuum, with maximum alertness at one extreme and absolute unconsciousness or coma on the other; in between are confusion, clouding of consciousness, delirium, and stupor.

In confusion there is disorientation as to time, place, and person and a feeling of bewilderment. It is often accompanied by an impairment of consciousness and is encountered in both organic states and functional disorders.

In clouding of consciousness there is a disturbance in perception, attention, and thought, and a subsequent amnesia.

Delirium is a psychic state characterized by disorientation in all spheres, confusion, clouding of consciousness, and bewilderment in association with anxiety, fear, illusions, and hallucinations. It is the result of an infection, tumor, hemorrhage, or toxic-metabolic disorder and is classically associated with acute brain syndromes.

Stupor is a state of relative nonresponsiveness to the environment. It differs from the total insensibility of coma in purely quantitative terms. Stupor can occur as a lesser stage of impaired consciousness in all the conditions causing coma. However, there are, in addition, psychogenic stupors, in which the patient is motionless, mute, and more or less nonresponsive to powerful stimuli but without organic brain disease or impairment of reflexes. In catatonic stupor, for example, the patient is aware of his surroundings but is intensely preoccupied. He is able to give a relatively full description of the happenings in his environment in retrospective accounts after the catatonic stupor has subsided. Patients who exhibit the basic symptoms of manic-depressive psychosis may present a picture of stupor instead of depression. Because of the reportedly better prognosis in these cases, these patients are said to exhibit benign stupor.

Coma is the term describing the most profound degree of unconsciousness, in which there is no detectable evidence of responsiveness. At its deepest levels, even reflex responses to painful stimuli and to breathing obstructions are abolished. Function is reduced to the mere vegetative persistence of circulation and respiration. Coma may be the result of diffuse inflammatory brain disease (encephalitis), vascular disease (intracranial hemorrhage, thrombosis, or embolism), brain tumor, poisoning, or factors of toxic-metabolic origin.

Coma vigil is a coma in which the eyes remain open. This condition may occur in a variety of acute organic brain disorders, particularly when the diencephalon is affected. On occasion, patients in coma vigil follow the human face with their eyes when they are responsive to no other stimuli. In such instances, tracking movements of the eyes can be elicited by means of a two-dimensional pictorial representation of the face as well as the actual face itself.

This curious phenomenon seems to represent a regression to a stage in development during the first year of life, when the infant fixes his gaze on the face of the mother during feeding.

## ATTENTION

Attention is an aspect of consciousness that relates to the amount of effort exerted in focusing on certain portions of an experience so that they become relatively more vivid. One may speak of primary attention—which is passive, involuntary, automatic, instinctive, or reflexive—and secondary attention, which is active or voluntary.

Attention in both its primary and secondary aspects may fluctuate in intensity from moment to moment in acute brain disorders, such as subdural hematoma and impending diabetic coma. Attention may remain basically alert and vigilant yet shift swiftly from topic to topic. In distractibility an individual's attention is too easily drawn away from a given content by extraneous or distracting stimuli. Although a certain amount of distractibility is normally present, it occurs in its extreme form in the manic state. Distracting stimuli may arise not only from the outer environment but from inner fantasies as well. The latter are present in the psychoneuroses and may play an important role in learning disability. They are also outstanding features in schizophrenia.

Attention span is measured by the length of time that an individual can apply himself to a given task. It is, in a sense, the reciprocal of distractibility. Attentiveness is the process of paying attention.

Selective inattention is a term used to describe an aspect of attentiveness in which the subject blocks out those data of consciousness that generate anxiety, guilt, and other unpleasant feelings. It is synonymous with the psychological defense mechanism known as denial. Blunting of attention is an extreme form of inattention in which responses to noxious stimuli are reduced.

## APPERCEPTION

Apperception, or comprehension, implies the clear and correct recognition of the meaning of the data of perception. When a mental image is clearly perceived but is falsely interpreted or understood, one speaks of abnormal apperception. This may occur in psychoneurosis in relation to severe anxiety, in psychotic states as a result of delusions, and in organic brain disease with sensory aphasia.

## SUGGESTIBILITY

Suggestibility exists when a patient responds compliantly with unusual readiness. Suggestibility is seen in psychoneurosis, especially in conversion reaction, and plays an important role in hypnosis. In psychosis it can be seen in automatic obedience, echolalia, echopraxia, and cerea flexibilitas. If the patient has a good and trusting relationship with an individual, this increases his suggestibility. Suggestion is the process of influencing a patient to accept uncritically an attitude or idea.

Negative suggestibility, in which the patient does the opposite of what is suggested, is seen normally in children and in catatonic schizophrenia as negativism, which means the perverse resistance to suggestions or advice.

Suggestion plays an important role in communicated insanity (*folie à deux*), a psychotic reaction in which two closely related and associated individuals simultaneously show the same symptoms and one member seems to have influenced the other. It may also affect three members of a family; then it is called *folie à trois*.

## HYPNOSIS

This is an artificially induced disturbance of consciousness that may superficially resemble sleep but is physiologically distinct from it. It is characterized by heightened suggestibility. As a result, a variety of sensory, motor, and memory abnormalities may be induced by the hypnotist.

## HYPNOID STATE

This was hypothesized by Freud to be an alteration of consciousness that occurs characteristically in hysteria during periods of emotional stress. It is characterized by heightened suggestibility and provides a basis for hysterical somatic symptom formation, feelings of depersonalization and derealization, and fugue states.

## STARTLE REACTION

This is a reflex response to an unexpected stimulus of great intensity. It is associated with a sudden increase in the level of consciousness and a diffuse motor response involving flexion movements of the trunk and extremities (hence, in German, *Zusammenschrecken* reflex). It occurs in normal individuals. It may be elicited more readily and with a greater motor excursion in acute anxiety neurosis, such as occurs following a traumatic battlefield experience during wartime.

## Effects of Pharmacological Agents

Various pharmacological agents affect the level of consciousness. Most sedative and hypnotic agents act on the central nervous system diffusely. In small amounts, they reduce perceptual acuity and motor skills. In larger amounts, they produce, in succession, somnolence, sleep, stupor, coma, and death.

Reduction of the level of consciousness by means of sedative and hypnotic medication is induced for the relief of mental or physical suffering. Some of the medications of the phenothiazine series act selectively on the central nervous system so as to reduce the affective experience of suffering without simultaneously reducing the overall level of sensorimotor efficiency.

It has been hypothesized that the phenothiazines and some other psychopharmacological agents selectively diminish the activity within the multisynaptic short circuits of the reticular activating system (RAS), thus leaving the functions of the cerebral cortex essentially unimpaired. This is in contrast to the barbiturates and other sedative medications, which diminish central nervous system activity diffusely, including the cerebral cortex and the long pathways.

## Sleep

Sleep is a complex state of altered consciousness consisting of at least four separate stages of varying depth, sensory and motor activity, and responsivity.

In clinical descriptive terms, sleep has many variants. It may be deep, continuous, and refreshing. It may be light, intermittent, and exhausting. It may seem dreamless or filled with dreams. When dreams appear, they may be good dreams or bad dreams.

There is relative unresponsiveness to stimuli in sleep, the degree of unresponsiveness depending on the stage of sleep, the amount of fatigue, the state of mind of the subject (whether troubled or at ease), the intensity and quality of the stimulus. For example, a mother may sleep deeply, unmindful of loud noises all about her, and yet awaken at once at the first soft cry of her baby. Among the strange expressions of consciousness in sleep is the commonly experienced ability to wake up at a specific time in the morning.

Sleep occupies most of the twenty-four hours of the day at birth and is interrupted only briefly because of hunger or physical discomfort. The period of sleep gradually shortens until it occupies seven to eight hours in the normal adult and becomes still shorter with advancing age. Normal sleep requirements vary widely from as little as four hours a night in exceptional intances at one extreme to ten hours or more at the other.

Insomnia is a pathological inability to sleep. In catatonic or manic excitement, the patient may remain uninterruptedly sleepless for twenty or more hours at a time. These reactions of extreme excitement may terminate with fatal exhaustion, which is at times associated with hyperthermia.

Early morning insomnia is a sleep disturbance occurring characteristically in depressions. In these instances the patient falls asleep readily enough but awakens in a few hours, bathed in anguished perspiration. This sleep pattern is commonly associated with anorexia, weight loss, feelings of sadness, and suicidal ideation.

Inability to fall asleep is a form of insomnia more characteristic of the psychoneuroses. In these instances the patient is often afraid to fall asleep because of nightmares. Patients with traumatic neuroses induced by battlefield experiences often are afraid to fall asleep because of the severity of their nightmares.

Pavor nocturnus is a type of sleep disturbance encountered in early childhood in which the child is usually found sitting up in bed screaming in terror, in the grip of a nightmare of hallucinatory intensity. In the course of the episode the youngster may seem to be reacting to frightening people or animals and acts as if unaware of the presence of reassuring parents. The episode is brief and self-limited, and the youngster spontaneously drops off to sleep after it. Often the child has no recollection of the episode the next morning. On the other hand, these episodes may become the basis of a fear of falling asleep.

Hypersomnia is often seen in depressive reactions occurring in psychoneurotics. In these instances sleep is a retreat from painful encounters with the real world.

Reversal of sleep habit is a common accompaniment of hypersomnia. In these instances the patient tends to sleep soundly through the early morning hours, wakes up gradually in the early afternoon, and achieves full wakefulness at a time when most people are going to bed.

Drowsiness is a state of consciousness that intervenes normally between sleep and waking and is characterized by a general slowing-up of the thought processes, with a tendency to concreteness in thinking, diminished perception, and clumsiness in motor responses.

Somnolence is abnormal drowsiness. It occurs in a variety of toxic, metabolic, and inflammatory disorders of the brain and with brain tumors that press on the floor of the third ventricle.

## EPILEPTIC AND CONVULSIVE DISORDERS

The essence of epilepsy from the standpoint of diagnosis is the periodic appearance of a recurring pattern of short-lived disturbances of consciousness.

Petit mal and grand mal seizures are characteristically associated with full loss of consciousness in the midst of the attack. In petit mal, consciousness blinks on and off, as it were, for intervals lasting between one and forty seconds each. These individual attacks are not associated with a preattack warning and are not followed by characteristic subjective or objective sequelae. EEG records in the midst of such attacks invariably reveal a spike and wave pattern having a frequency of approximately three of these complexes per second. The attacks may occur as often as one hundred times in a single day or as occasional, isolated attacks days or weeks apart.

The disturbances of consciousness associated with grand mal epilepsy are much more complicated. The actual muscular movements are typically preceded by an aura, which in itself may consist of a variety of clouded states of general awareness, including feelings of unreality and depersonalization. Commonly, these feeling states are not only vividly experienced but often remembered by the patient. Such preconvulsive alterations of consciousness may last for hours or even days before the actual seizure and may give the patient an opportunity to get to a place of safety. During the actual convulsion, loss of consciousness is complete, and amnesia for the events during the actual seizure is also complete. After the grand mal seizure, patients display an obtunded state of consciousness, which varies in duration from a few minutes to a period of hours. During this time, the EEG may show diffuse, symmetrical slow wave activity. Amnesia for the postseizure period may be complete or interspersed with fragmentary islands of recall. This period has been called the postictal twilight state.

Twilight states or dream states of consciousness can occur as independent phenomena apart from grand mal seizures. They are characterized by circumscribed periods of intellectual dulling, disturbance in consciousness, confusion, and disorientation. Brief auditory and visual hallucinatory symptoms and schizophrenic-like psychotic reactions have been described within the complex of the epileptic disorders. Generally, there is an amnesia for actions during this period. Characteristically, all these seizure patterns are associated with electroencephalographic abnormalities, which coincide in duration with the duration of the abnormality in the state of consciousness. Similar dream states are encountered in dissociative reactions, but with normal electroencephalograms.

The reticular activating system acts as an arousing mechanism that increases alertness when stimulated. Sensory stimulation serves a twofold function: It brings information from the environment, thus providing specific data concerning reality; and it arouses and alerts the organism through collateral pathways to the RAS.

Corticofugal pathways also send collaterals to the RAS, thereby placing the latter under the control of sensory stimuli from without and cerebral cortical elaboration from within. Stimulation of the

RAS facilitates both the general sensory inflow and the lower motor outflow. Inhibition of the RAS inhibits sensory inflow and lower motor outflow. In this way, the RAS can be said to affect both the cognitive and conative aspects of consciousness.

## DISTURBANCES OF ORIENTATION

Orientation may be defined as the ability to recognize one's surroundings and their temporal and spatial relationships to oneself or to appreciate one's relations to the social environment. The capacity for orientation involves the following categories: (1) Time: knowledge of the hour, day of the week, date, month, season, year. (2) Place: name of present location, the address, one's home address, the distance between present location and home address, reason for being in this place at this time. Inquiries in this area may reveal pathological denial of physical illness and the existence of other types of delusional systems. (3) Person: identity of self and others in the immediate environment. This includes not only a knowledge of names but also an appreciation of the role of each in that setting.

The capacity for orientation depends, in the main, on three factors: (1) the availability of perceptual data from the outer world, (2) the availability of the stored data of recent memory, and (3) a commitment to the demands of reality, which is part of the emotional equipment of the mature adult.

One may speak of a specific drive to seek out and maintain accurate orientation as a psychological quality characterizing the mature adult. Normally, the inability to establish one's bearings generates anxiety and appropriate orientation-seeking behavior. A normal person, for example, awakening in strange surroundings after a deep sleep may have a brief period of bewilderment, during which he scans his environment for clues, draws on his stored memory for recent events, and, finally, with a sense of relief, orients himself correctly. If he awakens from a particularly vivid dream characterized by a deep sense of the reality of the events in the dream, he may have a similar brief struggle to reestablish his orientation. If a patient wakes up from a coma, he may not be able to marshal sufficient data to orient himself. He may suffer from anxiety and bewilderment and respond to specific inquiries concerning orientation with panic and requests for information or by admitting that he does not know the answers to the questions.

In a variety of settings, individuals abdicate their firm commitment to reality. Adults in normal recreational settings, for example, deliberately cultivate flight from reality as part of the recreational process. In the theatre, surrender to the make-believe of the play may be so complete that it takes a period of active struggle to reestablish contact with the real world when the performance is over. Alcohol and other common central nervous system inhibitory substances encourage, and temporarily make possible, flights from reality and facilitate rapprochement with the world of make-believe.

The phenomenon of the imaginary companion may be cited as an example of flight from reality that takes place within the limits of normal. It has been commonly observed that an essentially normal child will create an imaginary companion for himself and will endow this product of his fantasy with qualities of reality. He gives the companion a name, a definite personality, and even an imaginary family. This phenomenon is seen most often when the subject is an only child or is for any reason shut off from real playmates. In general, the imaginary companion is so created by the child that it has everything the child desires but lacks. Thus, at this stage of development the child is able to enter into transient but easily reversible breaks with reality.

Patients with diffuse organic brain disease provide a paradigm for understanding the phenomena of disorientation. For many years the incorrect orientation answers of brain-injured patients were too briefly dismissed with "The patient is confused," or "The patient shows memory impairment." On close observation, orderly patterns can often be discerned within the overall picture of disorientation. In addition, what is sometimes described as an inability to remember is in actual fact a consistently repeated pattern of *mis*remembering.

## DISORIENTATION FOR TIME

Hospitalized patients without organic brain disease very commonly lose track of the date, the day of the week, and even the month. Thus, correct answers may be expressive of an alert and intact sensorium, but errors in these categories are not diagnostic of organic brain disease. An error in the year, on the other hand, *is* of diagnostic significance. It is in relation to the year that one commonly encounters a persistent pattern of misremembering.

A patient may give the year as 1958, and, even though he is corrected repeatedly, on each subsequent questioning he persists in stating that the year is 1958. Thus he "remembers" quite dependably the wrong year. To characterize this as a simple lapse of memory is to miss the point that the patient is remembering what he *wishes* to remember; that is, he is responding to a wish or to a feeling that he is living in a year that was, perhaps, the last time that he was in good health. The incorrect response, "The year is 1958," expresses a wish to be well rather than a simple failure of memory.

Errors for the time of day are not significant as evidence of organic brain disease unless the error crosses a mealtime. Brain-injured patients commonly show errors for time of day if awakened from a nap, thinking, for example, that lunch or supper is actually breakfast.

A patient cited by Weinstein and Kahn always gave the time of day as 7 P.M., "because that is when my daughter comes to visit me." This patient deliberately avoided contact with a clearly visible wall clock in the process of denying the correct time.

In giving their personal history, many patients condense incidents in time that should actually be separated.

A patient may report the birth of a younger sibling and the occurrence of an operation, such as a tonsillectomy, as taking place the same year when, in fact, the younger sibling was born when the patient was age 3 and the operation took place at age 6. In some such instances, it is possible to demonstrate that guilt over sibling rivalry on the one hand and the childish misinterpretation of an operative procedure as a punitive act on the other, although temporally separated, are condensed as a retrospective temporal falsification so that crime and punishment become fused in memory as a single event (see paramnesia).

Neurotic problems involving rebellious attitudes or a need to avoid painful reality may result in patterns of persistent tardiness. The affective state also plays a role in temporal orientation. During moods of elation, time seems to move quickly, whereas depressive moods are associated with a feeling that time is dragging.

Some anxious patients are unable to tolerate free time and have a need to fill all the temporal nooks and crannies of the day with prearranged activities. Such patients often suffer from a fear of loss of impulse control and defend themselves against acting out by overscheduling themselves. On the other hand, some patients, with a fear of their own passivity, will complain that they are too tightly scheduled. The outer controlling elements are experienced as potentially dangerous forces capable of overwhelming the victim. Such patients are incapable of tolerating authority and may present particular problems in relation to school and military service, where punctuality is a *sine qua non* for successful performance.

## DISORIENTATION FOR PLACE

The brain-injured patient in a general hospital may express the wish to be well by insisting that he is not in a hospital but in his home. When one such patient was asked to explain the presence of the doctors and nurses who were all around her, she answered, "These people have taken over my home and have made it over to look like a hospital, but it is really my home." Other patients will give the name of the institution correctly but will characterize it as a hotel, a restaurant, a convalescent home—that is, in various ways they will deny the gravity of the illness by denying that they are in a hospital. On occasion, the patient will give the name of the hospital correctly but will place the hospital close to home, saying, "I live a block away," or "I live across the street," when, in fact, home may be miles away. At times the patient will locate himself in another hospital in which he was treated many years ago for a relatively minor illness from which he recovered. In this spatial dislocation he is expressing a *déjà vu.* He says, in effect, "I've been here before, and I went home in good health." Temporal disorientation commonly accompanies this pattern of spatial disorientation. In duplication or reduplicative paramnesia, patients will give the name and location of the hospital correctly but insist that another "bad" hospital with the same name is located nearby.

These meaningful alterations, which are so clear in the case of the patient with diffuse brain disease, provide the clue for the disorientations in place encountered without organic brain disease. Schizophrenic patients may be disoriented for place in less predictable ways but always meaningfully in terms of their delusions.

A schizophrenic patient asserted that he was in a prison elaborately disguised to look like a hospital with a staff of jailers disguised as doctors and nurses who were all engaged in a charade to elicit incriminating facts about the patient and his family. He made a severe suicidal attempt because he believed that only upon his death would the jailers spare the lives of his loved ones.

## DISORIENTATION FOR PERSON

A married female patient displaying disorientation for person may give her maiden name and will insist that she is not married. Such denials often express elements of marital disharmony from which the patient wishes to take flight. It may also be associated with temporal disorientation representing regression to a time preceding the onset of illness.

Anosognosic patients may misidentify in a manner to confirm the denial of illness. The doctor in a white coat may be identified as a fish peddler and the place of their encounter the Fulton Fish Market. Some physical or characterological trait in a doctor or nurse may be the basis for a persistent misidentification of this person as a friend from the past who has no connection with illness. The doctor may be identified under such circumstances as a former teacher or an insurance salesman.

The tendency to divide the world into good and bad elements and then to create delusional systems that, in effect, embody this split resulted in a delusion expressed by a woman with one son named William. She claimed she had two sons, one named Bill, who was a good son, and one named Willie, who was bad. This duplication may involve not only the entire person but part of a person. For instance, a hemiplegic patient may insist that he has two left arms, one good left arm and one bad left arm.

Many times, patterns of disorientation in reversible brain disease will persist after the acute brain disease has subsided. Or it may clear up only to recur in a setting of emotional stress.

The concept of self may be so chaotic that the vulnerable individual tends to be highly suggestible and to identify with any dominant person he is with. He may incorporate specific mannerisms of speech and dress and self-destructive patterns of behavior, such as narcotic addiction. This instability of self-concept is particularly conspicuous in teen-aged girls. For this reason, they are vulnerable to mass hysterical behavior, as television audiences know from watching their responses to currently popular public performers. The chaotic concept of self is what Erikson referred to as the identity crisis. Confronted with an essentially insoluble dilemma concerning one's role in life, many teenagers go beyond experimental introjections and identifications and take flight into psychosis.

A teen-aged girl could not decide whether to be a successful writer and civic-spirited citizen like her father or a beautiful narcissistic woman like her mother. The patient had a prominent nose, which caused her to resemble her father. A plastic surgeon modified her nose, achieved an excellent cosmetic result, and succeeded in emphasizing delicate feminine features, which resembled her mother. Postoperatively, she went into an acute schizophrenic state, characterized by delusions that she was a sought-after beauty who had a great mission to save the world as a second Florence Nightingale.

Disorientations in all spheres tend to parallel and support each other. Through secondary elaboration, an inner consistency is achieved, like the consistency that often characterizes a dream. There is an expansion and embellishment of certain details to make for this consistency. If the time precedes the onset of the patient's illness, then the place is apt to be consistent with that time. The people are similarly misidentified, and the reason for everyone being together at that time and in that place is rationalized by complex delusional systems. When the disorientations in the delusional system are logically organized so that they have a "rational" inner consistency, the delusional system has been systematized. Systematized delusions are more resistant to correction and tend to carry a more serious prognosis.

## DISTURBANCES OF MEMORY

Memory is based on three essential processes: (1) registration, the ability to establish a record of an experience in the central nervous system; (2) retention, the persistence or permanence of a registered experience; and (3) recall, the ability to arouse and report in consciousness a previously registered experience.

A good memory involves the capacity to register data swiftly and accurately, the capacity to retain these data for long periods of time, and the capacity to recall them promptly in relation to reality-oriented goals.

During the process of registration, there must be a physiologically intact alert central nervous system. There must also be a sufficient number of repetitions of exposure to the data to stabilize the memory trace. An actor who needs many repetitions to memorize a script is called a slow study. At the other extreme are gifted individuals who in a single exposure can master a dramatic script, a musical score, or a school lesson.

Emotions associated with the learning process play a crucial role in determining the permanence of memories. In infancy and early childhood, the entire learning process is tied up with satisfactions based on the relief of biological needs by loving parents. Thus, in early childhood, there is a brain maximally receptive to learning in purely biological terms, there are attentive adults who are prepared to provide the repetitions necessary for learning, and there is a pattern of reward based on the loving responses of the parents as teachers. For all these reasons, it is no accident that the first language learned is called the mother tongue and that the mother tongue is normally the first language that returns on recovery from brain injury in patients who knew more than one language prior to the injury.

Although a good memory is one of the factors in the complex of mental capacities that make up intelligence, phenomenal feats of memory are occasionally encountered in settings of apparent mental retardation. The latter usually involve rote memory, the capacity to retain and reproduce data verbatim, without reference to meaning. In logical memory, on the other hand, problem-solving in relation to a reality-oriented goal is paramount.

In addition to quantitative there are also qualitative differences in memory. Some persons are particularly well-endowed with visual memory and can recall images with virtual hallucinatory intensity. Such subjects are called eidetic individuals, and the reproduced memories are called eidetic images. This eidetic capacity tends to occur in childhood and subside with age, so that it is rare after adolescence. Memory for music, mathematics, muscular movements such as those involved in the performing arts, spatial relationships, and emotional feelings may be cited as examples of nonverbal memory. Verbal memories depend on the development of verbal skills.

## DISTURBANCES IN REGISTRATION

Registration depends on the level of consciousness. Anything that diminishes consciousness, such as alcoholism or concussion, interferes with registration. A prizefighter may go on for several rounds to win a fight after a dazing blow to the head and yet have no recoverable memory for the events following the blow. A circumscribed memory loss of this kind occurring during the time after an acute brain injury is called anterograde amnesia. An alcoholic may behave in a socially acceptable manner for an entire evening and yet have no recoverable memory of the events of that evening. Disturbed states of consciousness lasting for weeks and months associated with encephalitis, subarachnoid hemorrhage, and severe brain trauma may be followed by a permanent inability to recall the events experienced during that period. In all of these instances, the subsequent defect in recall starts with primary defects involving registration and retention.

There are conditions in which registration seems to be impaired because the patient appears to be totally nonreactive. This occurs in catatonic schizophrenia and in severe panic states. However, when the brain is intact from an organic point of view but perceived experiences are repressed or denied for purely emotional reasons, registration is normal. In these instances, seemingly nonobserved events can be recalled subsequently, either directly or with the use of specific techniques for eliciting forgotten or repressed memories, such as hypnosis or narcoanalysis.

## DISTURBANCES IN RETENTION

In the establishment of lasting memories, there is a preliminary learning stage during which the memory trace is unstable. The memory curve or the curve of forgetting is a graphic representation of the relative amounts of memorized material that can be recalled after various intervals of time. For individuals with good memories, the memory traces are quickly established, and the curve of forgetting is prolonged and may extend over the entire lifetime of the individual. In some instances of organic brain disease, the curve of forgetting is accelerated. In Korsakoff psychosis, memory for recently acquired facts may decay in a matter of seconds, without any residual capacity for recall.

Retention is a property of nerve tissues in general. Nerve cells and their processes may be compared to tape recorders that retain at least a partial record of the impulses that have passed along them. There is an enormous capacity for units of information and for specificity of records of this kind in the brain.

It has been hypothesized that the registration stage of memory depends on the formation of ribonucleic acid (RNA) within the nerve cells and their processes and that specific memories derive their individuality from specific modifications in the RNA molecule. According to this hypothesis, each such RNA molecule is the storage device for the memory system and, at the same time, a template or stencil that can run off duplicates of the molecule as part of the mechanism of recall.

It has also been hypothesized that in the aging brain the basic supply of RNA is diminished and that this is the specific organic deficit underlying the proverbial weakness of memory in the aged.

Indeed, it has been suggested that additional RNA, parenterally supplied, can reverse the memory defects of senility.

## DISTURBANCES IN RECALL

Recall is, in the long run, the most important aspect of memory, since it is only in the examination of the process of recall that we acquire evidence that memory is intact or impaired.

*Amnesia.* Amnesia is the partial or total inability to recall past experiences. The events of infancy and early childhood up to the fifth year are commonly forgotten as part of the normal childhood amnesia.

According to psychoanalytic theory, an important basis for childhood amnesia is the need to control and repress various infantile wishes that are forbidden by parents. As infantile fears of punishment are relieved during psychoanalysis, many of the events of childhood amnesia are increasingly subject to voluntary recall.

From a theoretical point of view, a relatively sharp distinction can be made between the amnesias based on organic brain disease and those disturbances of purely emotional origin. The latter fulfill specific emotional needs and tend to subside when these are no longer operative. The amnesias of organic brain disease involve disturbances in registration and retention and are essentially nonrecoverable. Most often they affect the recall of recent events and leave the memory for remote events relatively intact. This is described as retrograde amnesia. Thus, in retrograde amnesia, there is amnesia for a period prior to a traumatic event. Such an amnesia may be psychological as well as organic in origin. If the brain disease is organic and progressive, impairment in recall worsens. The amnesias of emotional origin either improve with treatment or remain stationary.

The sharp distinction between amnesias of organic and emotional origins is made for purposes of description and clarification. Most amnesias seen in relation to organic brain disease are, in fact, mixed amnesias in which organic deficits and emotional interference with recall both play a role.

Hysterical amnesia is a loss of memory for a particular period of past life or for certain situations associated with great fear, rage, or shameful humiliation. This form of amnesia is highly selective and systematized to fulfill the patient's specific emotional needs (see hysterical fugue state).

The rule of Pitrés states that, in a person who knew more than one language prior to a brain insult, the first language that returns is the mother tongue.

E. E. Krapf cites a case of polyglot aphasia that illustrates the negative role emotion can play during the period of recovery. A brain-injured young man grew up in a Spanish-speaking country, but his mother tongue was English. In this case the mother-child relationship was a highly disturbed one, and the patient grew up with the image of his mother as a menacing figure. As memory for language returned in this brain-injured boy, he clearly preferred Spanish. Reduction in comprehension of English was especially noticeable during his mother's visits.

Halpern cites another case of polyglot aphasia. In this case, on recovery from a severe head injury, a Hebrew-speaking man whose mother tongue was English followed the rule of Pitrés and used English first. However, on return from the hospital to his Hebrew-speaking wife and children, he went into a severe depression when he found he could not communicate with them. During the following days, his mastery of Hebrew returned, and thereafter his fluency in Hebrew returned more rapidly than his recovery of English.

The brain-injured patient who is highly motivated may succeed in overcoming organically determined impairments of recall by a variety of mnemonic devices. For example, in response to a request to name an abstract word or concept, he may start with a concrete visual image that is charged with highly personal significance. In his search for the correct word he may then go on to make writing movements with his head. Finally, after much effort exerted over this tortuous path, he arrives at the abstract word for which he is searching. Thus, in order to discover subtle memory defects in brain-injured patients, it is necessary to inquire into the mechanism of remembering as well as the actual content of what is remembered.

In contrast to the aphasic impairments of recall, which are highly circumscribed and involve specific words or actions, is the impairment of recall associated with the hysterical fugue state (dissociative reaction). This is a form of amnesia that sets in following a severe emotional trauma. A terrifying experience on the battlefield or a momentary loss of impulse control that nearly leads to the murder of a loved one may be followed by a complete loss of memory concerning all personal identifying data. Following the precipitating psychological trauma, the patient enters into a period of actual physical flight, which takes place in a state of panic. When the victim comes to, he finds himself far removed from his accustomed habitat and unable to identify his surroundings, his reason for being there, or anything about his past. This form of amnesia is associated with a flattening of affect characteristic of hysteria. Usually, the lost memory is readily recoverable with hypnosis, narcoanalysis, or strong suggestion, particularly when offered in a setting that promises extended relief or actual physical separation from the traumatic life situation.

The dramatic extremes embodied in hysterical fugue states provide the model for more circumscribed examples of functional forgetting. Many psychologically traumatic experiences in early childhood are forgotten. What Freud referred to as *repression* in relation to these early childhood traumata is indistinguishable from forgetting in general. Such circumscribed amnesias may be the basis for a chronic state of psychological stress. According to psychoanalytic theory, these forgotten traumata threaten constantly to erupt into consciousness.

Symptom formation, to some degree, has its origin in the on-going need to keep these memories out of consciousness or to distort and disguise them if they do return. In a sense, the neurotic patient can be said to suffer from memories he is forgetting with only partial success, and in this way the psychopathology of memory is related to the psychopathology of the emotions.

Since nothing registered in the intact brain is ever really lost, in the functional diseases only the capacity for recall is impaired. In psychoanalytically oriented psychotherapy, the recall of forgotten traumata is facilitated by a systematic attack on the defenses.

*Paramnesia.* Paramnesia is a distortion of recall usually associated with the inclusion of false details or wrong temporal relationships.

Distortions in recall are encountered in normal individuals. The witness's errors in the courtroom are examples of this. There is in everyone a readiness to distort recall whenever accurate recall impinges on some painful reality. The presence of diffuse organic brain disease has the effect of facilitating and fixating this universally present tendency toward paramnesia.

*Fausse reconnaissance*, or false recognition, is the feeling of certainty that one is recalling accurately something that is patently inaccurate.

In retrospective falsification, a type of paramnesia sometimes called illusions of memory, false details, meanings, and recollections of a real memory are created in response to emotional needs. A patient may recall a true past event but distort it in accordance with a present need to support a symptom.

In confabulation, there is an unconscious filling in of gaps in memory by imagined experiences that the patient believes, although they have no basis in fact. These recollections change from moment to moment and are easily induced by suggestion. This phenomenon is most characteristic in Korsakoff's psychosis.

Pseudoreminiscence incorporates both confabulation and retrospective falsification.

*Déjà vu* is an illusion of recognition in which a new situation is incorrectly regarded as a repetition of a previous memory. It can occur in normal individuals, particularly in settings generating anxiety. It is more common in psychoneurotic states and occurs occasionally in the aura of an epileptic seizure. In *jamais vu* there is a false feeling of unfamiliarity with a real situation that one has experienced.

Related to *déjà vu* are *déjà entendu*, in which a comment never heard before is incorrectly regarded as a repetition of a previous conversation, and *déjà pensé*, in which a thought never entertained before is incorrectly regarded as a repetition of a previous thought.

Although the causes of these related phenomena are not known, psychoanalytic evidence suggests that they share with screen memories and daydreaming the function of psychological defense. Implicit in the feeling "I have experienced this before" is the reassuring further thought "and I have survived in spite of my fears." In short, *déjà vu* is a device to control the intensity of anticipatory anxiety.

The familiar type of nightmare known as the examination dream seems to serve the same function as *déjà vu*. Such dreams occur typically before a school examination or some other life trial. In the dream, the subject is asked to answer examination questions concerning a subject he never studied. In spite of the manifest anxiety in such dreams, the content typically deals with a test that was successfully passed some time ago. As such, it serves to reassure the dreamer that he will pass this test as well.

*Hypermnesia.*    Hypermnesia is an exaggerated degree of retention and recall. It can be elicited at times in a hypnotic trance. It is seen in certain prodigies, obsessive-compulsive neurosis, paranoia, and mania.

A screen memory consists of fragments of childhood recollection that break through the barrier of childhood amnesia. The screen memory is often striking for the minutiae recalled. Commonly, there are recollections of bright light. Characteristic also of the screen memory is its tendency to return to consciousness repeatedly in an obsessive fashion.

Paradoxically, the qualities of exaggerated accuracy and feelings of certainty that accompany these hypermnesias are deceptive. There are temporal and spatial alterations and an emphasis on trivia that combine to ward off from conscious recall specific traumatic memories of childhood. Thus, these memories may be more accurately classified among the paramnesias.

## DISTURBANCES IN PERCEPTION

Perception is the awareness of objects, qualities, or relations that follows stimulation of peripheral sense organs, as distinct from the awareness that results from memory. Thus, perception is the necessary precursor of memory and is connected with memory via the process of memory registration.

There are as many categories of perceived data as there are types of end organs. The latter include auditory, olfactory, gustatory, tactile, and kinesthetic.

Perception also includes discrimination—that is, the capacity to perceive the differences between two or more objects in respect to certain characteristics. Depth perception is the capacity to perceive the distance of a given object or objects from the observer or the relative distance from front to back in the perception of solid objects.

Agnosia is an inability to recognize and interpret the significance of sensory impressions because of organic brain disease.

Perception may be the result of relatively simple, affectively neutral stimuli, presented one at a time or two at a time (double simultaneous stimulation or DSS). Stimuli may be complex, involving both visual and kinesthetic factors in making a discriminatory judgment, as in binocular vision; or stimuli may be a combination of visual, olfactory, and gustatory in an essentially gustatory perception.

A disturbance of perception associated with organic brain disease forms the basis for the face-hand test (Bender). If a normal alert adult with eyes closed is touched on his face and hand simultaneously, he recognizes both touches accurately and promptly. In settings of diffuse organic brain disease, including cerebral arteriosclerosis, the subject reports the face touch accurately but does not report the hand touch at all or displaces it up toward the face and locates it inaccurately. Persistent errors on double simultaneous stimulation provide presumptive evidence of organic brain disease. This test is normally positive in children up to the age of 4 or 5. It then becomes negative until age 60, after which it tends to become positive again. In the intervening age groups, the test provides a useful presumptive sign. In elderly patients who are depressed and who give a positive response, the test tends to become negative as the depression lifts. In all instances of a positive response, further neurological studies are required to demonstrate absolutely that organic brain disease is indeed present.

Between the presentation of a stimulus and its recognition by the observer there is a time lapse called the perception time. This involves time for the transmission of the nerve impulse from the sensory receptor to the appropriate brain centers. More significant is the time involved to overcome an emotionally determined barrier to perception, which exists to protect the individual against traumatic stimuli.

Traumatic stimuli of all categories are modified adaptively by the barrier against stimuli. Alterations in the level of consciousness provide one example, with complete loss of consciousness (fainting) as an extreme example.

Whereas emotionally induced fainting eliminates all perception, circumscribed eliminations of perception may occur as a device for coping with traumatic stimuli. In negative hallucination, an individual with a physiologically intact nervous system fails to perceive a stimulus. It can be induced through hypnosis. When the nonperceived stimulus is excluded from conscious awareness because it is traumatic, it is usually part of the syndrome of hysteria.

Any modality of perception may be disordered in hysteria. Total anesthesia can occur, but diminution in sensation is more common. These perceptual disturbances do not follow recognizable neuroanatomical distributions but involve rather a part of a limb (glove and stocking distribution), half the body, and the mucous membranes (vagina, rectum, nose, mouth, and pharynx). Peculiar to the hysterical anesthesias is the usual involvement of all forms of sensation, superficial and deep, without the dissociation that so frequently occurs in organic sensory disturbances. If the sensory loss is limited to half the body, it is found to stop exactly at the midline, a condition contrary to the normal cutaneous overlapping. Similarly, psychogenic loss of sensation is attested to by the hysteric's perception of the tuning fork on only one side of the sternum or on only one side of the head, an obvious impossibility in view of the normal bone conduction of vibrations.

Repeated testing of visual fields in hysteria may result in a spiral contraction of the visual field. Hysterical blindness may occur.

Macropsia is a condition characteristic of hysteria in which objects appear larger than they really are. They may assume terrifying proportions.

Micropsia is a condition in which objects appear smaller than they really are. It may alternate with macropsia in hysteria, but it has also been described as an aura in some cases of epilepsy.

Hysterical patterns of perceptual disturbance do not by any means rule out organic disease. These perceptual disturbances often seem to emerge in response to repeated sensory testing. This is not at all the result of a conscious intent to deceive the examiner but is often a naive appeal for help.

> Brain-injured patients with left hemiplegia, hemianesthesia, and hemianopsia often steadfastly neglect the entire left side of the visual field. For example, they will eat all the food on the right side of the hospital tray right up to the midline; they will write only on the right half of the page; they will read only the right half of an individual word. In drawing the human figure, they draw only the mirrored representation of the right half of the body, neglecting entirely to draw the left half. In all these instances, there seems to be a selective inattention to the sick side, which manifests itself as an essentially hysterical disturbance in vision. The relationship of the latter to denial of illness seems quite clear: "The sick side does not exist."

Patients with organic hearing impairments have selectively more difficulty hearing emotionally disturbing auditory stimuli. In a sense, these patients with mixed (organic and functional) hearing disturbances are expressing in a selective and more circumscribed fashion the same phenomenon that is encountered in complete hysterical deafness without organic hearing impairment, namely, a blocking out of potentially traumatic auditory percepts.

Hysterical anesthesia has been described as a kind of localized fainting. Frigidity, including all degrees of anesthesia of the vagina and external genitalia, is a common hysterical defense against sexual excitement. In each circumstance, there is a withdrawal of attention from potentially traumatic external events.

Just as withdrawal of attention from a body part can reduce perception to the point of complete anesthesia, so can a sensory end organ be over-invested with attention because of anxiety. In the latter instance, there may be areas of hyperalgesia to touch, headaches, and other body pains. In spite of verbal expression of great suffering, the hysterical patient may show a characteristic attitude of unconcern. Complaints of pain may be associated with rigidity of muscles and occasionally bizarre flexion deformities of the extremities and spine. Although the physical complaints typically do not conform to recognizable clinical syndromes, actual physical disease, past or present, may set the stage for use of a specific body part in symptom formation that is without organic basis. This return to a previous symptom or the perpetuation and intensification of a present organic symptom is termed somatic compliance.

In all the perceptual disturbances of hysteria it is not enough to demonstrate that the pattern of sensory abnormality is impossible from the point of view of known neuroanatomical facts. One must also search out the emotional meaning of the perceptual disturbance in adaptational terms, recalling that anesthesia, hyperesthesia, or paralysis commonly serve to defend the patient against sexual or violent impulses that he fears may get out of control.

## HYPOCHONDRIASIS

A generalized withdrawal of attention from external objects is followed almost always by an increase in the attention focused on the self as an object. If this retreat from the world of real objects is complete enough, a pathological awareness of body feelings emerges, which is the basis for hypochondriasis.

Hypochondriasis is the unshakable belief that physical disease is present, in the face of all evidence to the contrary. As a symptom, it occurs in many forms of mental illness. It is most common in the depressions, particularly those of the involutional period. It may take extreme and bizarre forms in schizophrenia, in which case one may speak more appropriately of somatic delusions. (For example, "My insides are rotting," or "My intestines are filled with vermin or a solid plug of wax.") It may occur in a chronic low-grade form over a period of years as part of a psychoneurotic reaction. Abnormal body feelings associated with hysteria tend to be localized and serve to protect the individual against the still longed for but potentially traumatic encounters with circumscribed portions of the outer world. Abnormal body feelings associated with hypochondriasis, on the other hand, tend to be generalized, in the sense that the entire body is involved, and result from a relatively complete withdrawal from external objects. Thus, an important difference between the hysteric and the hypo-chondriac is the degree to which the real objects in the external world have been retained or surrendered.

## ILLUSIONS

In an illusion there is perceptual misinterpretation of a real external sen-sory experience. In a state of anxiety and loneliness, a traveler is apt to mistake a tree trunk for a menacing adversary or a mist for a terrifying apparition. This does not necessarily imply psychopathology. However, a schizophrenic patient may hear an insulting remark in the chime of a clock or feel the sinister hand of death in a casual handshake. This kind of misinterpretation is also known as an illusion. Illusions frequently occur in confused toxic conditions.

## HALLUCINATIONS

A hallucination is the apparent perception of an external object when no corresponding real object exists. That is, an internal psychological event is mistakenly attributed to an external source. A dream is a simple example of a hallucination in normal experience.

Any modality of perception may be involved in a hallucination. Within the framework of normal hallucinatory experience, hypnagogic and hyp-nopompic hallucinations should be mentioned. Hypnagogic hallucinations occur in the drowsy state preceding deep sleep. They may contain both auditory and visual elements with great clarity and intensity. At times they are associated with paresthesias in the mouth and hand, the sound of murmured voices, and vague visual images of large objects approaching and receding. The latter group of hypnagogic hallucinations has been called the Isakower phenomenon and seems to represent a reawakening of the memory of early nursing experiences.

Although it is said that hypnagogic hallucinations occur most often in individuals suffering from hysteria, they can also occur in normal individ-uals, particularly during childhood and early adolescence. What has been said of hypnagogic hallucinations is also true of hypnopompic hallucina-tions, except that the latter occur during the drowsy state following deep sleep and preceding awakening.

When the schizophrenic patient is wide awake by all neurophysiological criteria, he may experience hallucinations as vivid as those experienced by normal people during dreams. He very often acts on these inner percep-tions, as though they were more compelling than the external realities that compete for his attention. He may incorporate illusions into his hallucina-tions, so that the latter occur alongside of external perceptions and even intermingle with them.

The affective content of the schizophrenic hallucination is more like that of a nightmare. In the acute schizophrenic reactions, unpleasant (dysphoric) elements tend to prevail. This is probably a result of the fact that some unendurable reality being warded off in the psychotic state constantly threatens to break through and contradict the schizophrenic distortion of reality. Auditory hallucinations tend to predominate in schizophrenia as contrasted with the predominance of the visual sphere in the dream.

Hallucinosis is a term for psychotic states in which the patient is well oriented, in spite of the fact that he is hallucinating. Such patients slip in and out of the hallucinatory state, with intervals of insight and lucidity. (Hence, Hughling Jackson's term mental diplopia.)

There is a group of hallucinogenic psychotomimetic drugs that characteristically elicit hallucinosis—that is, hallucinations in a setting of relatively clear consciousness. Mescaline and lysergic acid diethylamide (LSD) are well known representatives of this group. The relative alertness of the subject makes it possible for him to communicate his hallucinations in considerable detail in an experimental situation.

Under mescaline, visual hallucinations, combined with visual illusions, are most frequently reported. These visual phenomena are vivid and change rapidly. Auditory hallucinations also occur, but less frequently.

Proprioceptive, cutaneous, and hypochondriacal sensations are also reported under the influence of LSD. Visual hallucinations tend to be much less frequent with LSD. In describing their reactions to hallucinatory drugs, particularly to LSD, patients have described compound hallucinations such as "color-hearing" or "sound-seeing." These occurrences have been termed synesthesias.

The relationship of drug-induced hallucinosis to schizophrenia and the value of these hallucinatory states as adjuvants to psychotherapy have been studied extensively, with only equivocal results.

In the convulsive disorders, relatively unformed percepts may occur during the aura. Olfactory and gustatory hallucinations occur in temporal lobe lesions in the so-called uncinate fits. Characteristically, the patient is unable to describe these sensations clearly except to say that they are unpleasant. Other patients may experience nausea or flashes of light as part of the aura. Less commonly, the aura in uncinate fits is associated with complex hallucinatory experiences involving visual and auditory components and possessing an affective quality of reminiscence (for example, *déjà vu*). The nature of the preseizure's sensory disturbance often provides important clues for the localization of seizure foci amenable to surgical removal.

Generalized organic brain disease of almost any etiology can be associated with hallucinatory states that are at times indistinguishable from schizophrenia. These reactions may be expressive of drug sensitivities. Atropine and its derivatives may cause characteristic Lilliputian hallucinations in drug-sensitive adults receiving relatively small quantities in the form of eyedrops or in children being treated for enuresis. In Lilliputian hallucinations the hallucinated objects, usually people, appear greatly reduced in size. Although they occur most characteristically in psychotic reactions to a variety of drugs and toxic-metabolic states, they can on occasion occur in psychotic reactions without organic brain disease. They are to be differentiated from micropsia, in which real objects in the environment appear reduced in size.

Similarly, relatively small doses of alcohol or marihuana can produce hallucinations in sensitive subjects. Even the phenothiazines, which are administered to decrease psychotic manifestations, may in specific sensitive subjects intensify hallucinations or elicit new ones.

Patients who are chronically habituated to any sedative substance (alcohol, barbiturates, meprobamate, diazepoxide, etc.) often experience hallucinations when these drugs are withdrawn (withdrawal reaction). These hallucinatory states are commonly associated with great terror.

A large range of toxic metabolic stressors can elicit hallucinations as part of their action on the brain—for example, uremia, hypoglycemia, diabetic acidosis, alkalosis, hyperparathyroidism, and heart failure. The relief of heart failure with digitalis will at times interrupt a hallucinatory psychosis. On the other hand, a sensitivity reaction to digitalis may start one.

Brain tumors, subarachnoid hemorrhage, uremia, strokes, a broad range of endocrine abnormalities, and a variety of drugs may all play a role in initiating hallucinatory psychosis. The main point is that different chemical agents can produce the same hallucinatory effect in a given individual, and, conversely, a given chemical can produce widely varying responses among different individuals (Kluever: equivalence of heterogeneous stimuli).

In a hallucinatory state the following elements are to be taken into account:

1. PROJECTION TO THE OUTER WORLD. At times, hallucinations are perceived with great intensity; at other times, they are perceived as barely audible whispers or barely visible shadows. At times, the hallucination is clearly placed in the outer world; at other times, it is experienced within the body: a picture or a voice located in the head, the chest, or some other part of the body. The images and words may be distinct or blurred. They shade off from unmistakable sensory experiences at one extreme, through vivid imaginations and inspired thoughts, to ordinary thoughts and ideas at the other extreme.

2. THE SENSORY MODALITY. For example, a haptic hallucination is one associated with the sensation of touch. Although it may occur in schizophrenia, it is probably more common in delirium tremens, in which these cutaneous hallucinations are commonly associated with visual hallucinations of tiny, crawling animals. Creepy sensations under the skin

are known as formication—for example, the "cocaine bug." Hallucinations of bad tastes and odors may be encountered as part of the aura of temporal lobe epilepsy (uncinate fit). The latter may also occur in schizophrenia, with complex delusional elaboration. The visual sphere is primarily involved in the hallucinatory phenomena seen in the toxic-metabolic disorders. Anton's syndrome is delusional denial of blindness, associated with hemiplegia of the nondominant side. The auditory sphere is probably the most frequently involved sensory modality in the hallucinations of schizophrenia. Reflex hallucinations may occur in one sensory sphere as the result of irritation in another; for example, a toothache may stimulate an auditory hallucination. Kinesthetic hallucinations may occur in amputees, as the phantom limb experience.

3. THE CIRCUMSTANCES THAT HAVE ELICITED THE HALLUCINATIONS. A careful history with physical and laboratory examinations must be carried out to diagnose psychoses with acute or chronic brain disease that might otherwise be indistinguishable from schizophrenia. In all cases involving organic brain disease, reactions of delirium are more apt to occur at night. The sensory deprivation, the loneliness, and the anxiety, which tend to be greater at night, may combine to reactivate a psychotic process that has become quiescent by day. Therefore, careful nursing and security precautions throughout the night are particularly important in the treatment of these cases.

4. INSIGHT. The degree to which the patient is aware of the pathological nature of his perceptual disturbances may have both diagnostic and prognostic significance. The element of insight is more likely to be present in the early stages of any psychosis and during the period of recovery. In either case, its presence tends to be associated with a good prognosis, and such patients are naturally more cooperative for treatment.

5. THE EMOTIONAL AND IDEATIONAL CONTENT OF THE HALLUCINATIONS. The acute reactions of withdrawal from drugs and the toxic deliria are associated typically with great terror. Reactions of flight are common, and such patients, if unattended, may leap out of a hospital window to escape the unspeakable horrors of their psychotic world.

During psychotic states of ecstasy and elation, hallucinatory experiences may involve sexual excitement and feelings of being infused with impregnating rays which result in conception. In paranoid states, voices may be threatening. Rays may cause diseases, poisonings, or strange feelings. Voices may order the patient to commit acts of violence to save himself or the world from unspeakable sin. In depressive states, voices may be derisive and humiliating. They may accuse him of sexual perversion and order him to commit some expiatory act of self-mutilation or self-destruction.

As in dreams, memory traces constitute the building blocks of hallucinations. The past history of each patient provides the clue for understanding their content. The content reflects the effort to master anxiety and to fulfill various wishes and needs. Whereas patients with organic brain disease tend to express simple ideas relating to the wish to be well and to be home, patients with functional psychoses express more complex ideas based on interactions with internalized objects and concern themselves primarily with sexual and aggressive drives that the individual has been unable to master in real life.

## DISTURBANCES IN AFFECT

Affect is the feeling tone, pleasurable or unpleasurable, that accompanies an idea. Affect and emotion are used interchangeably and include such feelings as rage, grief, and joy. It determines the general attitude, whether of rejection, acceptance, flight, fight, or indifference. Thus, the affects provide the motivational drive (or psychodynamic) component in relation to every life situation and play a determining role in the thoughts and actions of an individual in health and disease. When an affective state is sustained for a considerable period, we speak of a mood. Affect may be described as shallow or inadequate (emotional flatness), inappropriate (when the emotion does not correlate with the stimulus), or labile (changeable).

Attitude refers to the affective state with which a person habitually confronts his environment. Attitude is determined in early childhood by what Erikson called basic trust.

In the normal developmental sequence, an individual develops a capacity to relate to parents and to later parent figures in school and at work with an attitude of love and basic trust. In settings of family disorganization and in the absence of dependable sources of love and safety, the individual grows up with an attitude of basic distrust.

Where the individual's attitude is one of basic distrust, he tends to be rigidly hostile, suspicious, cynical, and pessimistic toward everyone, even when others attempt to relate to him in a positive way.

Disposition refers to the affective state with which an individual habitually confronts himself. Whenever what Erikson called basic security has evolved, there is also a clear sense of personal identity. Associated with this is a sense of well-being and optimism, which tides the individual over the inevitable recurrent life crises that generate anxiety and depression in everyone.

### ANXIETY

Anxiety may be defined as a disagreeable emotional state in which there are feelings of impending danger, characterized by uneasiness, tension, or apprehension. The cause is usually unconscious or unrecognized intrapsychic conflict. Anxiety is associated with a characteristic pattern of autonomic nervous system discharge involving altered rhythm of respiration, increased heart rate, pallor, dryness of the mouth, increased sweating, and musculoskeletal disturbance involving trembling and feelings of weakness.

Anxiety is to be differentiated from fear, in which the foregoing combination of feelings and nervous discharges occur as a reaction to a real conscious and external danger that is present or that threatens to materialize.

Tension should also be differentiated from anxiety. In tension, the patient feels tight psychologically as well as physically. Tension is associated with conflict as a component of anxiety.

Panic is a state of extreme, acute, intense anxiety, accompanied by disorganization of personality and function.

In infancy, anxiety is hypothesized to be a diffuse, objectless feeling of dread stemming from the discomforts of unsatisfied needs. As the infant comes to identify the people in the environment who satisfy his needs, anxiety appears as a response to separation from them. With biological development, he is able to make complex behavioral responses calculated to prevent separation or to take action to bring separation to an end. As part of the child's anxiety reaction, he develops physical maneuvers to protect the body, to fight off the attentions of unwelcome individuals, or to take flight. Anxiety at this point involves not only a feeling of dread and the concept of danger but also a positive relationship to a specific individual (usually the mother) capable of relieving the danger. As a consequence of this relationship, the anxiety reaction becomes mingled with a feeling of hope.

As the child develops, he learns to anticipate the danger of separation and to initiate maneuvers to avoid it before it starts. As this is accomplished with increasing success, the gross reaction of discomfort subsides, and in time anxiety is reduced to a mere signal of danger, which sets off appropriate responses so swiftly and silently that there is no conscious awareness of danger in the entire process.

When confronted with an unprecedented danger or when the previous solutions are no longer available, the silent signal of danger once again becomes a conscious clamor, and once again there are psychologically meaningful actions representing calls for help and preparations for fight or flight. If a solution is still not forthcoming, anxiety increases progressively. At one point, expressions of helplessness and hopelessness ensue, with panic and various pathological forms of withdrawal from the traumatic environment.

As the infant develops strength and understanding, he becomes increasingly capable of accepting periods of separation from his mother and increasingly capable of accepting suitable substitutes for her during periods of enforced separation.

Realistic dangers continue throughout life. Such stressful situations still call forth the feeling of dread, the impulse to fight or take flight, and all the associated physiological concomitants. Commonly, the stressor is readily identifiable—for example, an impending operation. At other times the source of anxiety is more difficult to identify. In the early stages of organic disease, a reaction of anxiety to the vaguely sensed organic impairment may be the earliest clinical symptom preceding the appearance of any other localizing somatic symptoms.

Whenever the psychological adaptational mechanisms threaten to decompensate, anxiety appears. This may occur in a chronic low-grade form as a constant accompaniment to life. This occurs when a more or less compensated mental disorder exists. Sudden changes in the life situation may evoke an increase of anxiety or precipitate an episode of panic as a warning that more disastrous emotional decompensation is in the offing. Thus, the presence of generalized anxiety or the occurrence of anxiety attacks are indicative not of any one clinical entity but are rather psychophysiological signals of danger that can occur in any diagnostic category of physical or emotional disease.

Free-floating anxiety is the nucleus and key symptom of neurosis. It consists of a feeling of dread that the patient cannot logically assign to a specific cause. In the quest for causality, patients suffering from free-floating anxiety are always ready to attach it to some suitable ideational content.

Anxiety reaction is a psychoneurotic state based primarily on free-floating anxiety. It is characterized by irritability, anxious expectation, pangs of conscience, and episodes of panic. There is a hypersensitivity to ordinary sights and sounds, as a result of which startle reactions occur frequently and with minimal sensory provocation. Cardiac palpitation, breathlessness, giddiness, nausea, dryness of mouth, diarrhea, compulsive eating, urinary frequency, seminal emissions, blurring of vision, general physical weakness, and other physical manifestations may occur chronically as part of anxiety neurosis. In an effort to reduce the unpleasant feelings associated with anxiety, the individual evolves a variety of defensive devices that in their entirety constitute many of the clinical manifestations of psychiatric disorder.

Conversion hysteria, for example, is a well-known pathological device for reducing or eliminating free-floating anxiety. It is a psychoneurotic reaction characterized by sensory and motor deficits without a corresponding structural organic lesion. The effect of a hysterical paraplegia, for example, may be to prevent access to a situation feared by the patient because of unconsciously desired and rejected erotic or aggressive impulses. Often the physical symptom is so effective in alleviating the anxiety that the patient displays an attitude of calm (*la belle indifférence*) that contrasts strangely with the extent of the physical disability. *La belle indiffér-*

*ence* is an example of inappropriate affect.

Anxiety hysteria is a psychoneurotic reaction in which the patient develops specific fears or phobias in relation to situations that might stimulate erotic or aggressive impulses unconsciously desired and rejected by the patient. A similar anxiety-relieving role can be made out for many of the symptoms of the obsessive-compulsive reaction and schizophrenic reaction.

Patients rarely employ a single fixed pattern for relieving anxiety. They try one and then another, and when these reactions fail, they may try still a third. This is repeated until the best adaptation possible under the circumstances is attained. And then, if the circumstances change, the pattern of adaptation may change again. In time, one pattern of adaptation does tend to become fixed in most patients.

In all instances, however, the clinical picture is best understood in adaptational terms in which a dangerous impulse is permitted some modicum of indirect or disguised discharge and the need for restraint and punishment is also permitted some degree of gratification, albeit in disguised form. These conflictual strivings are synthesized and harmonized in a way to reduce the amount of suffering caused by anxiety, and together they form the clinical symptom or reaction.

For example, a young woman was brought into the emergency room of a general hospital by her sister and brother-in-law with an adductor spasm of both lower extremities and an inability to walk. This motor abnormality was without accompanying organic disease. The emergency room physician gave her a small quantity of Amobarbital sodium intravenously, with the strong suggestion that her leg muscles would relax and return to normal when he finished counting to 10. At the appropriate signal, the patient relaxed, got off the table, and walked out of the emergency room, apparently elated. Four hours later, she was returned to the emergency room in a catatonic stupor, for which she had to be hospitalized. At that point, information was elicited for the first time that the patient had just recently moved into her sister's household and had suffered from guilt and anxiety as a result of illicit sexual play with her brother-in-law. Thus, removal of the hysterical defense (adductor spasm) caused this patient to regress to a psychotic defense (catatonia).

## DEPRESSION

Depression, or a feeling of sadness, shares with anxiety a preeminent place among the most frequently expressed human complaints. Depression may vary in intensity from mild dejection to feelings of deep melancholia and profound despair. Just as fear, as contrasted with anxiety, is a reaction to real danger, so grief, contrasted with depression, is a reaction to a real loss.

The reaction of grief or mourning, which is the appropriate emotional response to a real loss, can be encompassed within the limits of normal reaction patterns. At the outset, grief may be expressed by uncontrollable crying or a shocklike state, with confusion, temporary panic, and thoughts of self-destruction. There may be physical weakness and loss of appetite, withdrawal of attention from the surrounding world, and inconsolability. After the initial period of mourning, there is a restoration of interest in the world. However, each new reminder of the loss reawakens the reaction of grief. The associated affective changes may go on for months and constitute what Freud called the work of mourning. This reaction may be accompanied by irritability and feeling of guilt. In time, the bereaved accepts the irrevocability of the loss, works through the complex issues raised by his sense of guilt, and is restored to normal.

Where the emotional development of the bereaved is inadequate and where feelings of guilt are very great, the mourning reaction may go on more or less indefinitely and merge into a pathological state of reactive depression. Thus, reactive depression may be defined as a psychoneurotic reaction characterized primarily by feelings of sadness, pessimism, lassitude, and inadequacy. It is commonly associated with anxiety and is precipitated by some loss. The actual loss may involve a loved person, physical health, beauty, or social position.

Anaclitic depression refers to the syndrome shown by infants during the first years of life if deprived of the attentions of a suitable mothering figure. Anaclitic means "leaning on" and is a psychoanalytic term denoting an infant's dependency on his mother for his sense of well-being. On separation from the mother, the infant goes through a characteristic sequence of changes. There is an initial phase of protest, characterized by intense crying and struggling. If this state of affect deprivation continues, the infant lapses into the phase of despair. At this point behavior suggests hopelessness. Struggling decreases, and crying is softer and monotonous. In children's hospitals this quieter state is commonly misinterpreted as a state of diminished distress. Actually, it is a state of mourning. Some such infants fail to thrive. They may stop eating and then waste away and die, a state called marasmus. Those who survive lapse into a phase of detachment, in which the infant withdraws from human relationships and becomes preoccupied with inanimate objects or his own body parts, engaging in masturbation, fecal smearing, head banging, and rocking.

In children of grade school age, the loss of loving parental figures tends to result in aggressiveness, hyperactivity, self-injury due to frequent accidents, inattentiveness in school, fire-setting, and enuresis.

Many youngsters enter adolescence with a sense of loss relative to the simplicity of their previous life. Reactions of depression in adolescence are common. Sexual acting out is more often an expression of loneliness than of lack of morality. Because of his great vitality, the depressed teenager tends to act out not only sexually but antisocially. Juvenile delinquency, aggression, and reckless driving may be compared to the phase of protest previously mentioned. Suicidal threats and actions are used more to coerce adults than with deliberate self-destructive intent. However, successful acts of suicide are encountered with increasing frequency in the late teenage period.

Corresponding to the phase of detachment in early childhood is the "so what?" reaction in adolescence. An attitude of cynicism reinforces antisocial attitudes. Feelings of hopelessness, emptiness, and purposelessness may lead to addictions of all kinds. In fact, addictions—whether to alcohol, narcotics, other drugs, food, or even the company of other people— are typical adolescent expressions of the effort to overcome feelings of depression.

In adult life and thereafter, the picture of depression comes to resemble the picture of mourning more closely. In speech and behavior, the patient who expresses his helplessness often succeeds in recruiting support from the environment. In this context, suicidal threats and gestures are commonly employed as measures of protest or coercion.

Many fragile people maintain a marginal adaptation in highly supportive relationships in marriage or friendship. When these are disrupted, severe depression may emerge, which proceeds through all the phases: protest, despair, and detachment. Suicidal threats and gestures may occur during the reaction of protest. Alcohol, barbiturates, and other sedative drugs may be used to overcome feelings of despair.

A defense mechanism for dealing with the lost loved one is to act like that person—to adopt his interests, mannerisms, and way of life. This process is referred to as introjection. It is a form of identification that is potentially pathological in that it is often the result of feelings of helplessness and loneliness. Very commonly, depressed patients complain of symptoms that precisely reproduce the physical complaints of the deceased.

> In a case of transvestism (a compulsion to dress in the clothing of members of the opposite sex), a male patient periodically dressed in female attire as a way of retrieving his deceased mother.

A state of chronic depression may go on for years, with a progressive decrease of interest in the outside world. This intensifies the attention paid to the body, with a tendency to hypochondriasis. In later years, there may be an overlay of organic factors from cerebral arteriosclerosis, which complicates the clinical picture and renders the prognosis more grave. The reduction in energy output in depression also fulfills a self-preservation function in that it reduces the likelihood of self-destructive acting out.

Thoughts of self-destruction may occur transiently at one time or another during life within the limits of normal behavior. On the other hand, all verbally expressed suicidal thoughts must be given serious consideration, particularly where there is depression and there seems to be no promise of relief. In many instances, suicidal behavior represents a cry for help or an effort to induce protective behavior from an indifferent environment. With increasing age and progressive exhaustion of the reservoir of potential environmental helpers, the incidence of successful suicide goes up. Incidence of suicide rises uninterruptedly throughout life with males but tends to level off in the seventh decade with females.

## AGGRESSION

Aggression is forceful, goal-directed action that may be physical or verbal. It is the motor counterpart of the affect of rage, anger, or hostility. It may be realistic and healthy, thereby representing self-assertion, directed toward the external world or turned inward, resulting in impulses or acts of self-destruction. Aggression is constructive when it is problem-solving and appropriate as a defense against realistic attack. It is pathological when it is unrealistic, self-destructive, non-problem-solving, and the outcome of unresolved emotional conflict.

Rage tends to emerge whenever strong drives are frustrated. In early childhood, separation from the mother, which is experienced as frustration, tends to generate rage as well as anxiety. The need to share the mother with the father is a universally encountered frustration and provides the basis for the Oedipus complex. The need to share the mother's love with siblings also creates frustration and reactions of rage: sibling rivalry.

Uncontrolled rage in early childhood may result in loss of mother's love and incur punishment. As a result, the youngster growing up in the framework of normal family life experiences great pressure to control outward expressions of rage. To a considerable degree, the psychological developmental process involves the increasing capacity to control rage and to find substitutive outlets for it. Conversely, loss of control elicits feelings of guilt and anxiety.

Where there is family disorganization, particularly in the socioeconomically deprived group which is characterized by broken homes and absent fathers, the capacity to control outward expressions of rage is impaired. In such a population, the incidence of suicide due to inwardly turned rage is low, while the occurrence of assaultive behavior and homicide is high.

In pathological mother-child relationships, a spectrum of rage reactions may be discerned with postpartum depression and suicide at one end of the scale and child battering and infanticide at the other. There are innumerable intermediary ambivalent mothering reactions, resulting in infant neglect and failure of the youngster to thrive physically and emotionally.

Psychiatric symptom formation has as one of its primary goals the control of forbidden aggressive impulses. Phobias, hysterical paralyses, and hysterical fugue states are common examples of this type of defense. Obsessive-compulsive symptoms may develop as devices for expressing aggression in a diluted form. Typically, even these "modified aggressions" generate so much guilt that the obsessional patient feels compelled to *undo* the aggressive act by means of a variety of complex compulsive rituals. Pathological states of apathy and boredom may result as a defense against rage. In some patients, a small quantity of alcohol may suffice to precipitate an attack of pathological alcoholic intoxication, which is characterized by an outburst of homicidal fury. Morbid fear of death may be the result of a chronic fear of loss of control of aggression, with a concomitant anticipation of retaliation from the environment.

Rage, unexpressed because of guilt and fear of retaliation, has been hypothesized to result in a variety of physical symptoms involving various organ systems of the body in psychosomatic disease. Homicidal rage may occur episodically in postepileptic twilight states. Aggression verbally expressed may take the form of obscene speech, and the defense against this may take the form of stuttering or hysterical speech disturbances.

Irritability refers to a state in which chronic diffuse expressions of anger occur to ward off relationships viewed as threatening. This may be found in paranoid character disorders, various psychoneurotic reactions, and the early stages of psychotic depression and schizophrenia. It is commonly encountered in adolescents to ward off sexual feelings felt toward parents and siblings.

Outbursts of rage with delusional ideation may occur in schizophrenia as a defense against unconscious homosexual impulses or other impulses consciously unacceptable. Violence associated with criminal acts of breaking and entering may be encountered with perverse sexual impulses. Uncontrollable compulsive acts such as kleptomania, pyromania, and gambling may be masked expressions of rage. A major cause of suicidal behavior in depression is rage turned against oneself. In these instances, suicide becomes an internalized act of homicide.

Aggression merges with erotic thought and action in sadism and masochism. Sadism is the experience of pleasure derived from inflicting physical or psychological pain on others. Masochism is defined as pleasure derived from physical or psychological pain inflicted on oneself. Sadism and masochism may occur unconsciously within the limits of normal behavior as well as in sadistic or masochistic character disorders and in some psychoneurotic and psychotic reactions. These tendencies may also occur consciously in various sexual perversions, such as flagellantism, a masochistic or sadistic act in which one or both participants derive erotic stimulation from whipping or being whipped. Masochistic reactions are associated with unconscious guilt feelings, in response to which punishment is sought or invited.

## Pleasurable Affects

Implicit in the description of anxiety and depression are converse states, in which danger is absent and union with loved ones is perfect. In such a setting, the pressure of one's wishes and needs is balanced by the availability of adequate channels for impulse or drive discharge, and contentment prevails.

In infancy and early childhood, hunger and fatigue may rapidly transform a contented child into one who is fretful and unhappy. In the course of biopsychosocial maturation, the individual develops an increasing range of substitutive outlets and the capacity to delay immediate gratification. As a result, the capacity for affect stabilization increases. In the emotionally mature adult, there is an underlying stability of good mood that withstands the undermining traumata of daily life. The chronic absence of good feeling, anhedonia, is seen in chronic depressive states and in simple schizophrenia.

Normal recreation may be cited as an example of a substitutive outlet that allows for stabilization of mood. Recreation is characterized by a quality of irresponsibility, spontaneity, enthusiasm, hilarity, euphoria, elation, and other relatively uncontrolled expressions of emotion. During play, the emotionally mature adult is permitted to become a "child" again. Not only is this socially approved, but the capacity to act childishly in a controlled setting is a distinct asset. In play, it is possible to vent aggressive feelings against one's opponent. Mounting excitation culminating in a victorious climax may represent sublimation of sexual drives. Repetitive motor discharge through playing games is a device for achieving motor mastery in the developmental process and for recalling the sense of triumph upon accomplishing motor competence in the adult. Thus, while there are regressive elements in normal play, they are always within limits set by the rules of the game. The capacity to regress while maintaining disciplined contact with reality is not only part of recreation but of the esthetic experience in general and has been referred to by Kris as regression in the service of the ego.

Euphoria refers to the first, moderate level in the scale of pleasurable affects. It has been defined as a feeling of emotional and physical well-being. When it occurs in a manifestly inappropriate setting, it is indicative of mental disorder. Although it is usually psychogenic, it may be observed in organic brain disease.

Elation may be thought of as a second level in the scale of pleasurable affects. It is characterized by a definite affect of gladness in which there is an air of enjoyment and self-confidence, and motor activity is increased. This affect belongs within the limits of normal life experience. Yet it may be indicative of mental disorder when it occurs in a manifestly inappropriate setting.

Mood swings refer to the oscillations between periods of euphoria and feelings of depression and anxiety. To some degree, mood swings occur within normal limits throughout life. They may be more marked during adolescence. Another normal life situation characterized by mood instability is the premenstrual phase in women, which has been referred to as "the recurrent neurosis of women." Anxiety, excitability, and anger are common; other cases show fatigue, irritability, hypersensitivity, and weeping spells. In almost all instances there is some regression, as a result of which the capacity to delay immediate gratification of impulses is impaired, and frustration seems unbearable. In most adult women, the onset of menstrual flow is followed by emotional relief.

As Benedek has shown, hormonal influences undoubtedly play a large role in this premenstrual upheaval. However, psychological difficulties related to unresolved feminine identity problems may complicate the picture.

Ambivalence refers to the coexistence of antithetical emotions, attitudes, ideas, or wishes toward a given object or situation at the same time. Usually, only one attitude emerges into consciousness, the other remaining unconscious. Ambivalence is encountered in all instances of affective instability. Thus, it plays a role in the mood swings that occur within normal limits. However, it is fundamental in many pathological mental states, being particularly prominent in the obsessive-compulsive, manic-depressive, and schizophrenic reactions. Bleuler regarded marked ambivalence as one of the primary symptoms of schizophrenia.

Various pharmacological agents may induce euphoria or elation. Alcohol, narcotics, and the amphetamines may be cited as examples. Underlying most cases of addiction is an anxious-depressive state that drives the patient to use agents which will relieve the painful affective states. These substances enable the patient to repress or deny the existence of painful affects. Brain lesions may have a similar impact on painful affects.

It was once thought that lesions of the frontal lobe specifically elicited a mood of euphoria. It is now known that any brain lesion—anywhere and from any cause—that lowers the level of consciousness can have this effect. A small lesion involving the floor of the third ventricle may have a greater mood-elevating effect than a much larger one occurring elsewhere. Affability encountered in patients with senile dementia is an example of mood elevation associated with diffuse organic brain disease.

So far, the role of drugs and toxic and organic factors as affect-elevating agents has been emphasized. Some patients are able to eliminate from consciousness painful affects without the aid of chemical consciousness-impairing agents by utilizing defense mechanisms that are exclusively psychological. They deny not only depression but all object losses as well. The manic patient does not feel deprived; he feels elated. In place of pessimism and despair, he has feelings of unwarranted optimism and self-confidence, and he is physically overactive and high-spirited. He feels that he has unlimited resources and, as a result, squanders money with reckless abandon. This pattern is called the manic reaction, or mania. When less intense, this behavior is described as a hypomanic reaction. Because the clinical picture represents a complete break with reality, without awareness on the part of the patient, such reactions are defined as psychotic.

Often the manic reaction thinly disguises an underlying depression by which it may be abruptly replaced. Manic reactions tend to be relatively short-lived and are typically followed by depression, hence the term manic-depressive or cyclothymic psychosis. In some instances, a hypomanic reaction may be indefinitely prolonged.

Exaltation may be defined as extreme elation and is usually associated with delusions of grandeur. It merges into ecstasy, which represents a peak state of rapture. These affects in inappropriate circumstances are found almost exclusively in relation to psychosis, such as the schizophrenic reaction.

The ecstatic states occurring in acute schizophrenia are related to the ecstatic transports of religious mysticism. The mystical experience, whether religious or not, possesses certain distinguishing qualities:

1. INEFFABILITY. The subject often insists that his experience is inexpressible and indescribable, that it is impossible to convey what it is like to one who has never experienced it.

2. NOESIS. The subject has the feeling that the mystery of the universe has been plumbed, that an immense illumination or revelation has occurred. Along with this may go a curious sense of authority, the conviction that one is privileged to lead and to command. As for the revelation itself, it seems to consist of layer upon layer of truth that, as it unfolds, may find expression in some familiar or even commonplace thought that suddenly seems pregnant with new meaning. On occasion, the expression of the truth may take the form of a document of poetic beauty and great moral significance, such as are represented by the writings of the biblical prophets. On the other hand, the revelation may be expressed in words that are unintelligible to the speaker.

3. TRANSIENCY. The actual mystical state may last only a moment, or it may go on for an hour or two; but when the experience ceases, the particular quality of feeling it aroused is only imperfectly reproducible in memory. Yet it is as unforgettable as it is highly treasured, and it colors all subsequent activity.

4. PASSIVITY. In the mystical state there is an abeyance of the will, as if the subject were in the grip of a superior power to whose direction he is highly responsive.

5. UNIO MYSTICA. There is a sense of mystic unity with

an infinite power, an oceanic feeling in which opposites are reconciled, in which there are "darknesses that dazzle" and "voices of silence." There is a quality of timelessness, in which minutes and centuries are one and in which past and present are one.

The mystical experience seems to represent psychological regression at its most extreme. It has been hypothesized that it is a retreat to the very beginnings of conscious psychological life, and in a sense it is an ultimate counsel of despair. As the individual travels backward in memory in search of a time when life was endurable, finding no one on earth to whom he can turn for help, he comes at last to a time of contentment that preceded conscious awareness of other human beings. It is a retreat to a time when infant and mother were fused. In recapturing this mood, the individual may find in the mystical experience a way out in the form of psychosis or a compelling religious experience, whatever its nature, that may be life-saving in its impact on the subsequent behavior of a despairing human being.

## MECHANISMS FOR MAINTAINING MOOD CONTROL

The euphoric, manic, and ecstatic states are often based on painful affects, which are replaced in consciousness by their opposite. Other ways in which painful affects may be brought under control follow:

*Depersonalization.* This is a mental phenomenon characterized by a feeling of unreality and strangeness about oneself. The patient says, in effect, "This experience does not hurt *me* because I am not *me*."

The term depersonalization includes feelings of unreality, estrangement, amnesia, multiple personality states, and distortions in the body image. Depersonalization may be partial or complete, transient or long-lasting. It may be encountered in hysteria or as part of the aura of epilepsy. In schizophrenia it is complete and lasting.

*Derealization.* This is a mental phenomenon characterized by the loss of the sense of reality concerning one's surroundings. The patient says, in effect, "This environment is not dangerous to me because this environment does not really exist."

Derealization includes distortions of spatial and temporal relationships so that an essentially neutral environment seems strangely familiar (*déjà vu*) or strangely unfamiliar (*jamais vu*) or otherwise strange and distorted. Like depersonalization, to which it is closely related, derealization can be partial or complete, transient or long-lasting. Similarly, it may occur in hysteria or as part of the aura of epilepsy. It, too, is most complete and persistent in schizophrenia.

Although depersonalization and derealization occur as adaptational mechanisms to reduce unpleasant affects, they may in their own right create a feeling of impending catastrophe.

A feeling that could be shattering if experienced in a single episode becomes tolerable if "digested" piecemeal over an extended period.

The traumatic neuroses of wartime may be cited as an example. An experience capable of generating overwhelming terror may be dealt with at the moment of occurrence by depersonalization and derealization. When the catastrophe is over and the individual is no longer in danger, delayed reactions of anxiety may appear. Sleep may be disturbed by recurrent battle dreams. There may be an intolerance for sudden loud noises and for displays of aggression. After memories of the traumatic incident have been "revisited" repeatedly and the anxiety slowly mastered in small doses, the traumatic neurosis subsides.

## DISTURBANCES IN MOTOR ASPECTS OF BEHAVIOR

Conation, or the conative aspect of mental functioning, refers to the capacity to initiate action or motor discharge and concerns the basic strivings of an individual as expressed through his behavior. The affective component of an idea determines the force and the direction of the action that follows that idea. Thus, conation cannot be considered apart from affects, and, conversely, all affects represent potential energy via their conative components.

The schizophrenic seems to have a basic impairment of the conative capacity. He has difficulty initiating goal-directed activity. He may in some instances be capable of carrying on useful work if it is initiated for him and carried out under constant supervision, as in a sheltered workshop. Other examples of impaired conation in schizophrenia follow.

Echolalia is the pathological repetition by imitation of the speech of another person. In certain instances of catatonic schizophrenia, all speech is echolalic in nature.

Echopraxia is the pathological repetition by imitation of the movements of another person. The patient may act as the mirror image of his physician and assume his postures and gestures. Echopraxia is characteristic of catatonic schizophrenia. Waxy flexibility (*cerea flexibilitas*) is the maintenance by a patient of imposed postures with increased muscle tone, as when a limb remains passively in the position in which it is placed, however long or uncomfortable. This phenomenon may be induced during a hypnotic trance (catalepsy) in essentially normal individuals, but it is most characteristic of catatonic schizophrenia and organic brain disease. It is to be differentiated from cataplexy, which refers to a sudden, transient attack of muscular weakness, with or without loss of consciousness. Narcolepsy is paroxysmal sleep associated with cataplexy.

Echolalia, echopraxia, and waxy flexibility are cited as examples of command automatism, wherein commands or suggestions are automatically and uncritically fulfilled. Disturbances of motor activity may also be conveniently classified in terms of overactivity and underactivity.

## OVERACTIVITY

Some individuals are endowed biologically with a tendency to increased motor output, which can be demonstrated in studies of fetal movements antepartum. The hyperkinetic child is particularly prone to restlessness, aggressivity, destructiveness, and assaultive activity during periods of family disorganization and emotional deprivation. Pathological overactivity in childhood is particularly prevalent among boys. As they develop motor skills, boys become increasingly involved in athletic activities, which offer an opportunity for self-discipline and goal direction in the expression of their intense motor drives. Children may also develop hyperkinesis as a sequel to organic brain disease such as encephalitis.

Agitation is a state of chronic restless motor activity that is a manifestation of emotional tension. When a patient is restless and depressed, his diagnosis is agitated depression. The restlessness and uncontrolled motor activity associated with certain ataractic drugs such as the phenothiazines is called akathisia.

Learned sphincter control, which is part of motor development, may be lost during periods of stress. Thus, previously toilet-trained youngsters may become enuretic or encopretic during periods of enforced separation from the mother.

Patterns of hyperkinesis that start during the grade school period may carry over into adolescence and are, in part, the basis of antisocial behavior during this period. Thus, adolescent tendencies to reckless driving and sexual acting out, which have far-reaching social implications, are best understood and treated as manifestations of biopsychosocial stress. Overeating, excessive drinking, smoking, irritability, and restlessness may also occur as fragments of the anxiety and depression syndrome in the adult.

Patterns of increased motor activity can be observed in the psychoneurotic reactions. The hysterical convulsion, for example, also known as major hysteria or hystero-epilepsy, consists usually of pantomimic expressions of sexual and aggressive fantasies. Occasionally, a hysteric patient may mimic a *grand mal* seizure with extraordinary fidelity; the major differential diagnostic feature is the patient's failure to develop postseizure reflex abnormalities.

Sleep-walking (somnambulism) is a motor disturbance that occurs primarily during childhood and tends to occur more often in individuals prone to hysterical symptom formation. It is also commonly associated with enuresis. On a psychological motivational level, it seems to be related to nocturnal feelings of fear and loneliness and the wish to enter the parental bed. In spite of what seems to be a simple mechanism at work, in which a child acts out relatively superficial wishes in a half-waking state, sleep-walking (as well as sleep-talking and enuresis), when monitored electroencephalographically, appears to take place during stage IV sleep, a period of deep sleep during which dreaming rarely if ever occurs.

Psychoneurotic reactions of the obsessive-compulsive type are character-ized both by obsessive ideas and doubts and by complicated compulsive rituals. The range of compulsive actions is literally limitless, although cer-tain patterns tend to occur most frequently, such as compulsive hand-washing, counting, and repetitive ceremonial rituals, including the recita-tion of prayers and the repeated checking of door locks, water faucets, gas jets, and windows. In each instance, the compulsive symptom simultane-ously carries out a forbidden wish and then undoes it. The endlessly re-peated cycle of anxiety, the need to carry out the forbidden act, relief of anxiety by carrying out the compulsive act, and the need to undo the act, characterizes the compulsive symptom.

Various compulsive manias are, in effect, pathological preoccupations or compulsions associated with specific ideas, activities, or impulses. For ex-ample, dipsomania, the compulsion to drink alcohol excessively; egomania, the pathological preoccupation with self; kleptomania, compulsive steal-ing; megalomania, preoccupation with delusions of great power; monoma-nia, the preoccupation with a single idea; nymphomania, excessive sexual desire in a female; pyromania, the morbid compulsion to set fires; trichotil-lomania, the compulsive pulling out of one's hair.

A tic is an intermittent spasmodic twitching of the face or other body part, repeated at frequent intervals and without external stimulus. Al-though there seems to be some relationship between tics and motor dis-turbances of conversion hysteria, the tic is more stereotyped and difficult to influence with treatment. Tics occur automatically and are not under conscious control. They seem to originate as an accompaniment to affect: sex, rage, anxiety, grief, triumph, or embarrassment. In time, they become affect equivalents, in the sense that there is repetitive discharge without conscious awareness of the original affective significance.

Maladie des tics is a disorder characterized by a facial tic, which may spread to involve the head, neck, and upper and lower extremities. The tic is associated with stereotyped gestures, echolalia, coprolalia (preoccupa-tion with obscene words), and compulsive thoughts. It usually begins be-tween the ages of 7 and 15 and is essentially incurable. The muscular movements begin in the face and extend to the rest of the body. The patient opens his mouth, spits, jerks his head, claps his hands, scratches, jumps, and dances. Articulation and phonation are affected, and barking noises are often made. The patient repeats certain words or phrases, fre-quently expressing compulsive ideas. There may be some accompanying organic changes, but the nature of the pathology is unknown.

Manic patients may talk, sing, dance, and joke with apparently inex-haustible energy and good spirits. In agitated depression, there may be crying, pacing, and wringing of hands. In catatonic excitement, the pat-tern of overactivity is extreme from a quantitative point of view and bewil-dering from the point of view of content. Talking, which may be loud and voluble, is in response to delusions and hallucinations. The talk may consist of endless repetitions of sentences or phrases, the meaning of which is obscure (verbigeration). The severe ambivalence characterizing the schizophrenic process may result in great mood swings, ranging from abject terror to exaltation. There may be sudden eruptions of terror and rage, in response to which the patient may become homicidal. There may be moments of deep guilt and an urge for self-sacrifice, which may result in acts of self-mutilation. The excited catatonic patient may execute various gestures that have the intent of influencing the world by means of magical thinking. Catatonic excitement, because of qualitative intensity and a tendency to be prolonged, may result in severe exhaustive states, with dehydration, hyperthermia, and sudden death. The use of physical restraint tends to increase terror, intensify excitement, and increase the dangers of exhaustion and death.

## UNDERACTIVITY (PSYCHOMOTOR RETARDATION)

Just as there are individuals constitutionally predisposed to hyperkinesis, so there are others who react to stress with motor inhibition. In childhood and early adolescence, generalized patterns of inhibition and retreat tend to have a more grave clinical significance than they do in later years and suggest the presence of a schizophrenic process.

Simple depression, in contrast to the agitated depression, is characterized by the absence of anxiety and by decreased motor activity. There is a feeling of pronounced fatigue and great difficulty in initiating any activity, including speech. Responses to stimuli are slowed up on an ideational, verbal, and motor level. The patient's posture is expressive of the underlying affect of hopelessness and futility.

Hysterical motor disturbances can affect any of the voluntary muscle groups in patterns calculated to ward off forbidden sexual and aggressive discharges or to avoid situations of physical danger. They may present clinically as paralysis or muscular weakness (asthenia); abnormal posture, such as torticollis, camptocormia, pseudocontractures, and stiffness; gait disturbances ranging from hysterical paraplegia to astasia-abasia. The speech apparatus may be affected with aphonia, hoarseness, and stammering. Blepharospasm may occur in relation to forbidden scoptophilic wishes. The muscular abnormalities of hysteria are usually associated with an increase in muscular tonus. If sustained, they may produce painful orthopedic and gynecologic disorders. For example, hysterical spasm of the muscles of the pelvic floor may cause vaginismus. Concerning the physical findings in hysterical paralysis, Freud wrote, "The hysteric acts in his paralyses and other manifestations as if anatomy were nonexistent or as if he had no knowledge of it."

Although hysterical paralyses are usually associated with increased muscle tone and rigidity, on other occasions a total flaccidity, except for the retention of normal reflexes, is encountered. On occasion, an attitude of ambivalence will express itself in variations in muscle tone.

In the schizophrenic catatonic stupor, the patient is immobile. His face may be masklike in its lack of animation. He is unresponsive to questions or commands except when he occasionally manifests echolalia or echopraxia. When an attempt is made to bend his arm at the elbow, he may vigorously extend it. He may close his eyes tightly when asked to open them. These qualities, which may be regarded as contrariness or counter-suggestibility, are manifestations of a generalized oppositional attitude called negativism, wherein the patient does the opposite of what is requested. Ambivalence may modify the muscle tonus of the patient with catatonic stupor to the extent that he will permit bending of his arm but against a resistance, so that a tonus quality emerges known as waxy flexibility.

Motor disturbances may express themselves primarily in disorders of language. Stammering is a disorder characterized by spasmodic, halting or hesitating speech. Stuttering is a more severe degree of stammering. It tends to have a more explosive quality, based on violent expulsive respiratory movements associated with the production of speech. It usually appears between the ages of 2 and 6 years. It occurs much more frequently in males and is said to be more frequent in those who are left-handed.

When an individual encounters an affect-laden idea while speaking, he may hesitate and stammer. Such an interruption in the flow of words is analogous to a slip of the tongue and represents a momentary speech impediment based on an encounter with a circumscribed and personalized conflict. However, when the function of speech itself has acquired an objectionable emotional overlay, there is an ongoing disturbance in the capacity to speak more or less independent of the ideas themselves. Such is the situation in stuttering.

## DISTURBANCES OF PERSONALITY

Personality refers to the sum total of the patterns of thought, feeling, and behavior that an individual habitually employs in his on-going adaptation to life. Personality is often used synonymously with character. Normal personality implies a state of maximal fulfillment in terms of flexible adaptation to adult reality. For most people, however, personality development involves a process of becoming psychologically rigid and of making peace with one's own illogicalities, eccentricities, and follies. As a result of personality rigidity, there is a certain loss of freedom of thought and action. However, overt symptom formation is prevented thereby. The structural rigidities of personality often conceal deep-seated psychopathology. Under stressful conditions sufficient to disrupt these structures, severe symptom formation, including overt psychosis, may erupt.

Various personality disturbances may be distinguished. They include inadequate personality, schizoid personality, cyclothymic personality, paranoid personality, passive-aggressive personality, and compulsive personality.

The sexual perversions are also included among the personality disorders. Some of these are homosexuality, pedophilia, fetishism, transvestitism, exhibitionism, voyeurism, sadism and masochism, and zoophilia.

## DISTURBANCES IN APPEARANCES

It is relevant at this point to discuss the relationship of appearance to the clinical manifestations of psychiatric disorder. Extremes of meticulousness or slovenliness and attire which is manifestly inappropriate or bizarre and which calls attention to itself for these reasons may all be indicative of mental disturbance.

Excessive fastidiousness may suggest an obsessive-compulsive disorder. Deterioration from a previous normal level of neatness may be an early sign of depression or schizophrenia. When a female patient seeks to arouse sexual desire by her seductive dress, make-up, and manner, hysteria should be suspected as an element in the clinical diagnosis. Male homosexuals are distinguished for their exhibitionistic attire. A sexually fearful female may deliberately choose neutral or drab clothing to discourage the interest of potential sexual partners. Regressive clinging to childhood may be expressed in childish patterns of dress. For example, a mature woman may wear a large ribbon in her hair.

Rejection of normal sexual identity is encountered in adolescent females who affect boys' haircuts and blue jeans and in adolescent boys who affect female or childhood hair styles. Repulsive body odors due to lack of bathing may be designated "the skunk maneuver," calculated to keep a frightening world at a safe distance. Paranoid patients may wear dark glasses so that they may spy on others without themselves being spied upon. Eccentric patterns of dress, including large unkempt beards and excessively tight pants, may become a badge of rebellion or a conformity for membership in teenage groups.

Transvestites are sometimes acting out complex fantasies involving a wish to recapture a lost parent figure. Schizophrenic patients may first reveal the delusion of body change by complaining that a hat or a pair of eye glasses no longer fits properly. Powerful automobiles and other possessions may become extensions of the body image and serve to compensate for feelings of inferiority.

## LIFE PATTERN DISTURBANCES

In the psychiatric evaluation of an individual, the main concern should be with actual life performance rather than with the symptoms he displays or the psychodynamics of each symptom. The important question is not whether he has psychopathology but whether the psychopathology "has" him. To evaluate an individual in operational terms, the psychiatrist must make inquiry into four separate areas: family, work, play, and community. In each of these areas, the patient is expected to function in a specific role. The effectiveness with which he performs these roles is a measure of health, just as impairments in these areas are a measure of life pattern disturbances and mental illness.

## FAMILY

Within a family group, one can identify the following roles: (1) spouse (husband, wife), (2) parent (father, mother, grandparents), and (3) child (son, daughter, sibling).

Each of these roles involves a complex of capacities and responsibilities. The husband must be not only the wage earner but also the sexual partner and companion for his wife. The capacity for satisfactory sexual performance is implicit in his role. Potency disturbances can have a severe undermining effect on family happiness. Just as satisfactory sexual performance reinforces the male's concept of self as a man, the satisfactions he gives to his wife reinforces her identity as a woman and promotes acceptance of her female role. Ideally, from a psychological point of view, the husband should be the leader in the home. If he is unable to assume family leadership because of his personal psychopathology or because socioeconomic factors have displaced him from that role, he gets caught up in a vicious cycle that is destructive to both himself and the rest of the family.

The wife must be capable of accepting her feminine role both sexually and in her overall responsibilities in the household. If she is frigid and incapable of sexual satisfaction in spite of normal sexual potential in the husband, this may undermine his self-esteem and have a destructive impact on his overall performance. Thus, there is in the sexual life of the married couple a give and take in which there is mutual reinforcement of self-esteem when the sexual life is normal and mutual disturbance when it is not.

Perhaps the most important aspect of the parental role is the capacity to accept an attitude of passive dependence in others. There are periods of helplessness and dependency needs that fall within the range of normal, and a *sine qua non* for normal function as a spouse or parent is the mastery of one's own infantile dependency needs. A person who has achieved this is capable of providing maximal opportunity for normal emotional development in others. On the other hand, reversal of roles is often seen in disturbed households in which an emotionally immature parent makes unrealistic demands on a young child. A schizophrenic or depressed mother may take to her bed and expect her little daughter to mother her.

That the mother plays a role of special importance in the emotional development of the child is self-evident. However, the importance of the father in the developmental process is equally great. Not only does he consolidate the self-esteem of the mother, but he provides an identification for the son and, in his relation to the mother, an identification model for the daughter. Families without fathers are particularly prone to psychopathology.

Grandparents play a complex role in family life, with variations that are determined largely by cultural factors. Perhaps the most important fact is that the grandparent role permits the individual to continue the reproductive role vicariously, with many privileges that are not possible with one's own children.

Children must develop basic security and basic trust in their relationships to their parents. Where the opportunity for this does not exist, attitudes of cynicism and distrust emerge and seriously impair the social, intellectual, and emotional developmental process. One result of effective parental participation in family life is the setting of limits on the outward expression of sibling rivalry. The birth of a sibling is universally experienced as a trauma, resulting as it does in a displacement of the older child from the bosom of the mother. The displaced youngster has feelings of rage, for which he needs help from his parents. If this help is not forthcoming, the youngster does not internalize his aggression or learn to sublimate it. Instead, he expresses it outwardly. This is why the likelihood of homicide and other forms of violence is greatly increased in communities characterized by family disorganization and absent parents.

## WORK

At each stage of life every individual has a work role. For the school age youngster, this involves his capacity to function as a student. The wage earner must be able to work with reasonable effectiveness and personal satisfaction. The same is true for the wife in relation to her household chores. Many people work far below their potential because of psychopathological work inhibitions. Some are self-defeating out of a sense of guilt. Others are self-defeating because of a fear of success (those who are destroyed by success). Some fall behind because they must rebel in their quest for identity. On a school level, this expresses itself as an impaired capacity for learning and in the school drop-out problem.

Retirement from work may have a severe disruptive impact on the adaptational patterns in a family and may touch off a vicious cycle of psychopathology. Some people might be termed work addicts. These are guilt-ridden people who work compulsively and for whom loss of a job or retirement upsets a delicately balanced adaptational state; loss of work may at times result in severe mental illness and disruption of family life.

The chronic schizophrenic patient has a peculiar attitude to work. If he works at all, he chooses work settings that are highly structured and that permit isolation from other human beings. The postal clerk on the night shift occasionally is an example of this. Many schizophrenics refuse to work. In some instances at least, work is viewed as a threat to basic security in the sense that success might mean separation from parent figures and loss of a sheltered home setting. For this very reason, some patients who fear to work for pay will work on a volunteer basis. The inability to hold a job carries with it a particularly poor prognosis in schizophrenic patients.

## SOCIAL

Normal emotional development calls for a capacity to enjoy one's leisure. This involves not only a range of skills and interests but freedom from guilt and anxiety. The capacity for spontaneity, enthusiasm, and elation has already been mentioned in the description of normal recreation. Some people in recreational situations are like work addicts. They play compulsively, angrily, and anxiously. They are so demanding of themselves that they suffer severely if they make errors; if they lose, they become depressed. In these instances, the superego remains too much in control, and there is no opportunity for genuine sublimation.

## COMMUNITY

A concern for the welfare of others should extend beyond the confines of the family. The emotionally mature adult has a sense of duty toward his community and ideally involves himself in charitable, educational, or political groups to provide service to others without financial reward. This involves a capacity for idealism and self-sacrifice and the ability to get along with others. Needless to say, many become involved in this area for pathological reasons, such as guilt, exhibitionism, and a need for self-aggrandizement. In such instances the formal goal of the group may clash with the pathological informal goals of the individual. If such individuals have positions of leadership, they may exert a highly destructive influence on the group, which may necessitate their removal if formal group goals are to be achieved.

## REFERENCES

American Psychiatric Association. *Psychiatric Glossary*, ed. 2. American Psychiatric Association, Washington, 1964.

Arieti, S., editor. *American Handbook of Psychiatry*, 2 vols. Basic Books, New York, 1959.

Bender, M. B. *Disorders of Perception*. Charles C Thomas, Springfield, Ill., 1952.

Bleuler, E. *Textbook of Psychiatry*. Macmillan, New York, 1924.

Deutsch, H. *Psychology of Women*, 2 vols. Grune & Stratton, New York, 1944.

Engel, G. L. *Psychological Development in Health and Disease*. W. B. Saunders, Philadelphia, 1962.

Fenichel, O. *Psychoanalytic Theory of the Neuroses*. W. W. Norton, New York, 1945.

Hinsie, L. E., and Campbell, R. J. *Psychiatric Dictionary*, ed. 3. Oxford University Press, New York, 1960.

Jackson, D. D., editor. *The Etiology of Schizophrenia*. Basic Books, New York, 1960.

Linn, L. *A Handbook of Hospital Psychiatry*. International Universities Press, New York, 1955.

Piaget, J. *Judgment and Reasoning in Children*. Humanities Press, New York, 1952.

Rapaport, D., editor. *Organization and Pathology of Thought*. Columbia University Press, New York, 1951.

Warren, H. C. *Dictionary of Psychology*. Houghton Mifflin, New York, 1934.

Wechsler, D. *The Measurement and Appraisal of Adult Intelligence*. Williams & Wilkins, Baltimore, 1958.

Weinstein, E. A., and Kahn, R. L. *Denial of Illness*. Charles C Thomas, Springfield, Ill., 1955.

# CHAPTER EIGHT

# *Classification in Psychiatry*

## *HENRY BRILL, M.D.*

PSYCHIATRIC CLASSIFICATION is in many ways a deceptively simple matter. It can be carried out routinely by using less than 50 of the 132 pages of the American Psychiatric Association's *Diagnostic and Statistical Manual*, and a number of national systems are far shorter. It is surprising how quickly the average resident in training can learn to comply with the formal requirements by using one of these outlines as his main guide.

On somewhat closer examination, this seeming simplicity proves illusory because psychiatric classification approximates a kind of maximum condensation of contemporary psychiatry and embodies theoretical and practical implications of the utmost complexity. Exploring these can lead one into such collateral problems as communication theory, the science of systematics, the philosophy of science, the history of psychiatry, and the complex problems central to psychiatric nosology itself. Obviously, most of these topics can be barely mentioned in a review of this kind, but they cannot be completely ignored, since they are a part of the total perspective.

## CLASSICAL BACKGROUND OF CLASSIFICATION THEORY

Many current issues in psychiatric classification are neither new nor specific to the field, although, if seen as purely psychiatric problems, they do appear to be specific and perhaps subject to simple solutions. An interesting example is the often-repeated proposal that *all* psychiatric classification be abolished, on the ground that there are only quantitative differences among the disorders of various individuals and that all cases are *different* and, therefore, cannot be grouped but must be described individually.

It is difficult to avoid the impression that this is a replay in modern dress of a controversy that extended from the eleventh to the fourteenth century, when a bitter debate raged around the idea that all collective terms—such as animal, man, wood, stone—had no existence or reality and were mere words. The argument originated in Aristotle's "Categories," which propounded the problem of genera and species and which split Scholastics into three warring groups. This analogy may seem far-fetched, but it serves to recall that classification involves a very subtle and complex logic, although it is basic to even quite simple human thought. Common language itself is made up of classifications developed in a long-forgotten past, and Aristotle, as founder of the science of logic, gave classification a central place in it.

The heat of the discussion of the Scholastics arose not from the abstract merits of the issues themselves but as a displacement from certain very practical religious implications. Similarly today, there is considerable displacement of affect from certain practical implications of psychiatric classification onto the classification itself. Although this is quite human and understandable, it is not helpful in arriving at a scientific solution. In any case, it appears futile to speak of abolishing classification, unless one were to give up all generalization and communicate only in the most concrete, individualistic terms. In view of this, the question is not whether or not we shall have classification but rather what *kind* or *kinds* will best serve our purposes. The answer depends entirely on what our aims are.

## PURPOSES OF CLASSIFICATION

In general, classifications are a device for reducing complexity by noting the similarities in a given mass of observations and then grouping them abstractly in order to deal with them more easily as a conveniently small number of things. A multitude of concrete observations must be brought to some kind of order and simplification if they are to constitute a subject of effective communication that can be handled by logic or if they are to serve the needs of knowledge.

There is, of course, no one absolute means of arranging objects. They may be grouped in many different ways, depending on the purpose of the moment. For instance, water may be classified according to size (from puddles to oceans), temperature (from steam to ice), or purity (from pure to infected). Each classification is valid and useful for a particular purpose or interest, though each is made up of quite arbitrary points on a continuum, and not one is composed of entities with absolute differences.

In clinical psychiatry, classifications serve important functions with respect to education, treatment, professional communication for recording and retrieval of data, research, and administration.

# DEFINITIONS

Classification is a specialized science and a branch of logic with its own history, terminology, and definitions, and it has various subspecialties, of which psychiatric nosology is only one. A review of several of the important definitions is necessary here because various authors use terms in somewhat different ways.

## CLASSIFICATION

In medicine the term classification refers to a specifically ordered arrangement of selected terms in which various disorders are gathered into groups, and these in turn are gathered into larger classes, which in their turn are finally drawn into major categories. Thus, in the American Psychiatric Association (A.P.A.) classification, catatonic schizophrenia is a subdivision of schizophrenia, which is one of a family of psychoses. The purpose of the classification is to create groupings based on significant similarities among the properties and peculiarities of the items being arranged. Thus, the disorders gathered under the heading of "psychoses" are thought to have characteristics in common that distinguish them from those found under "neuroses."

Any particular classification must be like a sorting rack for experience, with one specific position for each type of case, including the unclassifiable and the partially unclassifiable. Individual terms may be, and usually are, part of a nomenclature or terminology; but the way in which the terms are grouped and arranged turns the list into a classification. There is some reason to consider the identification of entities as different in nature from the arrangement of entities into larger groups that correspond to genera and species, but this has not been widely accepted in psychiatry.

## ARTIFICIAL AND NATURAL CLASSIFICATIONS

When the products of human experience are arranged, satisfactory underlying principles are often lacking, and it becomes necessary to use arbitrary groupings based on superficial characteristics, as when patients are classified according to economic disability. Such a classification is called artificial. In some discussions of psychiatric classification, the assumption seems to be that this is unscientific and that the only acceptable form is the natural one—that is, some system based on a significant underlying characteristic. For example, a natural classification of disease would be by causes, such as infections, trauma, and prenatal influences.

The most advanced scientific classifications do today reflect great natural laws. An example of such a classification is the periodic table of Mendeleyev; but the vast inner meaning of this arrangement did not emerge until long after the arrangement had been devised on relatively superficial, or artificial, grounds. Another great natural law is that of evolution, which is linked to the classification of Linnaeus; but his classification is an outstanding example of the value of an artificial arrangement, since it preceded Darwin's work by a century and originated as a purely artificial grouping based entirely on external characteristics; its natural characteristics were not discovered until long afterward.

The major psychiatric nosologies are neither totally artificial nor totally natural. Their individual elements or entities did not originate from a single system but were each evolved separately in the course of a long history of cumulative observations. All important modern psychiatric nosologies show gradations from the clearly natural organic disorders to the clearly conventional wastebasket of the personality disorders, where much of our current lack of knowledge is gathered into one place. Yet the artificial elements are justified by the principle that a purely artificial and conventional system is far better than none at all and must be used when a natural one is not available.

## Nomenclature

An arrangement of the terminology specific to a science is called its nomenclature. The arrangement is arbitrary and often alphabetical and is independent of any underlying characteristics. There may be, and often are, overlapping among various terms and multiple names for a given object, although one is generally marked as "preferred." *Current Medical Terminology*, published by the American Medical Association, is an excellent example that covers the entire field of medical practice, including psychiatry. It represents a bold and revolutionary attempt to create and maintain a codification of current usage, quite in contrast to the decennial revisions of the classification systems.

## Nosology, Taxonomy, and Systematics

Specialists make various distinctions among these terms, but here they are considered synonymous with each other and with "classification."

## Statistics, Statisticians, and Code Numbers

Classification is as old as recorded psychiatry, but the current use of diagnosis for public health purposes can be fairly attributed to Florence Nightingale, who, with the medical statistician William Farr, first proved the devastating effect of well-marshaled medical statistics in a battle for medical reform. Since their time, it has become increasingly clear that diagnosis cannot be a strictly individual and personal affair between patient and physician because of the overriding implications for public health and prevention. As a result, the mechanism for collecting such data has been much expanded and formalized.

Each item in a modern classification is accompanied by its identifying code number, and these numbers, arranged in a sequence, together form a system for sorting cases into various categories. Contrary to the impression that might derive from a hasty glance at these impressive looking columns of figures (some of which are hyphenated and run to six digits), there is no computational principle involved. They are purely for identification, analogous to numbers on license plates of automobiles, for convenience in sorting cases according to diagnosis, and for carrying on various statistical analyses. The special requirements imposed on the psychiatrist by statistical needs are relatively slight, and in no case do they impinge on his freedom to make an adequate diagnosis. They do not, however, permit making multiple diagnoses, all of equal value. Given half a dozen such terms in each case, the statistician would, because of the vast number of permutations, find it difficult to identify more than a small number of patients with exactly the same diagnosis in any sample of reasonable size, thus ruling out all statistical analysis of diagnosis. Of course, there are some investigators who feel that classification should not be subject to statistical analysis, but they are as yet in the minority and stand contradicted by a vast amount of work being done in terms of classification.

## HISTORY OF CLASSIFICATION IN PSYCHIATRY

It is fair to say that there has never been any psychiatric practice without a classification, and each classification represents a condensation of an entire system of psychiatric thought; thus, a history of classification would be equivalent to a history of psychiatry. This section is limited to a review of some of the relevant and interesting facts.

In spite of many deviations and retrogressions, the record is one of cumulative observation, with gradual evolution of concepts and clarification of thinking over more than 4,000 years. Traces of the evolutionary process survive in current psychiatric terminology, and the evolution has been in part a reflection of advances in knowledge. In addition, there are other influences—social and religious influences, political conditions, and the state of general technology. Finally, time alone seems to bring changes in the language of psychiatry independent of external influences.

### EARLY CLASSIFICATION

The mental changes of old age were historically among the first to be clearly identified, although the differentiation between parenchymatous disease and cerebral arteriosclerosis had to wait for the development of histology at the end of the nineteenth century. Similarly, alcoholic mental disorders and deterioration were recognized in ancient times, in spite of the fact that distilled liquors were not invented until about 900 A.D. Curiously enough, opium was described in the earliest records, but addiction was not medically diagnosed until comparatively modern times, and the effects of abuse were not even mentioned until late in the Middle Ages.

From the beginning, a very important place was assigned to supernatural causes of disease, and these influences are still seen in current terminology. The term "obsession" survives as a memento of the time when it was thought that the mentally ill person was besieged by the devil from without—a less serious condition than "possession," where the devil was within the victim. Similarly, the term "alienated" originated with the same idea that the victim had alienated or given over control of his soul to the devil in barter, and the term is borrowed from business law.

Many modern entities have a history that goes back to ancient medicine. The homosexual was described by the Greeks under the name of "pathicus." The ancients recognized the deliria of fever, some depressive states, the patterns of epilepsy, and certain effects of brain trauma. They also showed considerable sophistication about the existence of psychosomatic influences, although these were limited to the more obvious autonomic reactions of pulse and the like. Malingering of psychosis was recognized, as was mental retardation in children. But there was much confusion of functional and organic disorders. Schizophrenia itself was not delineated until the nineteenth century, and the neuroses remained virtually unexplored nosologically until then.

## MODERN CLASSIFICATION

Modern classification begins in the late eighteenth century. Historical accounts stress the great influence of Linnaeus, whose success with biological taxonomy stimulated a vast amount of nosological activity in psychiatry. This effort, however, proved to be of little value or effect. Numerous classifications of mental disorder were created, one such coming from the pen of Erasmus Darwin, the grandfather of the great naturalist. All these are of purely academic interest, and it was not until the development of asylums brought the mentally ill under observation of specializing physicians that psychiatric nosology entered into its modern phase of rapid development.

The first of these physicians was Pinel, who provided a very simple system based solely on his own observations; he refused even to discuss the arbitrary distributions of other nosologists. Although fully aware of the work of his predecessors and his contemporaries, he consciously imitated only the methods that had "contributed to the rapid advance of modern natural history." He described melancholia, mania without delirium, mania with delirium, dementia, and idiotism. However, hallucinations in our modern sense are not described in his 1806 edition. And although Pinel uses the engaging term "mental indispositions," he does not discuss the neuroses as we know them today, nor does he describe the mental changes of age, although he mentions them briefly.

Objective, long-term observation in mental hospitals continued to support advances, which were accelerated by the use of the pathological laboratory, a German development that helped that country assume psychiatric leadership by the middle of the nineteenth century. It was from there that Griesinger's influential nosology was published. He had a strongly organicist approach, in contrast to the antiorganicism of Pinel, and for several generations the work of the pathologists in the mental hospitals played a significant role in neuropsychiatry. The organic and exogenous psychiatric disorders were rapidly delineated, and the studies of Alzheimer, Nissl, Wernicke, Bonhoeffer, and the Russian Korsakoff made psychiatric history. The clinical work of Itard and Séquin clarified the question of mental deficiency and cleared the way for a better delineation of the functional mental disorders.

As a result, a new concept, dementia praecox, began to emerge. Thomas Willis had noted regressive changes in previously normal children two centuries before. Morel used the term in 1850, but without delineating the syndrome, and in 1870 Hecker and Kahlbaum described "katatonia." But it remained for Kraepelin, on the basis of his asylum experience, to pull together katatonia, hebephrenia, various dementias, vesanias, and certain degenerations to create the new concept of dementia praecox. This was later modified to schizophrenia by Bleuler, but the basic syndrome described by Kraepelin was widely accepted, as was his subsequent delineation of the manic-depressive psychoses.

The personality disorders (still the most unfinished of all the categories) had long been recognized in relation to law and literature but did not become a part of psychiatry until noted in *Moral Insanity* by Prichard.

The concept of the psychoneuroses is often considered to be of rather late development, and this is true of its modern psychodynamic form. However, the hysteria of the ancients certainly dealt with psychoneuroses, and a vast amount of outpatient psychiatry with psychoneurotics was done by the Mesmerists of the nineteenth century and by their predecessors, who had practiced magnetism and the laying on of hands for centuries. An extensive background of clinical practice thus existed for the systematic work of Beard in neurasthenia, Janet in psychasthenia, and Charcot in hysteria and, finally, for the great syntheses by Freud, whose classification of mental mechanisms cuts across all others and operates in its own independent dimension.

By the end of the nineteenth century, the main outlines of current nosologies had been laid down, for both descriptive and dynamic psychiatry. In the next twenty years, the marked variability in nosology that had characterized the previous century gradually came to be replaced by standardizations based on the categories just outlined.

## STANDARDIZATION OF NOMENCLATURE AND CLASSIFICATION

Until relatively recent times, medical classification and nomenclature, including that of psychiatry, were local or even personal matters based on whatever authorities a physician was inclined to follow and on whatever influences a hospital or medical school might bring to bear. The example of Florence Nightingale and others proved the importance of medical statistics, and it was inevitable that from then on uniformity and comparability of data should become a key issue in public health matters. A standardized international list of causes of death was first authorized in 1853, and in 1900, after the death lists had been revised many times, the causes of morbidity began to be developed. An eighth revision of this now standard work has been prepared under the aegis of the World Health Organization (W.H.O.). Most of the psychiatric disorders are found in one section of this publication, although some are scattered elsewhere in the classification.

In the United States the first move toward psychiatric standardization occurred in 1917, with a statistical classification of mental diseases prepared by the American Medical Psychological Association. In 1928 the American Medical Association first moved to adopt a general standard nomenclature of morbidity and death, and organized psychiatry undertook to prepare the section on mental disorders, which appeared simultaneously as a manual of the Association. This pattern has been retained through successive revisions at intervals of about ten years, and the current A.P.A. manual dates from 1968.

## REFERENCES

American Association on Mental Deficiency. *A Manual on Terminology and Classification in Mental Retardation*. J. Ment. Defic., 64: No. 2, suppl., 1959.

American Medical Association. *Standard Nomenclature of Diseases and Operations*, ed. 5. McGraw-Hill, New York, 1961.

American Medical Association. *Current Medical Terminology*. American Medical Association, Chicago, 1971.

American Psychiatric Association. *Diagnostic and Statistical Manual of Mental Disorders*. American Psychiatric Association, Washington, 1968.

Jaspers, K. *General Psychopathology*. University of Chicago Press, Chicago, 1963.

Jenkins, R. L., and Cole, J. O. Diagnostic classification in child psychiatry. Psychiat. Res. Rep. Amer. Psychiat. Assn., 18: 1, 1964.

Stengel, E. Classification of mental disorders. Bull. W. H. O., 21: 601, 1959.

World Health Organization. *International Classification of Diseases, Eighth Revision*. World Health Organization, Geneva, 1968.

# CHAPTER NINE

# A Guide to the American Psychiatric Association's New Diagnostic Nomenclature

## ROBERT L. SPITZER, M.D., and
## PAUL T. WILSON, M.D.

FOR THE FIRST TIME since its initial publication in 1952, the *Diagnostic and Statistical Manual, Mental Disorders* (*DSM-I*) has been revised by the American Psychiatric Association. The second edition (*DSM-II*) became the official nomenclature for American psychiatrists on July 1, 1968. The purpose of this article is to explain how the new manual differs from the old one and how in many ways it is improved.

## BACKGROUND

Beginning before the turn of the century, there has been growing interest in developing an international classification of diseases to facilitate communication across national boundaries. For the past 20 years this task has been entrusted to the World Health Organization in Geneva, Switzerland. The classification of mental disorders in the sixth revision of the *International Classification of Diseases* (*ICD-6*), which appeared in 1948, was incompatible with the nomenclature introduced in this country in *DSM-I* in 1952. Because the U.S. Public Health Service felt that the

Reprinted with the permission of the *American Journal of Psychiatry*, 124: 12, June 1968.

goals of an international classification system were important, it sent American representatives to work with the international committees preparing revisions for the mental disorder section of the *ICD-8*, which was approved by WHO in 1966 to become effective in 1968.

In 1965 the American Psychiatric Association, which had maintained close liaison with these international committees, assigned to its Committee on Nomenclature and Statistics, under the chairmanship of Dr. Ernest M. Gruenberg, the task of preparing a new diagnostic manual for the A.P.A. that would be compatible with the *ICD-8* list of mental disorders. A draft of the new manual, *DSM-II*, was circulated to 120 psychiatrists in February 1967 and was revised on the basis of their criticisms and suggestions. After further careful study by a special task force, the A.P.A. Council gave it final approval in December 1967.

## MODIFICATIONS OF ICD-8 FOR DSM-II

Within some limitations, countries observing nomenclature regulations for using the *International Classification of Diseases* may modify it for their own use. *ICD-8* was modified in five ways for *DSM-II*: (1) by changing the organization and sequence of listed diagnoses; (2) by suggesting that certain diagnoses not be used in this country; (3) by adding new diagnoses (sometimes by subdividing existing diagnoses); (4) by changing the names of categories; and (5) by adding additional digits to the diagnostic code numbers.

### CHANGES IN ORGANIZATION AND SEQUENCE

Diagnosis in *ICD-8* are divided into three major groups, and code numbers are assigned in the following order: *psychoses, neuroses, personality disorders, and other non-psychotic mental disorders*; and *mental retardation*. Because this is not the way mental disorders are generally grouped in this country, it was necessary to rearrange them for *DSM-II*. Specifically, *mental retardation* was placed first to emphasize that it is to be diagnosed whenever it is present, even if due to some other disorder. In addition, the *non-psychotic organic brain syndromes* were grouped with the psychotic brain syndromes in keeping with psychiatric thinking in this country, which views these disorders, whether psychotic or not, as one group. Consequently, because it was essential that the *DSM-II* code numbers for each disorder be the same as those in *ICD-8*, the code numbers for *mental retardation* and the *non-psychotic organic brain syndromes* are out of sequence.

For greater clarity, mental disorders in *DSM-II* are divided into ten sections, indicated with Roman numerals, to further emphasize the way mental disorders are often viewed in the United States.

## DIAGNOSES NOT TO BE USED

*DSM-II* suggests that four *ICD-8* categories not be used in this country. They are: *reactive excitation, reactive confusion, acute paranoid reaction,* and *reactive psychosis, unspecified.*

## ADDITIONAL DIAGNOSES

Thirty-nine diagnoses were added to those in *ICD-8*, usually by subdividing existing *ICD-8* categories. For example, *hysterical neurosis* was divided into a conversion type and a dissociative type. All added categories intended for use only in the United States are indicated in Table I (and in *DSM-II*) by an asterisk.

## CHANGES IN TERMS

The names of several *ICD-8* categories were changed for *DSM-II*, either to correspond with usage in this country or to simplify the task of recording them. For example, the term *reactive depressive psychosis* has been changed to the more familiar term *psychotic depressive reaction*. Similarly, the term *mental disorders not specified as psychotic associated with physical conditions, with epilepsy* has been mercifully shortened to *nonpsychotic OBS with epilepsy*.

## ADDITIONAL CODING DIGITS

For tabulating purposes, *ICD-8* diagnoses in the mental disorders section are coded with a basic three-digit number (290 to 315) and a fourth digit (.0 to .9) for achieving greater specificity within each three-digit category. *DSM-II* has added a fifth digit to accommodate additional diagnoses and to permit the coding of several qualifying phrases (described below).

## DIFFERENCES BETWEEN DSM-I AND DSM-II

Several kinds of changes appear in *DSM-II*. The names of many disorders are modified; the nomenclature is organized in a different way; the recording of multiple psychiatric diagnoses and associated physical conditions is explicitly encouraged; and the qualifying phrases are changed. Finally, there are numerous changes in the definitions of the disorders themselves. Table I shows the entire list of recommended *DSM-II* diagnoses and their code numbers.

## MODIFICATION OF TERMS

One of the most striking differences between *DSM-I* and *DSM-II*, and perhaps the one that will generate the strongest feelings, is the elimination of the term *reaction* from many diagnostic labels. For example, the *DSM-I* diagnosis of *schizophrenic reaction* is now simply *schizophrenia*. The same is true of the *DSM-I* terms *psychoneurotic reactions, psychophysio-*

*logic reactions, affective reactions,* and *paranoid reactions.* The only disorders in *DSM-II* in which the term *reaction* is still used are *psychotic depressive reaction,* the *transient situational disturbances,* and a new section, *behavior disorders of childhood and adolescence.*

Some individuals may interpret this change as a return to a Kraepelinian way of thinking, which views mental disorders as fixed disease entities. Actually, this was not the intent of the A.P.A. Committee on Nomenclature and Statistics:

> [The Committee] tried to avoid terms which carry with them *implications* regarding either the nature of a disorder or its causes and has been explicit about casual assumptions when they are integral to a diagnostic concept. . . . In the case of diagnostic categories about which there is current controversy concerning the disorder's nature or cause, the Committee has attempted to select terms which it thought would least bind the judgment of the user. The Committee itself included representatives of many views. It did not try to reconcile these views but rather to find terms which could be used to label the disorders about which they wished to be able to debate.

## ORGANIZATION

The basic organization of the *DSM-I* and *DSM-II* nomenclatures can be seen in Figure 1. This figure shows that, whereas the *DSM-I* nomenclature fell logically into three major groups, *DSM-II* is divided into ten categories. It should be noted that the fundamental distinction in *DSM-I* between organic brain syndromes and all other conditions has been preserved in *DSM-II* (despite the blurring of this distinction in the organization of *ICD-8*). However, to record the further distinction between acute and chronic brain syndromes in *DSM-II,* one must use a qualifying phrase.

*Involutional psychotic reaction* in *DSM-I* now appears as a subcategory of *major affective disorders* in *DSM-II,* while *psychotic depressive reaction,* which was listed in *DSM-I* as an *affective reaction,* is now in a separate category.

There are several major departures from *DSM-I* in the organization of the *personality disorders* category. The subtle distinction between *pattern disturbances* and *trait disturbances* has been eliminated. All of these disorders are listed in *DSM-II* simply as *personality disorders.* The subcategory *sociopathic personality disturbance* has been eliminated, and three of its subtypes, *sexual deviation, alcoholism,* and *drug dependence* are listed separately in *DSM-II* at the same hierarchical level of organizations as the major category *personality disorders.* Another subtype of *sociopathic personality disturbance,* the *dyssocial reaction,* is listed under the major *DSM-II* section *conditions without manifest psychiatric disorder.* Only one disorder from *DSM-I's sociopathic* group—*antisocial reaction*—remains in the *personality disorder* category of *DSM-II.*

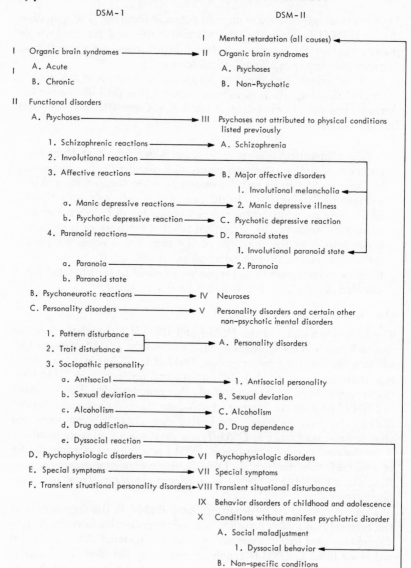

FIGURE 1. *Organization of nomenclature in DSM-I and DSM-II.*

In *DSM-I* *mental deficiency* was the last major group to be listed. In *DSM-II* *mental retardation* is the first.

## Multiple Psychiatric Diagnoses

*DSM-I* was inconsistent regarding multiple diagnoses. Although it gave support to the general notion of multiple diagnoses, it specifically prohibited certain combinations of them. For example, *alcoholism* could never be made as a separate diagnosis when it was associated with an "underlying" disorder. In contrast, *DSM-II* encourages clinicians to diagnose every disorder that is present, even if one is the symptomatic expression of another. (The only exception is a diagnosis from the section *special symptoms not elsewhere classified*, which, by definition, is listed only when it is not part of another disorder.)

Furthermore, *DSM-II* gives clear principles for determining which of two or more diagnoses should be listed first—the condition that most urgently requires treatment, or, when there is no issue of disposition or treatment priority, the more serious condition.

## Associated Physical Conditions

Whenever an organic brain syndrome or mental retardation is caused by a specific physical condition, *DSM-II* encourages clinicians to record the physical condition with a separate, additional diagnosis. To make it easier to do this, all *ICD-8* diagnoses (including both psychiatric and nonpsychiatric ones) are reproduced in a separate part of *DSM-II*. For example, an individual with cerebral arteriosclerosis causing a mild organic brain syndrome should be given two diagnoses: the psychiatric diagnosis of *nonpsychotic OBS with circulatory disturbance* and the physical diagnosis of *generalized ischemic cerebrovascular disease*.

## Qualifying Phrases

In *DSM-I* any of four qualifying phrases could be used (except where redundant) with any disorder; in *DSM-II* there are seven different qualifying phrases, but all except one are limited to specific sections (Table II).

The qualifying phrases *acute* and *chronic* can be used and coded in Section II (organic brain syndromes). This continues the distinction observed in this country between the two forms of these disorders.

The qualifying phrase *not psychotic* can be used and coded in Section III (functional psychoses) for patients who are not psychotic at the time of the evaluation but who nevertheless have a disorder traditionally classified as a psychosis. This paradox arises because these disorders, in the full-blown form in which they were first recognized, were generally seen in psychotic patients. This qualifying phrase would be appropriate, for example, for individuals who are not psychotic but who nevertheless show clear signs of schizophrenia.

The qualifying phrases *mild*, *moderate*, and *severe* are appropriate for

## TABLE I
### List of DSM-II Diagnoses and Code Numbers†

**I MENTAL RETARDATION**

| | |
|---|---|
| 310. | Borderline |
| 311. | Mild |
| 312. | Moderate |
| 313. | Severe |
| 314. | Profound |
| 315. | Unspecified |

With each: Following or associated with

| | |
|---|---|
| .0 | Infection or intoxication |
| .1 | Trauma or physical agent |
| .2 | Disorders of metabolism, growth, or nutrition |
| .3 | Gross brain disease (postnatal) |
| .4 | Unknown prenatal influence |
| .5 | Chromosomal abnormality |
| .6 | Prematurity |
| + .7 | Major psychiatric disorder |
| + .8 | Psycho-social (environmental) deprivation |
| .9 | Other condition |

**II ORGANIC BRAIN SYNDROMES (OBS)**

**A PSYCHOSES**

Senile and pre-senile dementia

| | |
|---|---|
| 290.0 | Senile dementia |
| 290.1 | Pre-senile dementia |

Alcoholic psychosis

| | |
|---|---|
| + 291.0 | Delirium tremens |
| + 291.1 | Korsakov's psychosis |
| + 291.2 | Other alcoholic hallucinosis |
| + 291.3 | Alcohol paranoid state |
| + 291.4* | Acute alcohol intoxication* |
| + 291.5* | Alcoholic deterioration* |
| + 291.6* | Pathological intoxication* |
| 291.9 | Other alcoholic phychosis |

Psychosis associated with intracranial infection

| | |
|---|---|
| 292.0 | General paralysis |
| 292.1 | Syphilis of CNS |
| 292.2 | Epidemic encephalitis |
| 292.3 | Other and unspecified encephalitis |
| 292.9 | Other intracranial infection |

Psychosis associated with other cerebral condition

| | |
|---|---|
| 293.0 | Cerebral arteriosclerosis |
| 293.1 | Other cerebrovascular disturbance |
| 293.2 | Epilepsy |
| 293.3 | Intracranial neoplasm |
| 293.4 | Degenerative disease of the CNS |
| 293.5 | Brain trauma |
| 293.9 | Other cerebral condition |

Psychosis associated with other physical condition

| | |
|---|---|
| 294.0 | Endocrine disorder |
| 294.1 | Metabolic and nutritional disorder |
| 294.2 | Systemic infection |
| 294.3 | Drug or poison intoxication (other than alcohol) |
| + 294.4 | Childbirth |
| 294.8 | Other and unspecified physical condition |

**B NON-PSYCHOTIC OBS**

| | |
|---|---|
| 309.0 | Intracranial infection |
| + 309.13* | Alcohol* (simple drunkenness) |
| + 309.14* | Other drug, poison or systemic intoxication* |
| 309.2 | Brain trauma |
| 309.3 | Circulatory disturbance |
| 309.4 | Epilepsy |
| 309.5 | Disturbance of metabolism, growth, or nutrition |
| 309.6 | Senile or pre-senile brain disease |
| 309.7 | Intracranial neoplasm |
| 309.8 | Degenerative disease of the CNS |
| 309.9 | Other physical condition |

**III PSYCHOSES NOT ATTRIBUTED TO PHYSICAL CONDITIONS LISTED PREVIOUSLY**

Schizophrenia

| | |
|---|---|
| 295.0 | Simple |
| 295.1 | Hebephrenic |
| 295.2 | Catatonic |
| + 295.23* | Catatonic type, excited* |
| + 295.24* | Catatonic type, withdrawn* |
| 295.3 | Paranoid |
| + 295.4 | Acute schizophrenic episode |
| + 295.5 | Latent |
| 295.6 | Residual |
| 295.7 | Schizo-affective |
| + 295.73* | Schizo-affective, excited* |

† Many of the titles here are listed in abbreviated form.
+ These are new diagnoses that do not appear in DSM-I.
* These diagnoses are for use in the U.S. only and do not appear in ICD-8.

Table I (*continued*)
*List of DSM-II Diagnoses and Code Numbers†*

295.74* Schizo-affective, depressed*
295.8* Childhood*
295.90* Chronic undifferentiated*
295.99* Other schizophrenia*

**Major affective disorders**
296.0 Involuntional melancholia
296.1 Manic-depressive illness, manic
296.2 Manic-depressive illness, depressed
296.3 Manic-depressive illness, circular
296.33* Manic-depressive, circular, manic*
296.34* Manic-depressive, circular, depressed*
296.8 Other major affective disorder

**Paranoid states**
297.0 Paranoia
297.1 Involutional paranoid state
297.9 Other paranoid state

**Other psychoses**
298.0 Psychotic depressive reaction

**V   NEUROSES**

300.0 Anxiety
300.1 Hysterical
300.13* Hysterical, conversion type*
300.14* Hysterical, dissociative type*
300.2 Phobic
300.3 Obsessive compulsive
300.4 Depressive
300.5 Neurasthenic
300.6 Depersonalization
300.7 Hypochondriacal
300.8 Other neurosis

**PERSONALITY DISORDERS AND CERTAIN OTHER NON-PSYCHOTIC MENTAL DISORDERS**

**Personality disorders**
301.0 Paranoid
301.1 Cyclothymic
301.2 Schizoid
301.3 Explosive
301.4 Obsessive compulsive
301.5 Hysterical
301.6 Asthenic
301.7 Antisocial
301.81* Passive-aggressive*

301.82* Inadequate*
301.89* Other specified types*

**Sexual deviation**
+ 302.0 Homosexuality
+ 302.1 Fetishism
+ 302.2 Pedophilia
+ 302.3 Transvestitism
+ 302.4 Exhibitionism
+ 302.5* Voyeurism*
+ 302.6* Sadism*
+ 302.7* Masochism*
  302.8 Other sexual deviation

**Alcoholism**
+ 303.0 Episodic excessive drinking
+ 303.1 Habitual excessive drinking
+ 303.2 Alcohol addiction
  303.9 Other alcoholism

**Drug dependence**
+ 304.0 Opium, opium alkaloids and their derivatives
+ 304.1 Synthetic analgesics with morphine-like effects
+ 304.2 Barbiturates
+ 304.3 Other hypnotics and sedatives or "tranquilizers"
+ 304.4 Cocaine
+ 304.5 Cannabis sativa (hashish, marihuana)
+ 304.6 Other psycho-stimulants
+ 304.7 Hallucinogens
  304.8 Other drug dependence

**VI   PSYCHOPHYSIOLOGIC DISORDERS**

305.0 Skin
305.1 Musculoskeletal
305.2 Respiratory
305.3 Cardiovascular
305.4 Hemic and lymphatic
305.5 Gastro-intestinal
305.6 Genito-urinary
305.7 Endocrine
305.8 Organ of special sense
305.9 Other type

**VII   SPECIAL SYMPTOMS**

306.0 Speech disturbance
306.1 Specific learning disturbance
+ 306.2 Tic

TABLE I (continued)
*List of DSM-II Diagnoses and Code Numbers†*

+ 306.3    Other psychomotor disorder
+ 306.4    Disorders of sleep
+ 306.5    Feeding disturbance
  306.6    Enuresis
+ 306.7    Encopresis
+ 306.8    Cephalalgia
  306.9    Other special symptom

## VIII    TRANSIENT SITUATIONAL DISTURBANCES

307.0*    Adjustment reaction of infancy*
307.1*    Adjustment reaction of childhood*
307.2*    Adjustment reaction of adolescence*
307.3*    Adjustment reaction of adult life*
307.4*    Adjustment reaction of late life*

## IX    BEHAVIOR DISORDERS OF CHILDHOOD AND ADOLESCENCE

+ 308.0*    Hyperkinetic reaction*
+ 308.1*    Withdrawing reaction*
+ 308.2*    Overanxious reaction*
+ 308.3*    Runaway reaction*

+ 308.4*    Unsocialized aggressive reaction
+ 308.5*    Group delinquent reaction*
  308.9*    Other reaction*

## X    CONDITIONS WITHOUT MANIFEST PSYCHIATRIC DISORDER AND NON-SPECIFIC CONDITIONS

**Social maladjustment without manifest psychiatric disorder**
+ 316.0*    Marital maladjustment*
+ 316.1*    Social maladjustment
+ 316.2*    Occupational maladjustment*
  316.3*    Dyssocial behavior*
+ 316.9*    Other social maladjustment*

**Non-specific conditions**
+ 317*    Non-specific conditions*

**No Mental Disorder**
+ 318*    No mental disorder*

## XI    NON-DIAGNOSTIC TERMS FOR ADMINISTRATIVE USE

319.0*    Diagnosis deferred*
319.1*    Boarder*
319.2*    Experiment only*
319.3*    Other*

TABLE II
*Qualifying Phrases and Their Code Numbers*

| Section II | Section III | Sections IV through IX | All Disorders |
|---|---|---|---|
| .X1 Acute | .X6 Not presently psychotic or not psychotic | .X6 Mild | .X5 In remission |
| .X2 Chronic | | .X7 Moderate | |
| | | .X8 Severe | |

disorders in Sections IV through IX. This should be particularly useful for recording many of those disorders, such as *phobic neurosis*, where the range of impairment may extend from trivial inconvenience to incapacitation.

Finally, the qualifying phrase *in remission* can be used and coded, at least theoretically, with all disorders. Because it should not be confused with a diagnosis of *no mental disorder*, it is most appropriate for conditions that consist of episodes separated by symptom-free intervals, such as the *manic-depressive illnesses*.

## I. MENTAL RETARDATION

In *DSM-I* this was called *mental deficiency* and was used only for the idiopathic or familial varieties of this disorder. When the retardation was due to a chronic brain syndrome, the disorder was classified as a chronic brain syndrome with an added qualifying phrase, *with mental deficiency*. In *DSM-II* *mental retardation* is diagnosed whenever present and from all causes. Of the nine specified causes of *mental retardation* listed in *DSM-II*, seven are brain syndromes that are roughly equivalent to *DSM-I* categories. The other two, *following major psychiatric disorder* and *with psycho-social (environmental) deprivation*, reflect new ways of thinking about the causes of mental retardation. Changes have also been made in the diagnoses indicating levels of severity: Whereas *DSM-I* had three levels, *DSM-II* has five.

## II. ORGANIC BRAIN SYNDROMES (OBS)

This section is divided into the psychotic and non-psychotic conditions; consequently, the distinction between the acute and chronic forms must now be indicated with a qualifying phrase. A condition is considered a psychosis if the patient is psychotic at any time during the episode being diagnosed. This principle avoids the necessity for changing a patient's diagnosis from day to day as he slips in and out of a psychosis during one episode; at the same time it permits giving a non-psychotic diagnosis to a patient who has not been psychotic during a particular episode yet has had past episodes of psychosis.

*DSM-II* defines psychosis more explicitly than did *DSM-I* and adds to the usual criterion of impaired reality-testing (for example, delusions and hallucinations) the further criterion of gross interference with the individual's capacity to meet the ordinary demands of life because of such things as profound alteration of mood and deficits in perception, language, and memory. These criteria for psychosis apply also to Section III, *Psychoses not attributed to physical conditions listed previously*.

One of the most significant changes in this section is the addition of eight specific alcoholic brain syndromes which in *DSM-I* were all subsumed under either *acute brain syndrome associated with alcohol intoxication* or *chronic brain syndrome associated with alcohol intoxication*. The new diagnoses are: *delirium tremens, Korsakov's psychosis, other alcoholic hallucinosis, alcohol paranoid state, acute alcohol intoxication, alcoholic deterioration, pathological intoxication*, and *non-psychotic OBS with alcohol (simple drunkenness)*.

This section contains another new diagnosis, *psychosis with childbirth*, which *DSM-II* cautions against using unless all other diagnoses have been ruled out.

## III. PSYCHOSES NOT ATTRIBUTED TO PHYSICAL CONDITIONS LISTED PREVIOUSLY

### SCHIZOPHRENIA

Several new subtypes of schizophrenia have been added by subdividing old categories. For example, catatonic schizophrenia is further divided into *excited* and *withdrawn* subtypes. Similarly, the schizo-affective type of schizophrenia is further divided into *excited* and *depressed* subtypes. In both cases, when the subtype cannot be specified, the more general diagnosis can be used.

The new diagnosis *acute schizophrenic episode* is identical in meaning to the *DSM-I* term *schizophrenic reaction, acute undifferentiated type*.

Another important new diagnosis, *schizophrenia, latent type*, has been added for disorders previously labeled unofficially as *incipient, prepsychotic, pseudoneurotic, pseudopsychopathic*, or *borderline* schizophrenia. It is for patients who have clear symptoms of schizophrenia but who are not psychotic at the time of examination and never have been. In *DSM-I* these same patients were classified under *schizophrenic reaction, chronic undifferentiated type*.

The definition of the *residual type* of schizophrenia is the same as before—that is, it applies to patients who have had a psychotic schizophrenic episode but who are no longer psychotic. The possibly confusing distinctions between the *chronic undifferentiated type* of schizophrenia in *DSM-I* and *DSM-II* and the *residual* and *latent* types of *DSM-II* depend on whether the patient is psychotic at the time of examination *and* whether he was ever psychotic in the past (Table III).

TABLE III

*Psychosis as a Criterion in Diagnosing Three Types of Schizophrenia*

| Term | Previously Psychotic | Presently Psychotic |
|---|---|---|
| **DSM-I** | | |
| Chronic undifferentiated | Yes or no | Yes or no |
| **DSM-II** | | |
| Chronic undifferentiated | Yes | Yes |
| Latent | No | No |
| Residual | Yes | No |

### MAJOR AFFECTIVE DISORDERS

*DSM-II* indicates that the disorder of mood in the *major affective disorders* does not seem to be related directly to a precipitating life experience and therefore is distinguishable from *psychotic depressive reaction* and *depressive neurosis*. Thus the term *major affective disorders* in *DSM-II* has a more restricted meaning than the corresponding term in *DSM-I*.

The increased emphasis on the presence or absence of a precipitating life experience is also reflected in a slight change in the definition of *psychotic depressive reaction*. Whereas DSM-I described *psychotic depressive reaction* as including *"frequent* presence of environmental precipitating factors"* (italics added), DSM-II states flatly that the depressive mood in this disorder is "attributable to some experience."

Two new subtypes of *manic-depressive illness, circular type* are now available to indicate the nature of the current episode; *manic-depressive illness, circular type, depressed* and *manic depressive illness, circular type, manic*.

The controversial diagnosis of *involutional psychotic reaction* in DSM-I has been split into two diagnoses in DSM-II: *involuntional melancholia* and *involutional paranoid state*. The latter is simply the paranoid variety of the old *involutional psychotic reaction* and is, therefore, included in DSM-II under the *paranoid states*. *Involutional melancholia* corresponds to the depressive variety of the old *involutional psychotic reaction*. As reflected by its inclusion in the *major affective disorder* group, it is limited to situations where "the disorder of mood is not due to some experience."

## Paranoid States

As mentioned above, *involutional paranoid state* has been added to this group of primary paranoid conditions. The rather elusive *DSM-I* diagnosis of *paranoid state* no longer exists as a discrete diagnosis.

## IV. NEUROSES

The names of the *DSM-I* diagnoses *conversion reaction* and *dissociative reaction* have been changed in *DSM-II* to *hysterical neurosis, conversion type*, and *hysterical neurosis, dissociative type*, respectively. These two subtypes were created by subdividing the single *ICD-8* diagnosis of *hysterical neurosis*, because the single *ICD-8* diagnostic term obliterates the very important distinction between these two conditions.

Three new diagnoses have been added: *neurasthenic neurosis, depersonalization neurosis*, and *hypochondriacal neurosis*. The first of these, *neurasthenic neurosis*, is equivalent to and replaces the *DSM-I* diagnosis of *psychophysiologic nervous system reaction*. The major difficulty in using the diagnosis of *depersonalization neurosis* will be in distinguishing it from episodes of depersonalization that either are part of some other mental disorder or not a symptom of illness.

## V. PERSONALITY DISORDERS AND CERTAIN OTHER NON-PSYCHOTIC MENTAL DISORDERS

This entire section is equivalent to the *DSM-I* section *personality disorders*, except that it no longer contains the diagnosis of *dyssocial reaction*, which now appears in *DSM-II* under *conditions without manifest psychiatric disorder.*

The *DSM-II* term *personality disorders* no longer includes disorders of sexual deviation, alcoholism, and drug dependence. Because these three disorders, in being maintained partially by physiological reinforcement, differ from the disorders listed as *personality disorders* in *DSM-II*, it is reasonable to group them separately.

## PERSONALITY DISORDERS

There are three new personality disorders: *explosive personality, hysterical personality,* and *asthenic personality.* The *explosive personality* has many features in common with the *DSM-I* diagnosis of *passive aggressive personality, aggressive type.* The concept of a *hysterical personality* is well known and common parlance in psychiatric discussions, despite the fact that it was not recognized in *DSM-I.* This diagnosis is appropriate for many patients who would have been given the *DSM-I* diagnosis of *emotionally unstable personality,* which does not appear in *DSM-II.*

*Asthenic personality* has no exact counterpart. *DSM-II* describes this category as "characterized by easy fatigability, low energy level, lack of enthusiasm, marked incapacity for enjoyment, and oversensitivity to physical and emotional stress." The major difficulty with this diagnosis will probably be in distinguishing it from *neurasthenic neurosis.*

In *DSM-II* there is no exact counterpart to the *DSM-I* diagnosis of *passive aggressive personality, passive dependent type.* Consequently, patients with this disorder should now be diagnosed *other personality disorder of specified type,* with the phrase "passive dependent personality" added.

## SEXUAL DEVIATION, ALCOHOLISM, AND DRUG DEPENDENCE

These three groups were single diagnoses in *DSM-I.* In *DSM-II* they are now major headings, under each of which appear whole sets of new diagnoses that allow far greater specificity than was possible before. In *DSM-I* a diagnosis of *drug addiction* could be made only while the individual was actually addicted. *DSM-II* provides a more comprehensive diagnosis, *drug dependence,* which does not require the presence of physiological addiction but merely "evidence of habitual use or a clear sense of need for the drug."

## VI. PSYCHOPHYSIOLOGIC DISORDERS

This section is the same as the corresponding *DSM-I* group except that *psychophysiologic nervous system reaction* has been eliminated and, as explained above, is now equivalent to *neurasthenic neurosis.* Anorexia nervosa, which was listed as an example in the *DSM-I* category of *psycho-*

*physiologic gastrointestinal reaction,* is mentioned in *DSM-II* as an example of *feeding disturbance* in the *special symptoms* section.

## VII. SPECIAL SYMPTOMS

In *DSM-I* this category included only four diagnoses: *learning disturbance, speech disturbance, enuresis,* and *somnambulism. DSM-II* adds six additional diagnoses: *tic, other psychomotor disorder, disorders of sleep, feeding disturbance, encopresis,* and *cephalalgia.*

## VIII. TRANSIENT SITUATIONAL DISTURBANCES

In *DSM-I, transient situational personality disorders* apparently did not include acute reactions to stress that were of psychotic proportion. *DSM-II* explicitly permits disturbances of psychotic proportion to be included here when they are considered clearly transient reactions to overwhelming environmental stress.

Three discrete changes have been made in this section. The *gross stress reaction* in *DSM-I* has been eliminated. The *adjustment reaction of childhood* is no longer further subdivided into *habit disturbances, conduct disturbances,* and *neurotic traits.* Many disorders previously diagnosed as one of these three subdivisions can now be classified more appropriately and with greater specificity with one of the *special symptoms* or *behavior disorders of childhood and adolescence.*

## IX. BEHAVIOR DISORDERS OF CHILDHOOD AND ADOLESCENCE

This is an entirely new set of diagnoses designed to describe disorders "occurring in childhood and adolescence that are more stable, internalized, and resistant to treatment than transient situational disturbances, but less so than psychoses, neuroses, and personality disorders. This intermediate stability is attributed to the greater fluidity of all behavior at this age." These disorders are: *hyperkinetic reaction, withdrawing reaction, overanxious reaction, runaway reaction, unsocialized aggressive reaction,* and *group delinquent reaction.*

## X. CONDITIONS WITHOUT MANIFEST PSYCHIATRIC DISORDER AND NON-SPECIFIC CONDITIONS

### CONDITIONS WITHOUT MANIFEST PSYCHIATRIC DISORDER

As stated in *DSM-II,* "this category is for recording the conditions of individuals who are psychiatrically normal but who nevertheless have severe enough problems to warrant examination by a psychiatrist." It is divided into four specific subtypes: *marital maladjustment, social maladjustment, occupational maladjustment,* and *dyssocial behavior.* The last category is equivalent to the *DSM-I* diagnosis of *sociopathic personality disturbance, dyssocial reaction.*

The far-reaching implications of this set of terms for forensic psychiatry and for insurance compensation will become clearer with time.

## Non-Specific Conditions

These are terms applicable to individuals who are having difficulties that cannot be categorized under any of the previous diagnoses but who cannot be considered to have *no mental disorder.*

## No Mental Disorder

This category did not appear in *DSM-I* although *disease none* was listed under *nondiagnostic terms for hospital record.* It will now be possible to report the finding of no mental disorder as a positive diagnosis.

## XI. NON-DIAGNOSTIC TERMS FOR ADMINISTRATIVE USE

This is the last section of *DSM-II.* Although the terms have been assigned numbers for tabulation purposes, they are not considered diagnoses.

## Conclusions

With the adoption of *DSM-II,* American psychiatrists for the first time in history will be using diagnostic categories that are part of an international classification of diseases. While this is an important first step, it is only an agreement to use the same sets of categories for classifying disorders. For many disorders, it is clear that clinicians in different countries will still define these categories in different ways.

The next step must be to establish a common set of definitions for these categories. This work has already begun under the auspices of the World Health Organization. Even this is not an end in itself. The ultimate purpose of this work is the improvement in treatment and prevention that will evolve with better communication among psychiatrists of all nations.

## REFERENCES

American Psychiatric Association. *Diagnostic and Statistical Manual, Mental Disorders,* ed. 1. American Psychiatric Association, Washington, 1952.

American Psychiatric Association. *Ibid.,* ed. 2, 1968.

World Health Organization. *International Classification of Diseases,* Sixth Revision. World Health Organization, Geneva, 1948.

World Health Organization. *Ibid.,* Eighth Revision, 1968.

# CHAPTER TEN

# *The New Diagnostic Nomenclature:*
# *Definition of Terms*

## I. MENTAL RETARDATION [1] (310-315)

MENTAL RETARDATION refers to subnormal general intellectual functioning which originates during the developmental period and is associated with impairment of either learning and social adjustment or maturation, or both. (These disorders were classified under "Chronic brain syndrome with mental deficiency" and "Mental deficiency" in DSM-I.) The diagnostic classification of mental retardation relates to IQ as follows[2]:

310 BORDERLINE MENTAL RETARDATION—IQ 68–83
311 MILD MENTAL RETARDATION—IQ 52–67
312 MODERATE MENTAL RETARDATION—IQ 36–51
313 SEVERE MENTAL RETARDATION—IQ 20–35
314 PROFOUND MENTAL RETARDATION—IQ UNDER 20

Classifications 310–314 are based on the statistical distribution of levels of intellectual functioning for the population as a whole. The range of intelligence subsumed under each classification corresponds to one standard deviation, making the heuristic assumption that intelligence is normally distributed. It is recognized that the intelligence quotient should not be the only criterion used in making a diagnosis of mental retardation or in

---

[1] For a fuller definition of terms, see the "Manual on Terminology and Classification in Mental Retardation" (supplement to *American Journal of Mental Deficiency*, Second Edition, 1961), from which most of this section has been adapted.

[2] The IQs specified are for the Revised Stanford-Binet Tests of Intelligence, Forms L and M. Equivalent values for other tests are listed in the manual cited in the footnote above.

Reprinted with the permission of the American Psychiatric Association from *Diagnostic and Statistical Manual of Mental Disorders*, ed. 2, 1968.

evaluating its severity. It should serve only to help in making a clinical judgment of the patient's adaptive behavioral capacity. This judgment should also be based on an evaluation of the patient's developmental history and present functioning, including academic and vocational achievement, motor skills, and social and emotional maturity.

### 3 1 5  Unspecified Mental Retardation

This classification is reserved for patients whose intellectual functioning has not or cannot be evaluated precisely but which is recognized as clearly subnormal.

## CLINICAL SUBCATEGORIES OF MENTAL RETARDATION

These will be coded as fourth digit subdivisions following each of the categories 310–315. When the associated condition is known more specifically, particularly when it affects the entire organism or an organ system other than the central nervous system, it should be coded additionally in the specific field affected.

### .0  Following Infection and Intoxication

This group is to classify cases in which mental retardation is the result of residual cerebral damage from intracranial infections, serums, drugs, or toxic agents. Examples are:

*Cytomegalic inclusion body disease, congenital.*   A maternal viral disease, usually mild or subclinical, which may infect the fetus and is recognized by the presence of inclusion bodies in the cellular elements in the urine, cerebrospinal fluid, and tissues.

*Rubella, congenital.*   Affecting the fetus in the first trimester and usually accompanied by a variety of congenital anomalies of the ear, eye, and heart.

*Syphilis, congenital.*   Two types are described, an early meningo-vascular disease and a diffuse encephalitis leading to juvenile paresis.

*Toxoplasmosis, congenital.*   Due to infection by a protozoan-like organism, Toxoplasma, contracted in utero. May be detected by serological tests in both mother and infant.

*Encephalopathy associated with other prenatal infections.*   Occasionally fetal damage from maternal epidemic cerebrospinal meningitis, equine encephalomyelitis, influenza, etc., has been reported. The relationships have not as yet been definitely established.

*Encephalopathy due to postnatal cerebral infection.*   Both focal and generalized types of cerebral infection are included and are to be given further anatomic and etiologic specification.

*Encephalopathy, congenital, associated with maternal toxemia of pregnancy.*   Severe and prolonged toxemia of pregnancy, particularly eclampsia, may be associated with mental retardation.

*Encephalopathy, congenital, associated with other maternal intoxica-*

*tions.* Examples are carbon monoxide, lead, arsenic, quinine, ergot, etc.

*Bilirubin encephalopathy (Kernicterus).* Frequently due to Rh, A, B, O blood group incompatibility between fetus and mother but may also follow prematurity, severe neonatal sepsis, or any condition producing high levels of serum bilirubin. Choreoathetosis is frequently associated with this form of mental retardation.

*Post-immunization encephalopathy.* This may follow inoculation with serum, particularly anti-tetanus serum, or vaccines such as smallpox, rabies, and typhoid.

*Encephalopathy, other, due to intoxication.* May result from such toxic agents as lead, carbon monoxide, tetanus, and botulism exotoxin.

### .1 FOLLOWING TRAUMA OR PHYSICAL AGENT

Further specification within this category follows:

*Encephalopathy due to prenatal injury.* This includes prenatal irradiation and asphyxia, the latter following maternal anoxia, anemia, and hypotension.

*Encephalopathy due to mechanical injury at birth.* These are attributed to difficulties of labor due to malposition, malpresentation, disproportion, or other complications leading to dystocia which may increase the probability of damage to the infant's brain at birth, resulting in tears of the meninges, blood vessels, and brain substance. Other reasons include venous-sinus thrombosis, arterial embolism and thrombosis. These may result in sequelae which are indistinguishable from those of other injuries, damage, or organic impairment of the brain.

*Encephalopathy due to asphyxia at birth.* Attributable to the anoxemia following interference with placental circulation due to premature separation, placenta praevia, cord difficulties, and other interferences with oxygenation of the placental circulation.

*Encephalopathy due to postnatal injury.* The diagnosis calls for evidence of severe trauma such as a fractured skull, prolonged unconsciousness, etc., followed by a marked change in development. Postnatal asphyxia, infarction, thrombosis, laceration, and contusion of the brain would be included and the nature of the injury specified.

### .2 WITH DISORDERS OF METABOLISM, GROWTH, OR NUTRITION

All conditions associated with mental retardation directly due to metabolic, nutritional, or growth dysfunction should be classified here, including disorders of lipid, carbohydrate, and protein metabolism and deficiencies of nutrition.

*Cerebral lipoidosis, infantile (Tay-Sach's disease).* This is caused by a single recessive autosomal gene and has infantile and juvenile forms. In the former there is gradual deterioration, blindness after the pathognomonic "cherry-red spot," with death occurring usually before age three.

*Cerebral lipoidosis, late infantile (Bielschowsky's disease).* This differs from the preceding by presenting retinal optic atrophy instead of the "cherry-red spot."

**Cerebral lipoidosis, juvenile** (*Spielmeyer-Vogt disease*). This usually appears between the ages of five and ten with involvement of the motor systems, frequent seizures, and pigmentary degeneration of the retina. Death follows in five to ten years.

**Cerebral lipoidosis, late juvenile** (*Kuf's disease*). This is categorized under mental retardation only when it occurs at an early age.

**Lipid histiocytosis of kerasin type** (*Gaucher's disease*). As a rule, this condition causes retardation only when it affects infants. It is characterized by Gaucher's cells in lymph nodes, spleen, or marrow.

**Lipid histiocystosis of phosphatide type** (*Niemann-Pick's disease*). Distinguished from Tay-Sach's disease by enlargement of liver and spleen. Biopsy of spleen, lymph, or marrow show characteristic "foam cells."

**Phenylketonuria.** A metabolic disorder, genetically transmitted as a simple autosomal recessive gene, preventing the conversion of phenylalanine into tyrosine with an accumulation of phenylalanine, which in turn is converted to phenylpyruvic acid detectable in the urine.

**Hepatolenticular degeneration** (*Wilson's disease*). Genetically transmitted as a simple autosomal recessive. It is due to inability of ceruloplasmin to bind copper, which in turn damages the brain. Rare in children.

**Porphyria.** Genetically transmitted as a dominant and characterized by excretion of porphyrins in the urine. It is rare in children, in whom it may cause irreversible deterioration.

**Galactosemia.** A condition in which galactose is not metabolized, causing its accumulation in the blood. If milk is not removed from the diet, generalized organ deficiencies, mental deterioration, and death may result.

**Glucogenosis** (*Von Gierke's disease*). Due to a deficiency in glycogen-metabolizing enzymes with deposition of glycogen in various organs, including the brain.

**Hypoglycemosis.** Caused by various conditions producing hypoglycemia which, in the infant, may result in epilepsy and mental defect. Diagnosis may be confirmed by glucose tolerance tests.

## .3 ASSOCIATED WITH GROSS BRAIN DISEASE (POSTNATAL)

This group includes all diseases and conditions associated with neoplasms, but not growths that are secondary to trauma or infection. The category also includes a number of postnatal diseases and conditions in which the structural reaction is evident but the etiology is unknown or uncertain, though frequently presumed to be of hereditary or familial nature. Structural reactions may be degenerative, infiltrative, inflammatory, proliferative, sclerotic, or reparative.

**Neurofibromatosis** (*Neurofibroblastomatosis, von Recklinghausen's* *disease*). A disease transmitted by a dominant autosomal gene but with reduced penetrance and variable expressivity. It is characterized by cutaneous pigmentation ("café au lait" patches) and neurofibromas of nerve, skin, and central nervous system with intellectual capacity varying from normal to severely retarded.

*Trigeminal cerebral angiomatosis* (*Sturge-Weber-Dimitri's disease*). A condition characterized by a "port wine stain" or cutaneous angioma, usually in the distribution of the trigeminal nerve, accompanied by vascular malformation over the meninges of the parietal and occipital lobes with underlying cerebral maldevelopment.

*Tuberous sclerosis* (*Epiloia, Bourneville's disease*). Transmitted by a dominant autosomal gene, characterized by multiple gliotic nodules in the central nervous system, and associated with adenoma sebaceum of the face and tumors in other organs. Retarded development and seizures may appear early and increase in severity along with tumor growth.

*Intracranial neoplasm, other.* Other relatively rare neoplastic diseases leading to mental retardation should be included in this category and specified when possible.

*Encephalopathy associated with diffuse sclerosis of the brain.* This category includes a number of similar conditions differing to some extent in their pathological and clinical features but characterized by diffuse demyelination of the white matter with resulting diffuse glial sclerosis and accompanied by intellectual deterioration. These diseases are often familial in character and, when possible, should be specified under the following:

ACUTE INFANTILE DIFFUSE SCLEROSIS
  (KRABBE'S DISEASE).
DIFFUSE CHRONIC INFANTILE SCLEROSIS
  (MERZBACHER-PELIZAEUS DISEASE, APLASIA
  AXIALIS EXTRACORTICALIS CONGENITA).
INFANTILE METACHROMATIC LEUKODYSTROPHY
  (GREENFIELD'S DISEASE).
JUVENILE METACHROMATIC LEUKODYSTROPHY
  (SCHOLZ' DISEASE).
PROGRESSIVE SUBCORTICAL ENCEPHALOPATHY
  (ENCEPHALITIS PERIAXIALIS DIFFUSA,
  SCHILDER'S DISEASE).
SPINAL SCLEROSIS (FRIEDRICH'S ATAXIA). Characterized by cerebellar degeneration, early onset followed by dementia.

*Encephalopathy, other, due to unknown or uncertain cause with the structural reactions manifest.* This category includes cases of mental retardation associated with progressive neuronal degeneration or other structural defects which cannot be classified in a more specific, diagnostic category.

## .4 Associated with Diseases and Conditions Due to Unknown Prenatal Influence

This category is for classifying conditions known to have existed at the time of or prior to birth but for which no definite etiology can be established. These include the primary cranial anomalies and congenital defects of undetermined origin as follows:

*Anencephaly* ( *including hemianencephaly* ).

*Malformations of the gyri.* This includes agyria, macrogyria (pachygyria), and microgyria.

*Porencephaly, congenital.* Characterized by large funnel-shaped cavities occurring anywhere in the cerebral hemispheres. Specify, if possible, whether the porencephaly is a result of asphyxia at birth or postnatal trauma.

*Multiple-congenital anomalies of the brain.*

*Other cerebral defects, congenital.*

CRANIOSTENOSIS. The most common conditions included in this category are acrocephaly (oxycephaly) and scaphocephaly. These may or may not be associated with mental retardation.

HYDROCEPHALUS, CONGENITAL. Under this heading is included only that type of hydrocephalus present at birth or occurring soon after delivery. All other types of hydrocephalus, secondary to other conditions, should be classified under the specific etiology when known.

HYPERTELORISM (GREIG'S DISEASE). Characterized by abnormal development of the sphenoid bone increasing the distance between the eyes.

MACROCEPHALY (MEGALENCEPHALY). Characterized by an increased size and weight of the brain due partially to proliferation of glia.

MICROCEPHALY, PRIMARY. True microcephaly is probably transmitted as a single autosomal recessive. When it is caused by other conditions, it should be classified according to the primary condition, with secondary microcephaly as a supplementary term.

LAURENCE-MOON-BIEDL SYNDROME. Characterized by mental retardation associated with retinitis pigmentosa, adiposo-genital dystrophy, and polydactyly.

## .5 With Chromosomal Abnormality

This group includes cases of mental retardation associated with chromosomal abnormalities. These may be divided into two sub-groups, those associated with an abnormal number of chromosomes and those with abnormal chromosomal morphology.

*Autosomal trisomy of group G* ( *Trisomy 21, Langdon-Down disease, Mongolism* ). This is the only common form of mental retardation due to chromosomal abnormality. (The others are relatively rare.) It ranges in degree from moderate to severe with infrequent cases of mild retardation. Other congenital defects are frequently present, and the intellectual development decelerates with time.

*Autosomal trisomy of group E.*

*Autosomal trisomy of group D.*

*Sex chromosome anomalies.* The only condition under the category which has any significant frequency is Klinefelter's syndrome.

*Abnormal number of chromosomes, other.* In this category would be included monosomy G and possibly others as well as other forms of mosaicism.

*Short arm deletion of chromosome 5—group B (Cri du chat).* A quite rare condition characterized by congenital abnormalities and a cat-like cry during infancy which disappears with time.

*Short arm deletion of chromosome 18—group E.*

*Abnormal morphology of chromosomes, other.* This category includes a variety of translocations, ring chromosomes, fragments, and isochromosomes associated with mental retardation.

## .6 ASSOCIATED WITH PREMATURITY

This category includes retarded patients who had a birth weight of less than 2500 grams (5.5 pounds) and/or a gestational age of less than 38 weeks at birth, and who do not fall into any of the preceding categories. This diagnosis should be used only if the patient's mental retardation cannot be classified more precisely under categories .0 to .5 above.

## .7 FOLLOWING MAJOR PSYCHIATRIC DISORDER

This category is for mental retardation following psychosis or other major psychiatric disorder in early childhood when there is no evidence of cerebral pathology. To make this diagnosis, there must be good evidence that the psychiatric disturbance was extremely severe. For example, retarded young adults with residual schizophrenia should not be classified here.

## .8 WITH PSYCHO-SOCIAL (ENVIRONMENTAL) DEPRIVATION

This category is for the many cases of mental retardation with no clinical or historical evidence of organic disease or pathology but for which there is some history of psycho-social deprivation. Cases in this group are classified in terms of psycho-social factors which appear to bear some etiological relationship to the condition as follows:

*Cultural-familial mental retardation.* Classification here requires that evidence of retardation be found in at least one of the parents and in one or more siblings, presumably because some degree of cultural deprivation results from familial retardation. The degree of retardation is usually mild.

*Associated with environmental deprivation.* An individual deprived of normal environmental stimulation in infancy and early childhood may prove unable to acquire the knowledge and skills required to function normally. This kind of deprivation tends to be more severe than that associated with familial mental retardation (q.v.). This type of deprivation may result from severe sensory impairment, even in an environment otherwise rich in stimulation. More rarely it may result from severe environmental limitations or atypical cultural milieus. The degree of retardation is always borderline or mild.

.9 WITH OTHER [AND UNSPECIFIED] CONDITION

## II. ORGANIC BRAIN SYNDROMES

(Disorders caused by or associated with impairment of brain tissue function)

These disorders are manifested by the following symptoms:
  (a) Impairment of orientation
  (b) Impairment of memory
  (c) Impairment of all intellectual functions such as comprehension, calculation, knowledge, learning, etc.
  (d) Impairment of judgment
  (e) Lability and shallowness of affect
The organic brain syndrome is a basic mental condition characteristically resulting from diffuse impairment of brain tissue function from whatever cause. Most of the basic symptoms are generally present to some degree regardless of whether the syndrome is mild, moderate, or severe.

The syndrome may be the only disturbance present. It may also be associated with psychotic symptoms and behavioral disturbances. The severity of the associated symptoms is affected by and related to not only the precipitating organic disorder but also the patient's inherent personality patterns, present emotional conflicts, his environmental situation, and interpersonal relations.

These brain syndromes are grouped into psychotic and non-psychotic disorders according to the severity of functional impairment. The psychotic level of impairment is described on page 23 [213 in this book] and the non-psychotic on pages 31–32 [220].

It is important to distinguish "acute" from "chronic" brain disorders because of marked differences in the course of illness, prognosis, and treatment. The terms indicate primarily whether the brain pathology and its accompanying organic brain syndrome is reversible. Since the same etiology may produce either temporary or permanent brain damage, a brain disorder which appears reversible (acute) at the beginning may prove later to have left permanent damage and a persistent organic brain syndrome which will then be diagnosed "chronic." Some brain syndromes occur in either form. Some occur only in acute forms (e.g., *Delirium tremens*). Some occur only in chronic form (e.g., *Alcoholic deterioration*). The acute and chronic forms may be indicated for those disorders coded in four digits by the addition of a fifth qualifying digit: .x1 *acute* and .x2 *chronic*.

## THE PSYCHOSES

Psychoses are described in two places in this Manual, here with the organic brain syndromes and later with the functional psychoses. The general discussion of psychosis appears here because organic brain syndromes are listed first in DSM-II.

Patients are described as psychotic when their mental functioning is sufficiently impaired to interfere grossly with their capacity to meet the ordinary demands of life. The impairment may result from a serious distortion in their capacity to recognize reality. Hallucinations and delusions, for example, may distort their perceptions. Alterations of mood may be so profound that the patient's capacity to respond appropriately is grossly impaired. Deficits in perception, language, and memory may be so severe that the patient's capacity for mental grasp of his situation is effectively lost.

Some confusion results from the different meanings which have become attached to the word "psychosis." Some non-organic disorders (295–298), in the well-developed form in which they were first recognized, typically rendered patients psychotic. For historical reasons these disorders are still classified as psychoses, even though it now generally is recognized that many patients for whom these diagnoses are clinically justified are not in fact psychotic. This is true particularly in the incipient or convalescent stages of the illness. To reduce confusion, when one of these disorders listed as a "psychosis" is diagnosed in a patient who is not psychotic, the qualifying phrase *not psychotic* or *not presently psychotic* should be noted and coded .x6 with a fifth digit.

Example: 295.06 *Schizophrenia, simple type, not psychotic*.

It should be noted that this Manual permits an organic condition to be classified as a psychosis only if the patient is psychotic during the episode being diagnosed.

If the specific physical condition underlying one of these disorders is known, indicate it with a separate, additional diagnosis.

## II. A. PSYCHOSES ASSOCIATED WITH ORGANIC BRAIN SYNDROMES (290–294)

### 290 SENILE AND PRE-SENILE DEMENTIA

**290.0 Senile dementia.** This syndrome occurs with senile brain disease, whose causes are largely unknown. The category does not include the pre-senile psychoses nor other degenerative diseases of the central nervous system. While senile brain disease derives its name from the age group in which it is most commonly seen, its diagnosis should be based on the brain disorder present and not on the patient's age at times of onset. Even mild cases will manifest some evidence of organic brain syndrome: self-centeredness, difficulty in assimilating new experiences, and childish emotionality. Deterioration may be minimal or progress to vegetative existence. (This condition was called "Chronic Brain Syndrome associated with senile brain disease" in DSM-I.)

**290.1 Pre-senile dementia.** This category includes a group of cortical brain diseases presenting clinical pictures similar to those of senile dementia but appearing characteristically in younger age groups. Alzheimer's and Pick's diseases are the two best known forms, each of which has a specific brain pathology. (In DSM-I Alzheimer's disease was classified as "Chronic Brain Syndrome with other disturbance of metabolism." Pick's disease was "Chronic Brain Syndrome associated with disease of unknown cause.") When the impairment is not of psychotic proportion, the patient should be classified under *Non-psychotic OBS with senile or pre-senile brain disease*.

### 291 ALCOHOLIC PSYCHOSES

Alcoholic psychoses are psychoses caused by poisoning with alcohol. When a pre-existing psychotic, psychoneurotic, or other disorder is aggravated by modest alcohol intake, the underlying condition, not the alcoholic psychosis, is diagnosed.

Simple drunkenness, when not specified as psychotic, is classified under *Non-psychotic OBS with alcohol*.

In accordance with ICD-8, this Manual subdivides the alcoholic psychoses into *Delirium tremens, Korsakov's psychosis, Other alcoholic hallucinosis*, and *Alcoholic paranoia*. DSM-II also adds three further subdivisions: *Acute alcohol intoxication, Alcoholic deterioration*, and *Pathological intoxication*. (In DSM-I "Acute Brain Syndrome, alcoholic intoxication" included what is now *Delirium tremens, Other alcoholic hallucinosis, Acute alcohol intoxication*, and *Pathological intoxication*.)

**291.0 Delirium tremens.** This is a variety of acute brain syndrome characterized by delirium, coarse tremors, and frightening visual hallucinations usually becoming more intense in the dark. Because it was first identified in alcoholics and until recently was thought always to be due to alcohol ingestion, the term is restricted to the syndrome associated with alcohol. It is distinguished from *Other alcoholic hallucinosis* by the tremors and the disordered sensorium. When this clinical picture is due to a nutritional deficiency rather than to alcohol poisoning, it is classified under *Psychosis associated with metabolic or nutritional disorder*.

**291.1 Korsakov's psychosis (alcoholic).** Also "Korsakoff." This is a variety of chronic brain syndrome associated with long-standing alcohol use and characterized by memory impairment, disorientation, peripheral neuropathy, and particularly by confabulation. Like delirium tremens, Korsakov's psychosis is identified with alcohol because of an initial error in identifying its cause, and therefore the term is confined to the syndrome associated with alcohol. The similar syndrome due to nutritional deficiency unassociated with alcohol is classified *Psychosis associated with metabolic or nutritional disorder*.

**291.2 Other alcoholic hallucinosis.** Hallucinoses caused by alcohol which cannot be diagnosed as delirium tremens, Korsakov's phychosis, or alcoholic deterioration fall in this category. A common variety manifests accusatory or threatening auditory hallucinations in a state of relatively clear consciousness. This condition must be distinguished from schizophrenia in combination with alcohol intoxication, which would require two diagnoses.

**291.3 Alcohol paranoid state** ((Alcoholic paranoia)).[3] This term describes a paranoid state which develops in chronic alcoholics, generally male, and is characterized by excessive jealousy and delusions of infidelity by the spouse. Patients diagnosed under primary paranoid states or schizophrenia should not be included here even if they drink to excess.

**291.4 * Acute alcohol intoxication.* [4]** All varieties of acute brain syndromes of psychotic proportion caused by alcohol are included here if they do not manifest features of delirium tremens, alcoholic hallucinosis, or pathological intoxication. This diagnosis is used alone when there is no other psychiatric disorder or as an additional diagnosis with other psychiatric conditions including alcoholism. The condition should not be confused with *simple drunkenness*, which does not involve psychosis. (All patients with this disorder would have been diagnosed "Acute Brain Syndrome, alcohol intoxication" in DSM-I.)

**291.5 * Alcoholic deterioration.*** All varieties of chronic brain syndromes of psychotic proportion caused by alcohol and not having the characteristic features of Korsakov's psychosis are included here. (This condition and Korsakov's psychosis were both included under "Chronic Brain Syndrome, alcohol intoxication with psychotic reaction" in DSM-I.)

**291.6 * Pathological intoxication.*** This is an acute brain syndrome

[3] Double parentheses indicate ICD-8 terms equivalent to U.S terms.
[4] Asterisk indicates categories added to ICD-8 for use in the United States only.

manifested by psychosis after minimal alcohol intake. (In DSM-I this diagnosis fell under "Acute Brain Syndrome, alcohol intoxication.")

**291.9** *Other [and unspecified]* [5] *alcoholic psychosis.* This term refers to all varieties of alcoholic psychosis not classified above.

## 292 PSYCHOSIS ASSOCIATED WITH INTRACRANIAL INFECTION

**292.0** *General paralysis.* This condition is characterized by physical signs and symptoms of parenchymatous syphilis of the nervous system and usually by positive serology, including the paretic gold curve in the spinal fluid. The condition may simulate any of the other psychoses and brain syndromes. If the impairment is not of psychotic proportion, it is classified *Non-psychotic OBS with intracranial infection.* If the specific underlying physical condition is known, indicate it with a separate, additional diagnosis. (This category was included under "Chronic Brain Syndrome associated with central nervous system syphilis (meningoencephalitic)" in DSM-I.)

**292.1** *Psychosis with other syphilis of central nervous system.* This includes all other varieties of psychosis attributed to intracranial infection by **Spirochaeta pallida.** The syndrome sometimes has features of organic brain syndrome. The acute infection is usually produced by meningovascular inflammation and responds to systemic antisyphilitic treatment. The chronic condition is generally due to gummata. If not of psychotic proportion, the disorder is classified *Non-psychotic OBS with intracranial infection.* (In DSM-I "Chronic Brain Syndrome associated with other central nervous system syphilis" and "Acute Brain Syndrome associated with intracranial infection" covered this category.)

**292.2** *Psychosis with epidemic encephalitis (von Economo's encephalitis).* This term is confined to the disorder attributed to the viral epidemic encephalitis that followed World War I. Virtually no cases have been reported since 1926. The condition, however, is differentiated from other encephalitis. It may present itself as acute delirium, and sometimes its outstanding feature is apparent indifference to persons and events ordinarily of emotional significance, such as the death of a family member. It may appear as a chronic brain syndrome and is sometimes dominated by involuntary, compulsive behavior. If not of psychotic proportions, the disorder is classified under *Non-psychotic OBS with intracranial infection.* (This category was classified under "Chronic Brain Syndrome associated with intracranial infection other than syphilis" in DSM-I.)

**292.3** *Psychosis with other [and unspecified] encephalitis.* This category includes disorders attributed to encephalitic infections other than epidemic encephalitis and also to encephalitis not otherwise specified.[6]

---

[5] Brackets indicate ICD-8 categories to be avoided in the United States or used by record librarians only.

[6] A list of important encephalitides may be found in *A Guide to the Control*

When possible, the type of infection should be indicated. If not of psychotic proportion, the disorder is classified under *Non-psychotic OBS with intracranial infection.*

**292.9 Psychosis with other [and unspecified] intracranial infection.** This category includes all acute and chronic conditions due to non-syphilitic and non-encephalitic infections, such as meningitis and brain abscess. Many of these disorders will have been diagnosed as the acute form early in the course of the illness. If not of psychotic proportion, the disorder should be classified under *Non-psychotic OBS with intracranial infection.* (In DSM-I the acute variety was classified as "Acute Brain Syndrome associated with intracranial infection" and the chronic variety as "Chronic Brain Syndrome associated with intracranial infection other than syphilis.")

### 293 PSYCHOSIS ASSOCIATED WITH OTHER CEREBRAL CONDITION

This major category, as its name indicates, is for all psychoses associated with cerebral conditions *other* than those previously defined. For example, the degenerative diseases following do *not* include the previous senile dementia. If the specific underlying physical condition is known, indicate it with a separate, additional diagnosis.

**293.0 Psychosis with cerebral arteriosclerosis.** This is a chronic disorder attributed to cerebral arteriosclerosis. It may be impossible to differentiate it from senile dementia and pre-senile dementia, which may coexist with it. Careful consideration of the patient's age, history, and symptoms may help determine the predominant pathology. Commonly, the organic brain syndrome is the only mental disturbance present, but other reactions, such as depression or anxiety, may be superimposed. If not of psychotic proportion, the condition is classified under *Non-psychotic OBS with circulatory disturbance.* (In DSM-I this was called "Chronic Brain Syndrome associated with cerebral arteriosclerosis.")

**293.1 Psychosis with other cerebrovascular disturbance.** This category includes such circulatory disturbances as cerebral thrombosis, cerebral embolism, arterial hypertension, cardio-renal disease, and cardiac disease, particularly in decompensation. It excludes conditions attributed to arteriosclerosis. The diagnosis is determined by the underlying organ pathology, which should be specified with an additional diagnosis. (In DSM-I this category was divided between "Acute Brain Syndrome associated with circulatory disturbance" and "Chronic Brain Syndrome associated with circulatory disturbance other than cerebral arteriosclerosis."

**293.2 Psychosis with epilepsy.** This category is to be used only for the condition associated with "idiopathic" epilepsy. Most of the etiological

*of Mental Disorders,* American Public Health Association, Inc., New York, 1962, pp. 40 ff.

agents underlying chronic brain syndromes can and do cause convulsions, particularly syphilis, intoxication, trauma, cerebral arteriosclerosis, and intracranial neoplasms. When the convulsions are symptomatic of such diseases, the brain syndrome is classified under those disturbances rather than here. The disturbance most commonly encountered here is the clouding of consciousness before or after a convulsive attack. Instead of a convulsion, the patient may show only a dazed reaction with deep confusion, bewilderment, and anxiety. The epileptic attack may also take the form of an episode of excitement with hallucinations, fears, and violent outbreaks. (In DSM-I this was included in "Acute Brain Syndrome associated with convulsive disorder" and "Chronic Brain Syndrome associated with convulsive disorder.")

*293.3 Psychosis with intracranial neoplasm.* Both primary and metastatic neoplasms are classified here. Reactions to neoplasms other than in the cranium should not receive this diagnosis. (In DSM-I this category included "Acute Brain Syndrome associated with intracranial neoplasm" and "Chronic Brain Syndrome associated with intracranial neoplasm.")

*293.4 Psychosis with degenerative disease of the central nervous system.* This category includes degenerative brain diseases not listed previously. (In DSM-I this was part of "Acute Brain Syndrome with disease of unknown or uncertain cause" and "Chronic Brain Syndrome associated with diseases of unknown or uncertain cause.")

*293.5 Psychosis with brain trauma.* This category includes those disorders which develop immediately after severe head injury or brain surgery and the post-traumatic chronic brain disorders. It does not include permanent brain damage which produces only focal neurological changes without significant changes in sensorium and affect. Generally, trauma producing a chronic brain syndrome is diffuse and causes permanent brain damage. If not of psychotic proportions, a post-traumatic personality disorder associated with an organic brain syndrome is classified as a *Non-psychotic OBS with brain trauma.* If the brain injury occurs in early life and produces a developmental defect of intelligence, the condition is also diagnosed *Mental retardation.* A head injury may precipitate or accelerate the course of a chronic brain disease, especially cerebral arteriosclerosis. The differential diagnosis may be extremely difficult. If, before the injury, the patient had symptoms of circulatory disturbance, particularly arteriosclerosis, and now shows signs of psychosis, he should be classified *Psychosis with cerebral arteriosclerosis.* (In DSM-I this category was divided between "Acute Brain Syndrome associated with trauma" and "Chronic Brain Syndrome associated with brain trauma.")

*293.9 Psychosis with other [and unspecified] cerebral condition.* This category is for cerebral conditions other than those listed above, and conditions for which it is impossible to make a more precise diagnosis. [Medical record librarians will include here *Psychoses with cerebral condition, not otherwise specified.*]

## 294 PSYCHOSIS ASSOCIATED WITH OTHER PHYSICAL CONDITION

The following psychoses are caused by general systemic disorders and are distinguished from the *cerebral* conditions previously described. If the specific underlying physical condition is known, indicate it with a separate, additional diagnosis.

**294.0 *Psychosis with endocrine disorder.*** This category includes disorders caused by the complications of diabetes other than cerebral arteriosclerosis and disorders of the thyroid, pituitary, adrenals, and other endocrine glands. (In DSM-I "Chronic Brain Syndrome associated with other disturbances of metabolism, growth, or nutrition" included the chronic variety of these disorders. DSM-I defined these conditions as "disorders of metabolism," but they here are considered endocrine disorders.)

**294.1 *Psychosis with metabolic or nutritional disorder.*** This category includes disorders caused by pellagra, avitaminosis, and metabolic disorders. (In DSM-I this was part of "Acute Brain Syndrome associated with metabolic disturbance" and "Chronic Brain Syndrome associated with other disturbance of metabolism, growth, or nutrition.")

**294.2 *Psychosis with systemic infection.*** This category includes disorders caused by severe general systemic infections, such as pneumonia, typhoid fever, malaria, and acute rheumatic fever. Care must be taken to distinguish these reactions from other disorders, particularly manic depressive illness and schizophrenia, which may be precipitated by even a mild attack of infectious disease. (In DSM-I this was confined to "Acute Brain Syndrome associated with systemic infection.")

**294.3 *Psychosis with drug or poison intoxication (other than alcohol).*** This category includes disorders caused by some drugs (including psychedelic drugs), hormones, heavy metals, gasses, and other intoxicants except alcohol. (In DSM-I these conditions were divided between "Acute Brain Syndrome, drug or poison intoxication" and "Chronic Brain Syndrome, associated with intoxication." The former excluded alcoholic acute brain syndromes, while the latter included alcoholic chronic brain syndromes.)

**294.4 *Psychosis with childbirth.*** Almost any type of psychosis may occur during pregnancy and the post-partum period and should be specifically diagnosed. This category is not a substitute for a differential diagnosis and excludes other psychoses arising during the puerperium. Therefore, this diagnosis should not be used unless all other possible diagnoses have been excluded.

**294.8 *Psychosis with other and undiagnosed physical condition.*** This is a residual category for psychoses caused by physical conditions other than those listed earlier. It also includes brain syndromes caused by physical conditions which have not been diagnosed. (In DSM-I this condition was divided between "Acute Brain Syndrome of unknown cause" and "Chronic Brain Syndrome of unknown cause." However, these categories also included the category now called *Psychosis with other [and unspecified] cerebral condition.*)

[*294.9 Psychosis with unspecified physical condition*].   This is not a diagnosis but is included for use by medical record librarians only.

## II. B. NON-PSYCHOTIC ORGANIC BRAIN SYNDROMES
### (309)

309 NON-PSYCHOTIC ORGANIC BRAIN SYNDROMES ((Mental disorders not specified as psychotic associated with physical conditions))

This category is for patients who have an organic brain syndrome but are not psychotic. If psychoses are present, they should be diagnosed as previously indicated. Refer to pages 22–23 [212–213] for description of organic brain syndromes in adults.

In children mild brain damage often manifests itself by hyperactivity, short attention span, easy distractability, and impulsiveness. Sometimes the child is withdrawn, listless, perseverative, and unresponsive. In exceptional cases there may be great difficulty in initiating action. These characteristics often contribute to a negative interaction between parent and child. If the organic handicap is the major etiological factor and the child is not psychotic, the case should be classified here. If the interactional factors are of major secondary importance, supply a second diagnosis under *Behavior disorders of childhood and adolescence*; if these interactional factors predominate, give only a diagnosis from this latter category.

*309.0 Non-psychotic OBS with intracranial infection*

*309.1 Non-psychotic OBS with drug, poison, or systemic intoxication*

309.13* NON-PSYCHOTIC OBS WITH ALCOHOL* (SIMPLE DRUNKENESS)

309.14* NON-PSYCHOTIC OBS WITH OTHER DRUG, POISON, OR SYSTEMIC INTOXICATION*

*309.2 Non-psychotic OBS with brain trauma*

*309.3 Non-psychotic OBS with circulatory disturbance*

*309.4 Non-psychotic OBS with epilepsy*

*309.5 Non-psychotic OBS with disturbance of metabolism, growth, or nutrition*

*309.6 Non-psychotic OBS with senile or pre-senile brain disease*

*309.7 Non-psychotic OBS with intracranial neoplasm*

*309.8 Non-psychotic OBS with degenerative disease of central nervous system*

*309.9 Non-psychotic OBS with other [and unspecified] physical condition*

[.91* ACUTE BRAIN SYNDROME, NOT OTHERWISE SPECIFIED*]

[.92\* CHRONIC BRAIN SYNDROME, NOT OTHERWISE
SPECIFIED\*]

## III. PSYCHOSES NOT ATTRIBUTED TO PHYSICAL CONDITIONS LISTED PREVIOUSLY (295–298)

This major category is for patients whose psychosis is not caused by physical conditions listed previously. Nevertheless, some of these patients may show additional signs of an organic condition. If these organic signs are prominent, the patient should receive the appropriate additional diagnosis.

### 295 SCHIZOPHRENIA

This large category includes a group of disorders manifested by characteristic disturbances of thinking, mood, and behavior. Disturbances in thinking are marked by alterations of concept formation which may lead to misinterpretation of reality and sometimes to delusions and hallucinations, which frequently appear psychologically self-protective. Corollary mood changes include ambivalent, constricted, and inappropriate emotional responsiveness and loss of empathy with others. Behavior may be withdrawn, regressive, and bizarre. The schizophrenias, in which the mental status is attributable primarily to a *thought* disorder, are to be distinguished from the *Major affective illnesses* (q.v.), which are dominated by a *mood* disorder. The *Paranoid states* (q.v.) are distinguished from schizophrenia by the narrowness of their distortions of reality and by the absence of other psychotic symptoms.

**295.0 Schizophrenia, simple type.** This psychosis is characterized chiefly by a slow and insidious reduction of external attachments and interests and by apathy and indifference leading to impoverishment of interpersonal relations, mental deterioration, and adjustment on a lower level of functioning. In general, the condition is less dramatically psychotic than are the hebephrenic, catatonic, and paranoid types of schizophrenia. Also, it contrasts with schizoid personality, in which there is little or no progression of the disorder.

**295.1 Schizophrenia, hebephrenic type.** This psychosis is characterized by disorganized thinking, shallow and inappropriate affect, unpredictable giggling, silly and regressive behavior and mannerisms, and frequent hypochondriacal complaints. Delusions and hallucinations, if present, are transient and not well organized.

**295.2 Schizophrenia, catatonic type**

295.23\* SCHIZOPHRENIA, CATATONIC TYPE, EXCITED\*

295.24\* SCHIZOPHRENIA, CATATONIC TYPE, WITHDRAWN\*

It is frequently possible and useful to distinguish two subtypes of catatonic schizophrenia. One is marked by excessive and sometimes violent motor activity and excitement and the other by generalized inhibition manifested by stupor, mutism, negativism, or waxy flexibility. In time, some cases deteriorate to a vegetative state.

*295.3 Schizophrenia, paranoid type.* This type of schizophrenia is characterized primarily by the presence of persecutory or grandiose delusions, often associated with hallucinations. Excessive religiosity is sometimes seen. The patient's attitude is frequently hostile and aggressive, and his behavior tends to be consistent with his delusions. In general the disorder does not manifest the gross personality disorganization of the hebephrenic and catatonic types, perhaps because the patient uses the mechanism of projection, which ascribes to others characteristics he cannot accept in himself. Three subtypes of the disorder may sometimes be differentiated, depending on the predominant symptoms: hostile, grandiose, and hallucinatory.

*295.4 Acute schizophrenic episode.* This diagnosis does not apply to acute episodes of schizophrenic disorders described elsewhere. This condition is distinguished by the acute onset of schizophrenic symptoms, often associated with confusion, perplexity, ideas of reference, emotional turmoil, dreamlike dissociation, and excitement, depression, or fear. The acute onset distinguishes this condition from simple schizophrenia. In time these patients may take on the characteristics of catatonic, hebephrenic, or paranoid schizophrenia, in which case their diagnosis should be changed accordingly. In many cases the patient recovers within weeks, but sometimes his disorganization becomes progressive. More frequently, remission is followed by recurrence. (In DSM-I this condition was listed as "Schizophrenia, acute undifferentiated type.")

*295.5 Schizophrenia, latent type.* This category is for patients having clear symptoms of schizophrenia but no history of a psychotic schizophrenic episode. Disorders sometimes designated as incipient, pre-psychotic, pseudoneurotic, pseudopsychopathic, or borderline schizophrenia are categorized here. (This category includes some patients who were diagnosed in DSM-I under "Schizophrenic reaction, chronic undifferentiated type." Others formerly included in that DSM-I category are now classified under *Schizophrenia, other [and unspecified] types* (q.v.).)

*295.6 Schizophrenia, residual type.* This category is for patients showing signs of schizophrenia but who, following a psychotic schizophrenic episode, are no longer psychotic.

*295.7 Schizophrenia, schizo-affective type.* This category is for patients showing a mixture of schizophrenic symptoms and pronounced elation or depression. Within this category it may be useful to distinguish excited from depressed types as follows:

295.73 * SCHIZOPHRENIA, SCHIZO-AFFECTIVE TYPE, EXCITED *

295.74 * SCHIZOPHRENIA, SCHIZO-AFFECTIVE TYPE, DEPRESSED *

**295.8 *** *Schizophrenia, childhood type.**   This category is for cases in which schizophrenic symptoms appear before puberty. The condition may be manifested by autistic, atypical, and withdrawn behavior; failure to develop identity separate from the mother's; and general unevenness, gross immaturity, and inadequacy in development. These developmental defects may result in mental retardation, which should also be diagnosed. (This category is for use in the United States and does not appear in ICD-8. It is equivalent to "Schizophrenic reaction, childhood type" in DSM-I.)

**295.90*** *Schizophrenia, chronic undifferentiated type.**   This category is for patients who show mixed schizophrenic symptoms and who present definite schizophrenic thought, affect, and behavior not classifiable under the other types of schizophrenia. It is distinguished from *Schizoid personality* (q.v.). (This category is equivalent to "Schizophrenic reaction, chronic undifferentiated type" in DSM-I except that it does not include cases now diagnosed as *Schizophrenia, latent type* and *Schizophrenia, other [and unspecified] types*.)

**295.99*** *Schizophrenia, other [and unspecified] types.**   This category is for any type of schizophrenia not previously described. (In DSM-I "Schizophrenic reaction, chronic undifferentiated type" included this category and also what is now called *Schizophrenia, latent type* and *Schizophrenia, chronic undifferentiated type*.)

## 296 MAJOR AFFECTIVE DISORDERS ((AFFECTIVE PSYCHOSES))

This group of psychoses is characterized by a single disorder of mood, either extreme depression or elation, that dominates the mental life of the patient and is responsible for whatever loss of contact he has with his environment. The onset of the mood does not seem to be related directly to a precipitating life experience and therefore is distinguishable from *Psychotic depressive reaction* and *Depressive neurosis*. (This category is not equivalent to the DSM-I heading "Affective reactions," which included "Psychotic depressive reaction.")

**296.0 *** *Involutional melancholia.**   This is a disorder occurring in the involutional period and characterized by worry, anxiety, agitation, and severe insomnia. Feelings of guilt and somatic preoccupations are frequently present and may be of delusional proportions. This disorder is distinguishable from *Manic-depressive illness* (q.v.) by the absence of previous episodes; it is distinguished from *Schizophrenia* (q.v.) in that impaired reality testing is due to a disorder of mood; and it is distinguished from *Psychotic depressive reaction* (q.v.) in that the depression is not due to some life experience. Opinion is divided as to whether this psychosis can be distinguished from the other affective disorders. It is, therefore, recommended that involutional patients not be given this diagnosis unless all other affective disorders have been ruled out. (In DSM-I this disorder was considered one of two subtypes of "Involutional Psychotic Reaction."

MANIC-DEPRESSIVE ILLNESSES (MANIC-DEPRESSIVE PSYCHOSES). These disorders are marked by severe mood swings and a tendency to remission and recurrence. Patients may be given this diagnosis in the absence of a previous history of affective psychosis if there is no obvious precipitating event. This disorder is divided into three major subtypes: manic type, depressed type, and circular type.

**296.1 Manic-depressive illness, manic type** ((Manic-depressive psychosis, manic type)). This disorder consists exclusively of manic episodes. These episodes are characterized by excessive elation, irritability, talkativeness, flight of ideas, and accelerated speech and motor activity. Brief periods of depression sometimes occur, but they are never true depressive episodes.

**296.2 Manic-depressive illness, depressed type** ((Manic-depressive psychosis, depressed type)). This disorder consists exclusively of depressive episodes. These episodes are characterized by severely depressed mood and by mental and motor retardation progressing occasionally to stupor. Uneasiness, apprehension, perplexity, and agitation may also be present. When illusions, hallucinations, and delusions (usually of guilt or of hypochondriacal or paranoid ideas) occur, they are attributable to the dominant mood disorder. Because it is a primary mood disorder, this psychosis differs from the *Psychotic depressive reaction*, which is more easily attributable to precipitating stress. Cases incompletely labelled as "psychotic depression" should be classified here rather than under *Psychotic depressive reaction*.

**296.3 Manic-depressive illness, circular type** ((Manic-depressive psychosis, circular type)). This disorder is distinguished by at least one attack of both a depressive episode *and* a manic episode. This phenomenon makes clear why manic and depressed types are combined into a single category. (In DSM-I these cases were diagnosed under "Manic depressive reaction, other.") The current episode should be specified and coded as one of the following:

296.33* MANIC-DEPRESSIVE ILLNESS, CIRCULAR TYPE, MANIC*

296.34* MANIC-DEPRESSIVE ILLNESS, CIRCULAR TYPE, DEPRESSED*

**296.8 Other major affective disorder** ((Affective psychosis, other)). Major affective disorders for which a more specific diagnosis has not been made are included here. It is also for "mixed" manic-depressive illness, in which manic and depressive symptoms appear almost simultaneously. It does not include *Psychotic depressive reaction* (q.v.) or *Depressive neurosis* (q.v.). (In DSM-I this category was included under "Manic depressive reaction, other.")

[*296.9 Unspecified major affective disorder*]

[AFFECTIVE DISORDER NOT OTHERWISE SPECIFIED]

[MANIC-DEPRESSIVE ILLNESS NOT OTHERWISE SPECIFIED]

## 297 PARANOID STATES

These are psychotic disorders in which a delusion, generally persecutory or grandiose, is the essential abnormality. Disturbances in mood, behavior, and thinking (including hallucinations) are derived from this delusion. This distinguishes paranoid states from the affective psychoses and schizophrenias, in which mood and thought disorders, respectively, are the central abnormalities. Most authorities, however, question whether disorders in this group are distinct clinical entities and not merely variants of schizophrenia or paranoid personality.

**297.0 *Paranoia*.** This extremely rare condition is characterized by gradual development of an intricate, complex, and elaborate paranoid system based on and often proceeding logically from misinterpretation of an actual event. Frequently the patient considers himself endowed with unique and superior ability. In spite of a chronic course the condition does not seem to interfere with the rest of the patient's thinking and personality.

**297.1 *Involutional paranoid state*** ((Involutional paraphrenia)). This paranoid psychosis is characterized by delusion formation with onset in the involutional period. Formerly it was classified as a paranoid variety of involutional psychotic reaction. The absence of conspicuous thought disorders typical of schizophrenia distinguishes it from that group.

**297.9 *Other paranoid state*.** This is a residual category for paranoid psychotic reactions not classified earlier.

## 298 OTHER PSYCHOSES

**298.0 *Psychotic depressive reaction*** ((Reactive depressive psychosis)). This psychosis is distinguished by a depressive mood attributable to some experience. Ordinarily the individual has no history of repeated depressions or cyclothymic mood swings. The differentiation between this condition and *Depressive neurosis* (q.v.) depends on whether the reaction impairs reality testing or functional adequacy enough to be considered a psychosis. (In DSM-I this condition was included with the affective psychoses.)

[**298.1 *Reactive excitation*]**
[**298.2 *Reactive confusion*]**
[ACUTE OR SUBACUTE CONFUSIONAL STATE]
[**298.3 *Acute paranoid reaction*]**
[**298.9 *Reactive psychosis, unspecified*]**

## [299 UNSPECIFIED PSYCHOSIS]

[DEMENTIA, INSANITY, OR PSYCHOSIS NOT OTHERWISE SPECIFIED]. This is not a diagnosis but is listed here for librarians and statisticians to use in coding incomplete diagnoses. Clinicians are expected to complete a differential diagnosis for patients who manifest features of several psychoses.

# IV. NEUROSES (300)

## 300 NEUROSES

Anxiety is the chief characteristic of the neuroses. It may be felt and expressed directly, or it may be controlled unconsciously and automatically by conversion, displacement, and various other psychological mechanisms. Generally, these mechanisms produce symptoms experienced as subjective distress from which the patient desires relief.

The neuroses, as contrasted to the psychoses, manifest neither gross distortion or misinterpretation of external reality nor gross personality disorganization. A possible exception to this is hysterical neurosis, which some believe may occasionally be accompanied by hallucinations and other symptoms encountered in psychoses.

Traditionally, neurotic patients, however severely handicapped by their symptoms, are not classified as psychotic because they are aware that their mental functioning is disturbed.

**300.0 Anxiety neurosis.**   This neurosis is characterized by anxious overconcern extending to panic and frequently associated with somatic symptoms. Unlike *Phobic neurosis* (q.v.), anxiety may occur under any circumstances and is not restricted to specific situations or objects. This disorder must be distinguished from normal apprehension or fear, which occurs in realistically dangerous situations.

**300.1 Hysterical neurosis.**   This neurosis is characterized by an involuntary psychogenic loss or disorder of function. Symptoms characteristically begin and end suddenly in emotionally charged situations and are symbolic of the underlying conflicts. Often they can be modified by suggestion alone. This is a new diagnosis that encompasses the former diagnoses "Conversion reaction" and "dissociative reaction" in DSM-I. This distinction between conversion and dissociative reactions should be preserved by using one of the following diagnoses whenever possible.

**300.13\* HYSTERICAL NEUROSIS, CONVERSION TYPE.\***   In the conversion type, the special senses or voluntary nervous system are affected, causing such symptoms as blindness, deafness, anosmia, anaesthesias, paraesthesias, paralyses, ataxias, akinesias, and dyskinesias. Often the patient shows an inappropriate lack of concern or *belle indifférence* about these symptoms, which may actually provide secondary gains by winning him sympathy or relieving him of unpleasant responsibilities. This type of hysterical neurosis must be distinguished from psychophysiologic disorders, which are mediated by the autonomic nervous system; from malingering, which is done consciously; and from neurological lesions, which cause anatomically circumscribed symptoms.

**300.14\* HYSTERICAL NEUROSIS, DISSOCIATIVE TYPE.\***   In the dissociative type, alterations may occur in the patient's state of consciousness or in his identity to produce such symptoms as amnesia, somnambulism, fugue, and multiple personality.

**300.2 *Phobic neurosis.*** This condition is characterized by intense fear of an object or situation which the patient consciously recognizes as no real danger to him. His apprehension may be experienced as faintness, fatigue, palpitations, perspiration, nausea, tremor, and even panic. Phobias are generally attributed to fears displaced to the phobic object or situation from some other object of which the patient is unaware. A wide range of phobias has been described.

**300.3 *Obsessive compulsive neurosis.*** This disorder is characterized by the persistent intrusion of unwanted thoughts, urges, or actions that the patient is unable to stop. The thoughts may consist of single words or ideas, ruminations, or trains of thought often perceived by the patient as nonsensical. The actions vary from simple movements to complex rituals such as repeated handwashing. Anxiety and distress are often present either if the patient is prevented from completing his compulsive ritual or if he is concerned about being unable to control it himself.

**300.4 *Depressive neurosis.*** This disorder is manifested by an excessive reaction of depression due to an internal conflict or to an identifiable event such as the loss of a love object or cherished possession. It is to be distinguished from *Involutional melancholia* (q.v.) and *Manic-depressive illness* (q.v.). *Reactive depressions* or *Depressive reactions* are to be classified here.

**300.5 *Neurasthenic neurosis*** ((Neurasthenia)). This condition is characterized by complaints of chronic weakness, easy fatigability, and sometimes exhaustion. Unlike hysterical neurosis, the patient's complaints are genuinely distressing to him and there is no evidence of secondary gain. It differs from *Anxiety neurosis* (q.v.) and from the *Psychophysiologic disorders* (q.v.) in the nature of the predominant complaint. It differs from *Depressive neurosis* (q.v.) in the moderateness of the depression and in the chronicity of its course. (In DSM-I this condition was called "Psychophysiologic nervous system reaction.")

**300.6 *Depersonalization neurosis*** ((Depersonalization syndrome)). This syndrome is dominated by a feeling of unreality and of estrangement from the self, body, or surroundings. This diagnosis should not be used if the condition is part of some other mental disorder, such as an acute situational reaction. A brief experience of depersonalization is not necessarily a symptom of illness.

**300.7 *Hypochondriacal neurosis.*** This condition is dominated by preoccupation with the body and with fear of presumed diseases of various organs. Though the fears are not of delusional quality, as in psychotic depressions, they persist despite reassurance. The condition differs from hysterical neurosis in that there are no actual losses or distortions of function.

**300.8 *Other neurosis.*** This classification includes specific psychoneurotic disorders not classified elsewhere, such as "writer's cramp" and other occupational neuroses. Clinicians should not use this category for patients with "mixed" neuroses, which should be diagnosed according to the predominant symptom.

[*300.9 Unspecified neurosis*]. This category is not a diagnosis. It is for the use of record librarians and statisticians to code incomplete diagnoses.

## V. PERSONALITY DISORDERS AND CERTAIN OTHER NON-PSYCHOTIC MENTAL DISORDERS (301–304)

### 301 PERSONALITY DISORDERS

This group of disorders is characterized by deeply ingrained maladaptive patterns of behavior that are perceptibly different in quality from psychotic and neurotic symptoms. Generally, these are life-long patterns, often recognizable by the time of adolescence or earlier. Sometimes the pattern is determined primarily by malfunctioning of the brain, but such cases should be classified under one of the non-psychotic organic brain syndromes rather than here. (In DSM-I "Personality Disorders" also included disorders now classified under *Sexual deviation, Alcoholism,* and *Drug dependence.*)

*301.0 Paranoid personality.* This behavioral pattern is characterized by hypersensitivity, rigidity, unwarranted suspicion, jealousy, envy, excessive self-importance, and a tendency to blame others and ascribe evil motives to them. These characteristics often interfere with the patient's ability to maintain satisfactory interpersonal relations. Of course, the presence of suspicion of itself does not justify this diagnosis, since the suspicion may be warranted in some instances.

*301.1 Cyclothymic personality* ((Affective personality)). This behavior pattern is manifested by recurring and alternating periods of depression and elation. Periods of elation may be marked by ambition, warmth, enthusiasm, optimism, and high energy. Periods of depression may be marked by worry, pessimism, low energy, and a sense of futility. These mood variations are not readily attributable to external circumstances. If possible, the diagnosis should specify whether the mood is characteristically depressed, hypomanic, or alternating.

*301.2 Schizoid personality.* This behavior pattern manifests shyness, over-sensitivity, seclusiveness, avoidance of close or competitive relationships, and often eccentricity. Autistic thinking without loss of capacity to recognize reality is common, as are daydreaming and the inability to express hostility and ordinary aggressive feelings. These patients react to disturbing experiences and conflicts with apparent detachment.

*301.3 Explosive personality* (*Epileptoid personality disorder*). This behavior pattern is characterized by gross outbursts of rage or of verbal or physical aggressiveness. These outbursts are strikingly different from the patient's usual behavior, and he may be regretful and repentant for them. These patients are generally considered excitable, aggressive, and over-responsive to environmental pressures. It is the intensity of the outbursts and the individual's inability to control them which distinguishes this group. Cases diagnosed as "aggressive personality" are classified here. If the patient is amnesic for the outbursts, the diagnosis of *Hysterical neurosis, Non-psychotic OBS with epilepsy,* or *Psychosis with epilepsy* should be considered.

**301.4 Obsessive compulsive personality** ((Anankastic personality)). This behavior pattern is characterized by excessive concern with conformity and adherence to standards of conscience. Consequently, individuals in this group may be rigid, over-inhibited, over-conscientious, over-dutiful, and unable to relax easily. This disorder may lead to an *Obsessive compulsive neurosis* (q.v.), from which it must be distinguished.

**301.5 Hysterical personality (Histrionic personality disorder).** These behavior patterns are characterized by excitability, emotional instability, over-reactivity, and self-dramatization. This self-dramatization is always attention-seeking and often seductive, whether or not the patient is aware of its purpose. These personalities are also immature, self-centered, often vain, and usually dependent on others. This disorder must be differentiated from *Hysterical neurosis* (q.v.).

**301.6 Asthenic personality.** This behavior pattern is characterized by easy fatigability, low energy level, lack of enthusiasm, marked incapacity for enjoyment, and oversensitivity to physical and emotional stress. This disorder must be differentiated from *Neurasthenic neurosis* (q.v.).

**301.7 Antisocial personality.** This term is reserved for individuals who are basically unsocialized and whose behavior pattern brings them repeatedly into conflict with society. They are incapable of significant loyalty to individuals, groups, or social values. They are grossly selfish, callous, irresponsible, impulsive, and unable to feel guilt or to learn from experience and punishment. Frustration tolerance is low. They tend to blame others or offer plausible rationalizations for their behavior. A mere history of repeated legal or social offenses is not sufficient to justify this diagnosis. *Group delinquent reaction of childhood (or adolescence)* (q.v.), and *Social maladjustment without manifest psychiatric disorder* (q.v.) should be ruled out before making this diagnosis.

**301.81\* Passive-aggressive personality.\*** This behavior pattern is characterized by both passivity and aggressiveness. The aggressiveness may be expressed passively, for example by obtructionism, pouting, procrastination, intentional inefficiency, or stubbornness. This behavior commonly reflects hostility which the individual feels he dare not express openly. Often the behavior is one expression of the patient's resentment at failing to find gratification in a relationship with an individual or institution upon which he is over-dependent.

**301.82\* Inadequate personality.\*** This behavior pattern is characterized by ineffectual responses to emotional, social, intellectual, and physical demands. While the patient seems neither physically nor mentally deficient, he does manifest inadaptability, ineptness, poor judgment, social instability, and lack of physical and emotional stamina.

301.89* *Other personality disorders of specified types* (*Immature personality, Passive-dependent personality, etc.*)*

301.9 [*Unspecified personality disorder*]

## 302 SEXUAL DEVIATIONS

This category is for individuals whose sexual interests are directed primarily toward objects other than people of the opposite sex, toward sexual acts not usually associated with coitus, or toward coitus performed under bizarre circumstances, as in necrophilia, pedophilia, sexual sadism, and fetishism. Even though many find their practices distasteful, they remain unable to substitute normal sexual behavior for them. This diagnosis is not appropriate for individuals who perform deviant sexual acts because normal sexual objects are not available to them.

302.0 *Homosexuality*

302.1 *Fetishism*

302.2 *Pedophilia*

302.3 *Transvestitism*

302.4 *Exhibitionism*

302.5* *Voyeurism**

302.6* *Sadism**

302.7* *Masochism**

302.8 *Other sexual deviation*

[302.9 *Unspecified sexual deviation*]

## 303 ALCOHOLISM

This category is for patients whose alcohol intake is great enough to damage their physical health or their personal or social functioning or when it has become a prerequisite to normal functioning. If the alcoholism is due to another mental disorder, both diagnoses should be made. The following types of alcoholism are recognized:

303.0 *Episodic excessive drinking.*   If alcoholism is present and the individual becomes intoxicated as frequently as four times a year, the condition should be classified here. Intoxication is defined as a state in which the individual's coordination or speech is definitely impaired or his behavior is clearly altered.

303.1 *Habitual excessive drinking.*   This diagnosis is given to persons who are alcoholic and who either become intoxicated more than 12 times a year or are recognizably under the influence of alcohol more than once a week, even though not intoxicated.

303.2 *Alcohol addiction.*   This condition should be diagnosed when there is direct or strong presumptive evidence that the patient is dependent on alcohol. If available, the best direct evidence of such dependence is the appearance of withdrawal symptoms. The inability of the patient to go one day without drinking is presumptive evidence. When heavy drinking continues for three months or more, it is reasonable to presume addiction to alcohol has been established.

*303.9 Other [and unspecified] alcoholism*

## 304 DRUG DEPENDENCE

This category is for patients who are addicted to or dependent on drugs other than alcohol, tobacco, and ordinary caffeine-containing beverages. Dependence on medically prescribed drugs is also excluded so long as the drug is medically indicated and the intake is proportionate to the medical need. The diagnosis requires evidence of habitual use or a clear sense of need for the drug. Withdrawal symptoms are not the only evidence of dependence; while always present when opium derivatives are withdrawn, they may be entirely absent when cocaine or marihuana are withdrawn. The diagnosis may stand alone or be coupled with any other diagnosis.

*304.0 Drug dependence, opium, opium alkaloids, and their derivatives*

*304.1 Drug dependence, synthetic analgesics with morphine-like effects*

*304.2 Drug dependence, barbiturates*

*304.3 Drug dependence, other hypnotics and sedatives or "tranquilizers"*

*304.4 Drug dependence, cocaine*

*304.5 Drug dependence, Cannabis sativa ( hashish, marihuana )*

*304.6 Drug dependence, other psycho-stimulants ( amphetamines, etc. )*

*304.7 Drug dependence, hallucinogens*

*304.8 Other drug dependence*

*[304.9 Unspecified drug dependence]*

## VI. PSYCHOPHYSIOLOGIC DISORDERS (305)

### 305 PSYCHOPHYSIOLOGIC DISORDERS ((Physical disorders of presumably psychogenic origin))

This group of disorders is characterized by physical symptoms that are caused by emotional factors and involve a single organ system, usually under autonomic nervous system innervation. The physiological changes involved are those that normally accompany certain emotional states, but in these disorders the changes are more intense and sustained. The individual may not be consciously aware of his emotional state. If there is an additional psychiatric disorder, it should be diagnosed separately, whether or not it is presumed to contribute to the physical disorder. The specific physical disorder should be named and classified in one of the following categories.

*305.0 Psychophysiologic skin disorder.* This diagnosis applies to skin reactions such as neurodermatosis, pruritis, atopic dematitis, and hyperhydrosis in which emotional factors play a causative role.

*305.1 Psychophysiologic musculoskeletal disorder.* This diagnosis applies to musculoskeletal disorders such as backache, muscle cramps, and myalgias, and tension headaches in which emotional factors play a causative role. Differentiation from hysterical neurosis is of prime importance and at times extremely difficult.

**305.2 Psychophysiologic respiratory disorder.** This diagnosis applies to respiratory disorders such as bronchial asthma, hyperventilation syndromes, sighing, and hiccoughs in which emotional factors play a causative role.

**305.3 Psychophysiologic cardiovascular disorder.** This diagnosis applies to cardiovascular disorders such as paroxysmal tachycardia, hypertension, vascular spasms, and migraine in which emotional factors play a causative role.

**305.4 Psychophysiologic hemic and lymphatic disorder.** Here may be included any disturbances in the hemic and lymphatic system in which emotional factors are found to play a causative role. ICD-8 has included this category so that all organ systems will be covered.

**305.5 Psychophysiologic gastrointestinal disorder.** This diagnosis applies to specific types of gastrointestinal disorders such as peptic ulcer, chronic gastritis, ulcerative or mucous colitis, constipation, hyperacidity, pylorospasm, "heartburn," and "irritable colon" in which emotional factors play a causative role.

**305.6 Psychophysiologic genito-urinary disorder.** This diagnosis applies to genito-urinary disorders such as disturbances in menstruation and micturition, dyspareunia, and impotence in which emotional factors play a causative role.

**305.7 Psychophysiologic endocrine disorder.** This diagnosis applies to endocrine disorders in which emotional factors play a causative role. The disturbance should be specified.

**305.8 Psychophysiologic disorder of organ of special sense.** This diagnosis applies to any disturbance in the organs of special sense in which emotional factors play a causative role. Conversion reactions are excluded.

**305.9 Psychophysiologic disorder of other type**

## VII. SPECIAL SYMPTOMS (306)

### 306 Special Symptoms not Elsewhere Classified

This category is for the occasional patient whose psychopathology is manifested by discrete, specific symptoms. An example might be anorexia nervosa under *Feeding disturbance* as listed below. It does not apply, however, if the symptom is the result of an organic illness or defect or other mental disorder. For example, anorexia nervosa due to schizophrenia would not be included here.

**306.0 Speech disturbance**
**306.1 Specific learning disturbance**

*306.2 Tic*
*306.3 Other psychomotor disorder*
*306.4 Disorder of sleep*
*306.5 Feeding disturbance*
*306.6 Enuresis*
*306.7 Encopresis*
*306.8 Cephalalgia*
*306.9 Other special symptom*

## VIII. TRANSIENT SITUATIONAL DISTURBANCES (307)

### 3 0 7 * TRANSIENT SITUATIONAL DISTURBANCES[7]

This major category is reserved for more or less transient disorders of any severity (including those of psychotic proportions) that occur in individuals without any apparent underlying mental disorders and that represent an acute reaction to overwhelming environmental stress. A diagnosis in this category should specify the cause and manifestations of the disturbance so far as possible. If the patient has good adaptive capacity, his symptoms usually recede as the stress diminishes. If, however, the symptoms persist after the stress is removed, the diagnosis of another mental disorder is indicated. Disorders in this category are classified according to the patient's developmental stage as follows:

**307.0\* Adjustment reaction of infancy.\*** Example: A grief reaction associated with separation from patient's mother, manifested by crying spells, loss of appetite, and severe social withdrawal.

**307.1\* Adjustment reaction of childhood.\*** Example: Jealousy associated with birth of patient's younger brother and manifested by nocturnal enuresis, attention-getting behavior, and fear of being abandoned.

**307.2\* Adjustment reaction of adolescence.\*** Example: Irritability and depression associated with school failure and manifested by temper outbursts, brooding, and discouragement.

**307.3\* Adjustment reaction of adult life.\*** Example: Resentment with depressive tone associated with an unwanted pregnancy and manifested by hostile complaints and suicidal gestures.

Example: Fear associated with military combat and manifested by trembling, running, and hiding.

Example: A Ganser syndrome associated with death sentence and

[7] The terms included under DSM-II Category 307\*, "Transient situational disturbances," differ from those in Category 307 of the ICD. DSM-II Category 307\*, "Transient situational disturbances," contains adjustment reactions of infancy (307.0\*), childhood (307.1\*), adolescence (307.2\*), adult life (307.3\*), and late life (307.4\*). ICD Category 307, "Transient situational disturbances," includes only the adjustment reactions of adolescence, adult life, and late life. ICD 308, "Behavioral disorders of children," contains the reactions of infancy and childhood. These differences must be taken into account in preparing statistical tabulations to conform to ICD categories.

manifested by incorrect but approximate answers to questions.

**307.4\* *Adjustment reaction of late life*.\*** Example: Feelings of rejection associated with forced retirement and manifested by social withdrawal.

## IX. BEHAVIOR DISORDERS OF CHILDHOOD AND ADOLESCENCE (308)

3 0 8 \* B E H A V I O R  D I S O R D E R S  O F  C H I L D H O O D  A N D A D O L E S C E N C E ((Behavior disorders of childhood))[8]

This major category is reserved for disorders occurring in childhood and adolescence that are more stable, internalized, and resistant to treatment than *Transient situational disturbances* (q.v.) but less so than *Psychoses, Neuroses,* and *Personality disorders* (q.v.). This intermediate stability is attributed to the greater fluidity of all behavior at this age. Characteristic manifestations include such symptoms as overactivity, inattentiveness, shyness, feeling of rejection, over-aggressiveness, timidity, and delinquency.

**308.0\* *Hyperkinetic reaction of childhood* (*or adolescence*).\*** This disorder is characterized by overactivity, restlessness, distractibility, and short attention span, especially in young children; the behavior usually diminishes in adolescence. If this behavior is caused by organic brain damage, it should be diagnosed under the appropriate non-psychotic *organic brain syndrome* (q.v.).

**308.1\* *Withdrawing reaction of childhood* (*or adolescence*).\*** This disorder is characterized by seclusiveness, detachment, sensitivity, shyness, timidity, and general inability to form close interpersonal relationships. This diagnosis should be reserved for those who cannot be classified as having *Schizophrenia* (q.v.) and whose tendencies toward withdrawal have not yet stabilized enough to justify the diagnosis of *Schizoid personality* (q.v.).

**308.2\* *Overanxious reaction of childhood* (*or adolescence*).\*** This disorder is characterized by chronic anxiety, excessive and unrealistic fears, sleeplessness, nightmares, and exaggerated autonomic responses. The patient tends to be immature, self-conscious, grossly lacking in self-confidence, conforming, inhibited, dutiful, approval-seeking, and apprehensive in new situations and unfamiliar surroundings. It is to be

[8] The terms included under DSM-II Category 308\*, "Behavioral disorders of childhood and adolescence," differ from those in Category 308 of the ICD. DSM-II Category 308\* includes "Behavioral disorders of childhood and adolescence," whereas ICD Category 308 includes only "Behavioral disorders of childhood." DSM-II Category 308\* *does not* include "Adjustment reactions of infancy and childhood," whereas ICD Category 308 does. In the DSM-II classification, "Adjustment reactions of infancy and childhood" are allocated to 307\* (Transitional situational disturbances). These differences should be taken into account in preparing statistical tabulations to conform to the ICD categories.

distinguished from *Neuroses* (q.v.).

**308.3\*** *Runaway reaction of childhood* (*or adolescence*).\* Individuals with this disorder characteristically escape from threatening situations by running away from home for a day or more without permission. Typically they are immature and timid and feel rejected at home, inadequate, and friendless. They often steal furtively.

**308.4\*** *Unsocialized aggressive reaction of childhood* (*or adolescence*).\* This disorder is characterized by overt or covert hostile disobedience, quarrelsomeness, physical and verbal aggressiveness, vengefulness, and destructiveness. Temper tantrums, solitary stealing, lying, and hostile teasing of other children are common. These patients usually have no consistent parental acceptance and discipline. This diagnosis should be distinguished from *Antisocial personality* (q.v.), *Runaway reaction of childhood* (*or adolescence*) (q.v.), and *Group delinquent reaction of childhood* (*or adolescence*) (q.v.).

**308.5\*** *Group delinquent reaction of childhood* (*or adolescence*).\* Individuals with this disorder have acquired the values, behavior, and skills of a delinquent peer group or gang to whom they are loyal and with whom they characteristically steal, skip school, and stay out late at night. The condition is more common in boys than girls. When group delinquency occurs with girls, it usually involves sexual delinquency, although shoplifting is also common.

**308.9\*** *Other reaction of childhood* (*or adolescence*).\* Here are to be classified children and adolescents having disorders not described in this group but which are nevertheless more serious than transient situational disturbances and less serious than psychoses, neuroses, and personality disorders. The particular disorder should be specified.

## X. CONDITIONS WITHOUT MANIFEST PSYCHIATRIC DISORDER AND NON-SPECIFIC CONDITIONS (316–318\*)

### 316\* SOCIAL MALADJUSTMENTS WITHOUT MANIFEST PSYCHIATRIC DISORDER

This category is for recording the conditions of individuals who are psychiatrically normal but who nevertheless have severe enough problems to warrant examination by a psychiatrist. These conditions may either become or precipitate a diagnosable mental disorder.

**316.0\*** *Marital maladjustment.\** This category is for individuals who are psychiatrically normal but who have significant conflicts or maladjustments in marriage.

**316.1\*** *Social maladjustment.\** This category is for individuals thrown into an unfamiliar culture (culture shock) or into a conflict arising from divided loyalties to two cultures.

**316.2\*** *Occupational maladjustment.\** This category is for psychiatrically normal individuals who are grossly maladjusted in their work.

*316.3\* Dyssocial behavior.\** This category is for individuals who are not classifiable as anti-social personalities but who are predatory and follow more or less criminal pursuits, such as racketeers, dishonest gamblers, prostitutes, and dope peddlers. (DSM-I classified this condition as "Sociopathic personality disorder, dyssocial type.")

*316.9\* Other social maladjustment\**

## 3 1 7* Non-Specific Conditions*

This category is for conditions that cannot be classified under any of the previous categories, even after all facts bearing on the case have been investigated. This category is not for "Diagnosis deferred" (q.v.).

## 3 1 8* No Mental Disorder*

This term is used when, following psychiatric examination, none of the previous disorders is found. It is not to be used for patients whose disorders are in remission.

# XI. NON-DIAGNOSTIC TERMS FOR ADMINISTRATIVE USE
## (319*)

### 3 1 9* Non-Diagnostic Terms for Administrative Use*

*319.0\* Diagnosis deferred \**
*319.1\* Boarder\**
*319.2\* Experiment only\**
*319.9\* Other\**

## CHAPTER ELEVEN

# Comparative Listing of DSM-I and DSM-II

### MORTON KRAMER, Sc.D., and

### FRANCES C. NEMEC

### INTRODUCTION

THIS CHAPTER provides a cross-reference between the titles and codes used in DSM-II and those used in DSM-I.

The International Classification of Diseases consists of a basic code of three digits and a fourth digit for achieving greater detail within each of the three-digit categories. The A.P.A. Committee on Nomenclature and Statistics found it necessary to add a fifth digit to the ICD code to obtain still further detail within each four-digit ICD category for the mental disorders and to maintain continuity with DSM-I. When statistics are produced for categories designated by these five-digit codes, the codes for these categories should be clearly earmarked as not part of the official ICD. In the following table all such code numbers are identified with a single asterisk.

To facilitate the coding of all disorders, a zero (o) is used as the fifth digit for those codes in which no special fifth digit is required.

Whenever a category in one manual corresponds to several categories in the other, the latter categories are enclosed in one brace. If more than one DSM-II diagnosis corresponds to a single DSM-I diagnosis, the appropriate DSM-II diagnosis must be chosen.

Reprinted with the permission of the American Psychiatric Association from *Diagnostic and Statistical Manual of Mental Disorders*, ed. 2, 1968.

Finally, selected additional ICD codes are indicated in parentheses for use when detail is desired regarding the specific condition with which a mental disorder is associated.

Asterisk indicates categories added to ICD-8 for use in the United States only. Brackets indicate ICD-8 categories to be avoided in the United States or used by record librarians only.

TABLE I

*Comparative Listing of Titles and Codes, DSM-I and DSM-II*

(Refer to preceding page concerning use of symbols)

| DSM-I Code Numbers and Titles[a] | DSM-II Code Numbers and Titles |
|---|---|
| 01-09 ACUTE BRAIN DISORDERS | |
| 01 Acute Brain Syndrome associated with infection | |
| 01.0 Intracranial infection (except epidemic encephalitis) | 292.91* Psychosis with other [and unspecified] intracranial infection. **Specify infection with additional code.** |
| 01.1 Epidemic encephalitis | 292.21* Psychosis with epidemic encephalitis |
| 01.2 With systemic infection, NEC | 294.21* Psychosis with systemic infection. **Specify infection with additional code.** |
| 02 Acute Brain Syndrome associated with intoxication | 291.01* Delirium tremens |
| | 291.21* Other alcoholic hallucinosis |
| 02.1 Alcohol intoxication | 291.41* Acute alcohol intoxication. **Excludes simple drunkness.** |
| | 291.61* Pathological intoxication |
| 02.2 Drug or poison intoxication (except alcohol) | 294.31* Psychosis with drug or poison intoxication. **Specify drug or poison. Excludes alcoholic psychosis (291).** |
| 03 Acute Brain Syndrome associated with trauma | 293.51* Psychosis with brain trauma. **Specify type of trauma with additional code (800–804; 850–854; 998).** |
| 04 Acute Brain Syndrome associated with circulatory disturbance | 293.11* Psychosis with other cerebrovascular disturbance. **Specify disturbance with additional code (430–436; 438).** |
| | 294.81* Psychosis with other and undiagnosed physical condition. **Specify circulatory disturbance with additional code (393–429; 440–458).** |
| 05 Acute Brain Syndrome associated with convulsive disorder | 293.21* Psychosis with epilepsy |

[a] The code numbers and titles referred to here are those found on pages 78-86 of DSM-I.

TABLE I (continued)

Comparative Listing of Titles and Codes, DSM-I and DSM-II

| | | | |
|---|---|---|---|
| o6 | Acute Brain Syndrome associated with metabolic disturbance | 294.11* | Psychosis with metabolic or nutritional disorder. Specify disorder with additional code (240–279). |
| o7 | Acute Brain Syndrome associated with intracranial neoplasm | 293.31* | Psychosis with intracranial neoplasm. Specify type of neoplasm with additional code. |
| o8 | Acute Brain Syndrome with disease of unknown or uncertain cause | 293.41* | Psychosis with degenerative disease of the central nervous system. Specify disease with additional code. |
| o9 | Acute Brain Syndrome of unknown cause | 294.81* [294.91*] | Psychosis with other and undiagnosed physical condition. Specify condition with additional code. Psychosis with unspecified physical condition] |
| 10-19 | CHRONIC BRAIN DISORDERS | | |
| 10 | Chronic Brain Syndrome associated with diseases and conditions due to prenatal (constitutional) influence | | |
| 10.0 | With congenital cranial anomaly | | |
| 10.00 | Without qualifying phrase | 309.92* | Non-psychotic OBS with other [and unspecified] physical condition. Specify type of congenital cranial anomaly with additional code (740–743). |
| 10.01 | With psychotic reaction | 294.82* | Psychosis with other and undiagnosed physical condition. Specify type of congenital cranial anomaly with additional code (740–743). |
| 10.02 | With neurotic reaction | 309.92* | See above. |
| 10.03 | With behavioral reaction | | |
| 10.1 | With congenital spastic paraplegia | | |
| 10.10 | Without qualifying phrase | 309.22* | Non-psychotic OBS with brain trauma. Specify congenital spastic paraplegia with additional code (343). |
| 10.11 | With psychotic reaction | 293.52* | Psychosis with brain trauma. Specify congenital spastic paraplegia with additional code (343). |

## Table I (continued)
### Comparative Listing of Titles and Codes, DSM-I and DSM-II

| | Code | Description |
|---|---|---|
| 10.12 With neurotic reaction<br>10.13 With behavioral reaction | 309.22* | See above. |
| 10.2 With mongolism<br>10.20 Without qualifying phrase | 309.92* | Non-psychotic OBS with other [and unspecified] physical condition. Specify mongolism and degree of retardation with an additional code (310.52, 311.52, 312.52, 313.52, 314.52, 315.52). |
| 10.21 With psychotic reaction | 294.82* | Psychosis with other and undiagnosed physical condition. Specify mongolism and degree of retardation with an additional code (310.52, 311.52, 312.52, 313.52, 314.52, 315.52). |
| 10.22 With neurotic reaction<br>10.23 With behavioral reaction | 309.92* | See above. |
| 10.3 Due to prenatal maternal infectious diseases<br>10.30 Without qualifying phrase | 309.02* | Non-psychotic OBS with intracranial infection. Specify maternal infection with additional code (761). |
| 10.31 With psychotic reaction | 292.92* | Psychosis with other [and unspecified] intracranial infection. Specify maternal infection with additional code (761). |
| 10.32 With neurotic reaction<br>10.33 With behavioral reaction | 309.02* | See above. |
| 11 Chronic Brain Syndrome associated with central nervous system syphilis | | |
| 11.0 Meningoencephalitic<br>11.00 Without qualifying phrase | 309.02* | Non-psychotic OBS with intracranial infection. Specify syphilis of CNS with additional code (094.1). |
| 11.01 With psychotic reaction | 292.02* | Psychosis with general paralysis |
| 11.02 With neurotic reaction<br>11.03 With behavioral reaction | 309.02* | See above. |

Table I *(continued)*

*Comparative Listing of Titles and Codes, DSM-I and DSM-II*

11.1 Meningovascular

11.10 Without qualifying phrase — 309.02* — Non-psychotic OBS with intracranial infection. **Specify** other syphilis of CNS with additional code (094.9).

11.11 With psychotic reaction — 292.12* — Psychosis with other syphilis of central nervous system. **Specify** other syphilis of CNS with additional code (094.9).

11.12 With neurotic reaction ⎫
11.13 With behavioral reaction ⎭ — 309.02* — See above.

11.2 Other central nervous system syphilis

11.20 Without qualifying phrase — 309.02* — Non-psychotic OBS with intracranial infection. **Specify** other syphilis of CNS with additional code (094.9).

11.21 With psychotic reaction — 292.12* — Psychosis with other syphilis of central nervous system. **Specify** other syphilis of CNS with additional code (094.9).

11.22 With neurotic reaction ⎫
11.23 With behavioral reaction ⎭ — 309.02* — See above.

12 Chronic Brain Syndrome associated with intracranial infection other than syphilis

12.0 Epidemic encephalitis

12.00 Without qualifying phrase — 309.02* — Non-psychotic OBS with intracranial infection. **Specify** encephalitis with additional code (062–065).

12.01 With psychotic reaction — 292.22* — Psychosis with epidemic encephalitis

12.02 With neurotic reaction ⎫
12.03 With behavioral reaction ⎭ — 309.02* — See above.

12.1 Other intracranial infections

12.10 Without qualifying phrase — 309.02* — Non-psychotic OBS with intracranial infection. **Specify** infection with additional code.

12.11 With psychotic reaction — 292.92* — Psychosis with other [and unspecified] intracranial infection. **Specify** infection with additional code.

## Table I (continued)
### Comparative Listing of Titles and Codes, DSM-I and DSM-II

| | | |
|---|---|---|
| 12.12 With neurotic reaction<br>12.13 With behavioral reaction } | 309.02* | See above. |
| **13** Chronic Brain Syndrome associated with intoxication | | |
| 13.0 Alcohol intoxication | | |
| 13.00 Without qualifying phrase | — | No exact counterpart in DSM-II. Closest approximation is 291.52* (Alcohol deterioration). |
| 13.01 With psychotic reaction | 291.12*<br>291.32*<br>219.52* } | Korsakov's psychosis (alcoholic)<br>Alcohol paranoid state<br>Alcoholic deterioration* |
| 13.02 With neurotic reaction<br>13.03 With behavioral reaction } | | No exact counterpart in DSM-II. Closest approximation is 291.52* (Alcohol deterioration). |
| 13.1 Drug or poison intoxication, except alcohol | | |
| 13.10 Without qualifying phrase | 309.14* | Non-psychotic OBS with other drug, poison, or systemic intoxication.* **Excludes drug dependence (304). This code and title are used for both the acute and chronic forms of the disorder. Specify drug or poison with additional code (960–979; 981–989).** |
| 13.11 With psychotic reaction | 294.32* | Psychosis with drug or poison intoxication. **Excludes alcoholic psychosis (291). Specify drug or poison with additional code (960–979; 981–989).** |
| 13.12 With neurotic reaction<br>13.13 With behavioral reaction } | 309.14* | See above. |
| **14** Chronic Brain Syndrome associated with trauma | | |
| 14.0 Birth trauma | | |
| 14.00 Without qualifying phrase | 309.22* | Non-psychotic OBS with brain trauma with additional code (764.0, 765.0, 766.0, 767.0, 768.0, 772.0). **Specify type of birth trauma** |
| 14.01 With psychotic reaction | 293.52* | Psychosis with brain trauma. **Specify type of birth trauma with additional code (764.0, 765.0, 766.0, 767.0, 768.0, 77.0).** |

TABLE I (continued)

Comparative Listing of Titles and Codes, DSM-I and DSM-II

| | | |
|---|---|---|
| 14.02 With neurotic reaction<br>14.03 With behavioral reaction | 309.22* | See above. |
| 14.1 Brain Trauma, gross force | | |
| 14.10 Without qualifying phrase | 309.22* | Non-psychotic OBS with brain trauma. Specify type of trauma with additional code (800–804; 850–854). |
| 14.11 With psychotic reaction | 293.52* | Psychosis with brain trauma. Specify type of trauma with additional code (800–804; 850–854). |
| 14.12 With neurotic action<br>14.13 With behavioral reaction | 309.22* | See above. |
| 14.2 Following brain operation | | |
| 14.20 Without qualifying phrase | 309.22* | Non-psychotic OBS with brain trauma. Specify brain operation with additional code (998). |
| 14.21 With psychotic reaction | 293.52* | Psychosis with brain trauma. Specify brain operation with additional code (998). |
| 14.22 With neurotic reaction<br>14.23 With behavioral reaction | 309.22* | See above. |
| 14.3 Following electrical brain trauma | | |
| 14.30 Without qualifying phrase | 309.22* | See above. Specify type of trauma with additional code (994.8). |
| 14.31 With psychotic reaction | 293.52* | Psychosis with brain trauma. Specify type of trauma with additional code (994.8). |
| 14.32 With neurotic reaction<br>14.33 With behavioral reaction | 309.22* | See above. |
| 14.4 Following irradiational brain trauma | | |
| 14.40 Without qualifying phrase | 309.22* | Non-psychotic OBS with brain trauma. Specify type of trauma with additional code (990). |
| 14.41 With psychotic reaction | 293.52* | Psychosis with brain trauma. Specify type of trauma with additional code (990). |

Table I (continued)

Comparative Listing of Titles and Codes, DSM-I and DSM-II

| | | |
|---|---|---|
| 14.42 With neurotic reaction<br>14.43 With behavioral reaction | 309.22* | See above. |
| 14.5 Following other trauma | | |
| 14.50 Without qualifying phrase | 309.22* | Non-psychotic OBS with brain trauma. Specify type of trauma with additional code. |
| 14.51 With psychotic reaction | 293.52* | Psychosis with brain trauma. Specify type of trauma with additional code. |
| 14.52 With neurotic reaction<br>14.53 With behavioral reaction | 309.22* | See above. |
| 15 Chronic Brain Syndrome associated with circulatory disturbance | | |
| 15.0 With cerebral arteriosclerosis | | |
| 15.00 Without qualifying phrase | 309.32* | Non-psychotic OBS with circulatory disturbance. Specify cerebral arteriosclerosis with additional code (437). |
| 15.01 With psychotic reaction | 293.02* | Psychosis with cerebral arteriosclerosis |
| 15.02 With neurotic reaction<br>15.03 With behavioral reaction | 309.32* | See above. |
| 15.1 With circulatory disturbance other than cerebral arteriosclerosis | | |
| 15.10 Without qualifying phrase | 309.32* | See above. Specify other circulatory disturbance with additional code 393–436; 438–458). |
| 15.11 With psychotic reaction | 293.12* | Psychosis with other cerebrovascular disturbance. Specify disturbance with additional code (393–436; 438–458). |
| 15.12 With neurotic reaction<br>15.13 With behavioral reaction | 309.32* | See above. |
| 16 Chronic Brain Syndrome associated with convulsive disorder | | |

TABLE I (continued)

Comparative Listing of Titles and Codes, DSM-I and DSM-II

| | | |
|---|---|---|
| 16.00 | Without qualifying phrase | 309.42* | Non-psychotic OBS with epilepsy |
| 16.01 | With psychotic reaction | 293.22* | Psychosis with epilepsy |
| 16.02 | With neurotic reaction | 309.42* | See above. |
| 16.03 | With behavioral reaction | | |
| 17 | Chronic Brain Syndrome associated with disturbance of metabolism, growth, or nutrition | | |
| 17.1 | With senile brain disease | | |
| 17.10 | Without qualifying phrase | 290.02* | Non-psychotic OBS with senile or presenile brain disease |
| 17.11 | With psychotic reaction | | Senile dementia |
| 17.12 | With neurotic reaction | 309.62* | See above. |
| 17.13 | With behavioral reaction | | |
| 17.2 | Presenile brain disease | | |
| 17.20 | Without qualifying phrase | 309.62* | Non-psychotic OBS with senile or presenile brain disease |
| 17.21 | With psychotic reaction | 290.12* | Presenile dementia |
| 17.22 | With neurotic reaction | 309.62* | See above. |
| 17.23 | With behavioral reaction | | |
| 17.3 | With other disturbance of metabolism, etc., except presenile brain disease | | |
| 17.30 | Without qualifying phrase | 309.52* | Non-psychotic OBS with disturbance of metabolism, growth, or nutrition. Specify disturbance with additional code (240–279). |
| 17.31 | With psychotic reaction | 294.02* | Psychosis with endocrine disorder. Specify disorder with additional code (240–258). |
| | | 294.12* | Psychosis with metabolic or nutritional disorder. Specify disorder with additional code (260–279). |
| 17.32 | With neurotic reaction | 309.52* | See above. |
| 17.33 | With behavioral reaction | | |

## Table I (continued)
### Comparative Listing of Titles and Codes, DSM-I and DSM-II

| | Title | Code | Description |
|---|---|---|---|
| 18 | Chronic Brain Syndrome associated with new growth | | |
| 18.0 | With intracranial neoplasm | | |
| 18.00 | Without qualifying phrase | 309.72* | Non-psychotic OBS with intracranial neoplasm |
| 18.01 | With psychotic reaction | 293.32* | Psychosis with intracranial neoplasm |
| 18.02 | With neurotic reaction | 309.72* | See above. |
| 18.03 | With behavioral reaction | | |
| 19 | Chronic Brain Syndrome associated with diseases of unknown or uncertain cause; chronic brain syndrome of unknown or unspecified cause | | |
| 19.0 | Multiple sclerosis | | |
| 19.00 | Without qualifying phrase | 309.82* | Non-psychotic OBS with degenerative disease of CNS. Specify multiple sclerosis with additional code (340). |
| 19.01 | With psychotic reaction | 293.42* | Psychosis with degenerative disease of CNS. Specify multiple sclerosis with additional code (340). |
| 19.02 | With neurotic reaction | 309.82* | See above. |
| 19.03 | With behavioral reaction | | |
| 19.1 | Huntington's chorea | | |
| 19.10 | Without qualifying phrase | 309.82* | Non-psychotic OBS with degenerative disease of CNS. Specify Huntington's chorea with additional code (331.0). |
| 19.11 | With psychotic reaction | 293.42* | Psychosis with degenerative disease of the CNS. Specify Huntington's chorea as additional code (331.0). |
| 19.12 | With neurotic reaction | 309.82* | See above. |
| 19.13 | With behavioral reaction | | |
| 19.2 | Pick's disease | | |
| 19.20 | Without qualifying phrase | 309.62* | Non-psychotic OBS with senile or presenile brain disease |
| 19.21 | With psychotic reaction | 290.12* | Presenile dementia |
| 19.22 | With neurotic reaction | 309.62* | See above. |
| 19.23 | Without qualifying reaction | | |

## TABLE I (continued)
### Comparative Listing of Titles and Codes, DSM-I and DSM-II

| | | |
|---|---|---|
| 19.3 Other diseases of unknown or uncertain cause | | |
| 19.30 Without qualifying phrase | 309.92* | Non-psychotic OBS with other [and unspecified] physical condition. **Specify condition when known.** |
| 19.31 With psychotic reaction | 294.82* | Psychosis associated with other and undiagnosed physical condition. **Specify condition when known.** |
| 19.32 With neurotic reaction } 19.33 With behavioral reaction | 309.92* | **See above.** |
| 19.4 Chronic brain syndrome of unknown or unspecified cause | | |
| 19.40 Without qualifying phrase | 309.92* | **See above.** |
| 19.41 With psychotic reaction | { 293.92* 294.82* | Psychosis with other [and unspecified] cerebral condition / Psychosis with other and undiagnosed physical condition |
| 19.42 With neurotic reaction } 19.43 With behavioral reaction | 309.92* | **See above.** |
| 20–24 PSYCHOTIC DISORDERS | 295–298 | Psychoses not attributed to physical conditions listed previously |
| 20 Involutional Psychotic Reaction | { 296.00 297.10 | Involutional melancholia / Involutional paranoid state |
| 21 Affective Reactions | | |
| 21.0 Manic depressive reaction, manic type | 296.10 | Manic-depressive illness, manic type |
| 21.1 Manic depressive reaction, depressed type | 296.20 | Manic-depressive illness, depressed type. **Includes "Endogenous depression."** |
| 21.2 Manic depressive reaction, other | { 296.30 [296.80] 296.90 | Manic-depressive illness, circular type / Other major affective disorder / Unspecified major affective disorder] |
| 21.3 Psychotic depressive reaction | 298.00 | Psychotic depressive reaction |
| 22 Schizophrenic Reactions | 295 | Schizophrenia |
| 22.0 Schizophrenic reaction, simple type | 295.00 | Schizophrenia, simple type |
| 22.1 Schizophrenic reaction, hebephrenic type | 295.10 | Schizophrenia, hebephrenic type |

## TABLE I (continued)

### Comparative Listing of Titles and Codes, DSM-I and DSM-II

| | | |
|---|---|---|
| 22.2 Schizophrenic reaction, catatonic type | 295.20 | Schizophrenia, catatonic type |
| 22.3 Schizophrenic reaction, paranoid type | 295.30 | Schizophrenia, paranoid type |
| 22.4 Schizophrenic reaction, acute undifferentiated type | 295.40 | Acute schizophrenic episode. Excludes acute schizophrenia of types listed above. |
| 22.5 Schizophrenic reaction, chronic undifferentiated type | { 295.90* | Schizophrenia, chronic undifferentiated type |
| | 295.50 | Schizophrenia, latent type |
| 22.6 Schizophrenic reaction, schizo-affective type | 295.70 | Schizophrenia, schizo-affective type |
| 22.7 Schizophrenic reaction, childhood type | 295.80* | Schizophrenia, childhood type[b] |
| 22.8 Schizophrenic reaction, residual type | 295.60 | Schizophrenia, residue type |
| 22.9 Other and unspecified | 295.99* | Schizophrenia, other [and unspecified] types |
| 23 Paranoid Reactions | 297 | Paranoid states |
| 23.1 Paranoia | 297.00 | Paranoia |
| 23.2 Paranoid state | 297.90 | Other paranoid state |
| 24 Psychotic Reaction Without Clearly Defined Structural Change Other than Above | [299 | Unspecified psychosis] |
| | 298.10 | Reactive excitation] |
| | 298.20 | Reactive confusion] |
| No Matching Codes and Titles | 298.30 | Acute paranoid reaction] |
| | 298.90 | Reactive psychosis, unspecified] |
| 30–39 PSYCHOPHYSIOLOGIC AUTONOMIC AND VISCERAL DISORDERS | 305 | Psychophysiologic disorders |
| 30 Psychophysiologic Skin Reaction | 305.00 | Psychophysiologic skin disorder |
| 31 Psychophysiologic Musculo-skeletal Reaction | 305.10 | Psychophysiologic musculo-skeletal disorder |
| 32 Psychophysiologic Respiratory Reaction | 305.20 | Psychophysiologic respiratory disorder |
| 33 Psychophysiologic Cardiovascular Reaction | 305.30 | Psychophysiologic cardiovascular disorder |

b The code designated as "Schizophrenia, childhood type" is for use in the USA only. ICD code 295.8 is "Schizophrenia, other."

## TABLE I (continued)
### Comparative Listing of Titles and Codes, DSM-I and DSM-II

| DSM-I | | DSM-II |
| --- | --- | --- |
| 34 | Psychophysiologic Hemic and Lymphatic Reaction | 305.40 Psychophysiologic hemic and lymphatic disorder |
| 35 | Psychophysiologic Gastro-intestinal Reaction | 305.50 Psychophysiologic gastro-intestinal disorder |
| 36 | Psychophysiologic Genito-urinary Reaction | 305.60 Psychophysiologic genito-urinary disorder |
| 37 | Psychophysiologic Endocrine Reaction | 305.70 Psychophysiologic endocrine disorder |
| 38 | Psychophysiologic Nervous System Reaction | 300.50 Neurasthenic neurosis |
| 39 | Psychophysiologic Reaction of Organs of special sense | 305.80 Psychophysiologic disorder of organ of special sense |
| | PSYCHONEUROTIC DISORDERS | PSYCHONEUROTIC DISORDERS |
| 40 | Psychoneurotic Reactions | 300 Neuroses |
| | | 300.00 Anxiety neurosis |
| 40.0 | Anxiety reaction | |
| 40.1 | Dissociative reaction | 300.13* Hysterical neurosis, dissociative type* |
| 40.2 | Conversion reaction | 300.13* Hysterical neurosis, conversion type* |
| 40.3 | Phobic reaction | 300.20 Phobic neurosis |
| 40.4 | Obsessive compulsive reaction | 300.30 Obsessive compulsive neurosis |
| 40.5 | Depressive reaction | **300.40** Depressive neurosis |
| | | 300.50 Neurasthenic neurosis |
| | | 300.60 Depersonalization neurosis |
| 40.6 | Psychoneurotic reaction, other | 300.70 Hypochrondriacal neurosis |
| | | 300.80 Other neurosis |
| | | [300.90] Unspecified neurosis] |
| 50–53 | PERSONALITY DISORDERS | 301 Personality disorders |
| 50 | Personality Pattern Disturbance | |
| 50.0 | Inadequate personality | 301.82* Inadequate personality* |
| 50.1 | Schizoid personality | 301.20 Schizoid personality |
| 50.2 | Cyclothymic personality | 301.10 Cyclothymic personality |
| 50.3 | Paranoid personality | 301.00 Paranoid personality |
| 50.4 | Personality pattern disturbance, other | 301.89* Other personality disorders of specified types* |
| 51 | Personality Trait Disturbance | |
| 51.0 | Emotionally unstable personality | 301.50 Hysterical personality |

TABLE I (continued)

Comparative Listing of Titles and Codes, DSM-I and DSM-II

| | | |
|---|---|---|
| 51.1 Passive-aggressive personality* c | 301.81* | Passive-aggressive personality* c |
| 51.2 Compulsive personality | 301.40 | Obsessive-compulsive personality |
| 51.3 Personality trait disturbance, other | 301.89* | Other personality disorders of specified types* |
| 52 Sociopathic Personality Disturbance | | |
| 52.0 Antisocial reaction | 301.70 | Antisocial personality |
| 52.1 Dyssocial reaction | 316.30* | Dyssocial behavior* |
| 52.2 Sexual deviation | [302.90] | Unspecified sexual deviation] |
| | 302.00 | Homosexuality |
| | 302.10 | Fetishism |
| | 302.20 | Pedophilia |
| | 302.30 | Transvestitism |
| | 302.40 | Exhibitionism |
| Detailed subdivisions not contained in DSM-I | 302.50* | Voyeurism* |
| | 302.60* | Sadism* |
| | 302.70* | Masochism* |
| | 302.80 | Other sexual deviation |
| 52.3 Alcoholism (addiction) | 303.90 | Other [and unspecified] Alcoholism. **Excludes alcoholic psychosis (291); acute poisoning by alcohol (980, E860).** |
| | 303.00 | Episodic excessive drinking |
| Detailed subdivisions not contained in DSM-I | 303.10 | Habitual excessive dinking |
| | 303.20 | Alcoholic addiction |
| | 303.90 | Other [and unspecified] alcoholism |
| 52.4 Drug addiction | [304.90] | Unspecified drug dependence] |

c Diagnoses recorded as "Passive aggressive personality, passive dependent type" are now equivalent to 301.89.* "Other personality disorders of specified type."

## TABLE I (continued)
### Comparative Listing of Titles and Codes, DSM-I and DSM-II

| | | |
|---|---|---|
| | 304.00 | Drug dependence, opium, opium alkaloids, and their derivatives |
| | 304.10 | Drug dependence, synthetic analgesics with morphine-like effects |
| | 304.20 | Drug dependence, barbiturates |
| Detailed subdivisions not contained in DSM-I | 304.30 | Drug dependence, other hypnotics and sedatives or "tranquilizers" |
| | 304.40 | Drug dependence, cocaine |
| | 304.50 | Drug dependence, Cannabis sativa (hashish, marijuana) |
| | 304.60 | Drug dependence, other psycho-stimulants |
| | 304.70 | Drug dependence, hallucinogens |
| | 304.80 | Other drug dependence |
| 53 Special Symptom Reaction | 306 | Special symptoms not elsewhere classified |
| 53.0 Learning disturbance | 306.10 | Specific learning disturbance |
| 53.1 Speech disturbance | 306.00 | Speech disturbance |
| 53.2 Enuresis | 306.60 | Enuresis |
| 53.3 Somnambulism | 306.40 | Disorder of Sleep |
| | 306.20 | Tic |
| | 306.30 | Other psychomotor disorder |
| 53.4 Other | 306.50 | Feeding disturbance |
| | 306.70 | Encopresis |
| | 306.80 | Cephalalgia |
| | 306.90 | Other special symptom |
| 54 TRANSIENT SITUATIONAL PERSONALITY DISORDERS | 307* | Transient situational disturbances |
| 54.0 Gross stress reaction | 307.30* | Adjustment reaction of adult life* |
| 54.1 Adult situational reaction | 307.30* | Adjustment reaction of adult life* |
| 54.2 Adjustment reaction of infancy | 307.00* | Adjustment reaction of infancy* |
| 54.3 Adjustment reaction of childhood | 307.10* | Adjustment reaction of childhood* |
| 54.4 Adjustment reaction of adolescence | 307.20* | Adjustment reaction of adolescence* |
| 54.5 Adjustment reaction of late life | 307.40* | Adjustment reaction of late life* |
| 54.6 Other transient situational personality disturbance | | No corresponding diagnosis (Assign another diagnosis 307 category based upon patient's age). |

TABLE I (continued)

Comparative Listing of Titles and Codes, DSM-I and DSM-II

| | | |
|---|---|---|
| **6o–62 MENTAL DEFICIENCY** | **310–315** | **Mental Retardation** |
| **6o** Mental Deficiency (**Familial** or **Hereditary**) | | |
| 60.0 Mild (I.Q. 70–85) | 310.80 | Borderline mental retardation (**I.Q.** 70–85) |
| | 310.80 | Borderline mental retardation (**I.Q.** 68–69) |
| 60.1 Moderate (I.Q. 50–69) | 311.80 | Mild mental retardation (**I.Q.** 52–67) |
| | 312.80 | Moderate mental retardation (**I.Q.** 50–51) |
| | 312.80 | Moderate mental retardation (**I.Q.** 36–49) |
| 60.2 Severe (I.Q. Below 50) | 313.80 | Severe mental retardation (**I.Q.** 20–35) |
| | 314.80 | Profound mental retardation (**I.Q. Below 20**) |
| 60.3 Severity not specified | 315.80 | Unspecified mental retardation |
| **61** Mental Deficiency, Idiopathic | | |
| 61.0 Mild (I.Q. 70–85) | 310.90 | Borderline mental retardation (**I.Q.** 70–85) |
| | 310.90 | Borderline mental retardation (**I.Q.** 68–69) |
| 61.1 Moderate (I.Q. 50–69) | 311.90 | Mild mental retardation (**I.Q.** 52–67) |
| | 312.90 | Moderate mental retardation (**I.Q.** 50–51) |
| | 312.90 | Moderate mental retardation (**I.Q.** 36–49) |
| 61.2 Severe (I.Q. below 50) | 313.90 | Severe mental retardation (**I.Q.** 20–35) |
| | 314.90 | Profound mental retardation (**I.Q. Below 20**) |
| 61.3 Severity not specified | 315.90 | Unspecified mental retardation |

# CHAPTER TWELVE

---

# *Neurosis, Psychosis, and the Borderline States*

---

## *MILTON H. MILLER, M.D.*

FOR MANY YEARS, two standard questions in medical school examinations have been, "Differentiate between psychosis and neurosis" and "Discuss the borderline psychotic states." However, the usefulness of these diagnostic concepts has become increasingly suspect in recent decades. Menninger states, "These old names are wrong labels and have wrong implications. They have become obsolete and hence dangerous." And, indeed, no diagnostic categorization can be expected to be more than a partial approximation, naming, at best, one or another truth regarding the subject and often ignoring or obscuring others. Diagnostic categories are man-made orderings, useful if they point to significant variables, obfuscating if some spurious or irrelevant order is suggested.

In attempting to utilize diagnostic labels for human beings, one confronts another problem. Jung put it this way, "Even if everyone knows how everything in a given person has come about, that person would still be only half-understood." In the same spirit, May commented: "We may know a great deal about a patient from his case record, let us say, and may have a fairly good idea of how other interviewers have described him. But when the patient himself steps in, we often have a sudden, sometimes powerful experience of here-is-a-new-person, an experience that normally carries with it an element of surprise, not in the sense of perplexity or bewilderment but in its etymological sense of being 'taken from above.' This is, of course, in no sense a criticism of one's colleagues' reports. . . . The data we learned about the patient may have been accurate and well worth learning. But the point rather is that the grasping of the being of the other person occurs on a quite different level from our knowledge of specific things about him."

At the same time, however, a 3,000-year record of attempts to categorize mental disorders attests the need for some standards of classification. Certainly, in every other area of medicine, meaningful diagnosis and effective remedy have proven inseparable. The task then is to find a variety of psychiatric nosology that tells more truths about a patient than it implies things that are not true.

Diagnostic categorizations of mental disorder have usually separated conditions with known gross organic precipitants from those that seem rooted in psychological or some subtle, as yet undiagnosable, organic cause. A second variable ordinarily included in diagnostic classification has been an assessment of the seriousness or the magnitude of disruption produced in the life of the person by the disorder. Finally, and especially in recent years, most efforts at the categorization of mental disorder have emphasized the adaptational, the dynamic, the changing and the integrating functions of personality demonstrated as a given individual deals with the opportunities and frustrations of his life.

## NEUROSIS

The term "neurosis" has had differing connotations over the years. At one time, it implied a very severe mental disorder; but at the present time, it suggests a less serious syndrome with a mild to mildly moderate level of psychological pain, anxiety, hyperalertness, and/or withdrawal. The term implies a kind of maladaptation that restricts to some extent the individual's overall judgment, his ability to make good contact with reality, and his capacity to relate effectively with others in the environment.

In the phenomenological sense, the neurotic diagnosis implies that the individual's world of experience is one in which much anxiety and psychological pain will be encountered unless careful precautionary steps are taken. These precautionary steps may be in the nature of avoidance mechanisms or some form of denial or substitution, usually with an accompanying level of discomfort. A diagnosis of neurosis suggests a kind of person who is fundamentally mistrustful of his own general level of competence and basic merit and of the basic friendliness and accepting nature of the environment. Thus the psychoneurotic individual is conceived of as an individual who lives in a world in which there is real and immediate danger of encountering painful anxiety and/or humiliating self-doubt. He must thus direct an inordinate part of his activities in such a way as to avoid these dangers. As a consequence, he may deny himself the hearty and spontaneous experience of life events and may complain that he is missing many of the good things life has to offer.

In the current American Psychiatric Association classification of mental disorders, a number of psychoneurotic reactions are listed, each naming one predominant kind of defensive pattern operative in the general framework just described. The subdivisions include anxiety reaction, dissociative reaction, conversion reaction, phobic reaction, obsessive-compulsive reaction, depressive reaction (mild to moderate), and psychoneurotic reaction.

## PSYCHOSIS

Contrasting terms to neurosis have been normalcy and psychosis. The latter term has been reserved ordinarily for mental disorders characterized by pervasive and profound alterations of mood, disorganization of thinking, and an associated withdrawal from the real world into a world of highly personalized preoccupations. Menninger has enumerated five classical syndromes that accompany the majority of psychotic patterns: "(1) Pervasive feelings of sadness, guilt, despondence, and hopelessness, with convictions of inadequacy, incompetence, unworthiness, or wickedness; (2) more or less continuous erratic, disorganized excitement, accompanied by a corresponding excess of verbal and motor production and emotional heightening, elation, excitement, irrascibility, etc.; (3) autistic regression and self-absorption, silliness, mannerisms of speech and behavior, bizarre delusional ideation, irrelevancy and incoherence of speech, posturing, and gross (apparent) indifference to social expectations; (4) delusional preoccupation with one or several themes, usually persecutory in trend and usually accompanied by defensiveness, resentment, suspiciousness, grandiosity, condescension, irrascibility, etc.; (5) confused, delirious states with disorientation, bewilderment, amnesia, confabulation, and sometimes hallucinations and hyperactivity."

All these symptoms are to be viewed in the context of active adaptations of personality in the face of disorganizing threat.

## SHIFTING PATTERNS OF NEUROSIS AND PSYCHOSIS

Ordinarily, in thinking of the circumstances leading to the emergence of psychosis, an image of mounting anxiety and progressively more disabling symptomatology comes to mind. However, all combinations and permutations of symptomatology are seen in clinical experience. Thus, one encounters individuals with neurotic symptoms who are somehow unable to work or relate effectively and whose overall life patterns are very disrupted. At the other end of the continuum, one not infrequently sees overtly psychotic individuals with delusions, hallucinations, or disorganized symptomatic patterns and profound periods of anxiety who are, nevertheless, highly successful and creative people. This is, of course, not the rule but tends to be the exception.

The same is true of anxiety. On occasion, one sees extremely severe, disabling, sustained anxiety in neurotic patients and, at the other extreme, individuals who develop pervasive psychotic symptomatology with little or no evidence of accompanying anxiety or stress.

Joan was one of monozygotic twins born to a South Dakota middle class family. She was the more passive of the two girls in personality structure but adjusted well within the family unit, school, and community to all outward appearances until she left home and went to college. At that time, the family decision was to split up the twin girls. Joan went west to a California college, and her sister went east.

Within a few days after arriving at college, Joan became extremely homesick, began to cry uncontrollably, and experienced the first gross anxiety of her life. She sought medical help at the school infirmary because she feared she was having a heart attack. She weathered this crisis and, ten days after arriving on the campus, met Bob. Within two weeks, she had become his steady. Theirs was an idyllic four-year college romance. All other friends, teachers, learning experiences, etc., were subsidiary to this relationship. They ate most of their meals together, took many classes in common, and were, in a sense, not only sweethearts and lovers but best friends.

They were married one week following graduation and moved to a small suburban community in Pennsylvania. Two children were born during the first four years of their married life. They remained devoted to each other, yet each was successful in his own respective areas of community activity and family life.

In 1950, unexpectedly, Bob was called to active duty as a pilot during the Korean War. Joan was very shaken and, during the weeks before his departure, cried a great deal, experienced much anxiety, but finally pulled herself together and bravely bid her husband farewell.

Within a few days after his departure, however, Joan began to experience extreme anxiety and tearfulness. In an effort to retain her self-control, she composed a schedule of projects for herself, including a three-month project of refinishing furniture in the home, a several-month project of sewing for the children, and a project of sewing new clothes for herself in anticipation of her husband's arrival home. She threw herself tirelessly into the furniture-sanding project, using all her spare time and working late into the evening in this effort.

About two months after Bob's departure, she became concerned about heart palpitations and entered the local hospital for a three-day period of tests and examinations. The results of the hospital examinations were "essentially negative," and she was placed on mild sedatives. Her apprehension continued, however, and she began to supplement the sedatives with alcohol. She was particularly agitated during the late evening hours, and her sleeping patterns were disrupted by early morning awakening, bad dreams, and preoccupation with night noises in the house.

Four months after her husband's departure, she precipitously took her children back to the family home in South Dakota and remained with her family for a month. She then returned to Pennsylvania with the children, despite the objections of her parents, who were very concerned over her restlessness. The next several months saw a steady increase in the level of her agitation, attested to by a number of contacts with her physician, two late evening calls to the police department because she felt the house was being invaded, a progressive loss of weight, and the total abandonment of her work projects. By the seventh month after her husband's departure, Joan's condition had deteriorated alarmingly. She cried a great deal, was extremely anxious, felt certain that she would die of a heart attack before her husband returned, and at times would sit mutely for hours, giving little attention to her home or children. Her mother was called by the physician, and ultimately she came to help Joan.

Seven and a half months after Bob's departure, efforts were undertaken by the family physician through the American Red Cross to return Bob to his family. Joan handled this newest development in a peculiar way. There was a sudden demonstration of an outward calm. She insisted on completing dental work before her husband's return, explaining to her mother, "I want to be perfect when he comes back." The family dentist told her that five teeth needed filling and was startled when she asked him to remove these teeth. He declined her urgent request, and Joan began a search of the community to find a dentist who would remove all of the "decayed and rotten teeth." She was ultimately successful.

Immediately afterward, she became frantically agitated, alternately fearful and elated, grandiose, and delusional. She stated that she was the Virgin Mary awaiting the return of God. She was floridly psychotic and actively suicidal when her husband returned.

Joan required two years of continuous hospitalization, and she continued to receive out-patient psychotherapeutic help for some years after release from the hospital and return to her husband and children.

Joan was, then, within an eight-month period of time in her life, a normal wife and mother, anxious and edgy, obsessively preoccupied, phobic, somatically fixated, dependent on alcohol, suicidally depressed, and, finally, delusional. She was, to all appearances, normal, neurotic, and psychotic within a relatively short interval. Of course, not all neurotic or psychotic patterns are characterized by this level of fluidity and change.

## BORDERLINE STATES

Compounding the effort to describe inclusive categories of neurotic versus psychotic individuals is the clinical picture presented by a large group of patients who have been variously labeled "borderline psychotics," "psychoneurotic schizophrenics," "ambulatory psychotics," etc. The unifying characteristic in such patients, who vary considerably in terms of individual complaints, is the tendency toward the episodic emergence of very profound psychotic behavioral patterns during times of stress, often with relatively prompt restitution of a less disordered neurotic or even normal clinical picture when stress is relieved.

Hoch and Polatin described such patients as suffering pseudoneurotic mental disorders. This has been an appealing concept to many clinicians, since, among other things, it explained why some apparently neurotic patients proved to be quite refractory to the kinds of psychological therapies that ordinarily were useful in treating neurotic patients. Miller has described the special diagnostic problems posed for the family physician by these patients who present fluctuating psychological pictures, pointing out the tendency of doctors to misinterpret bizarre somatic complaints that have emerged in the face of life stress and thus reflect organismic rather than organ disorder. Knight, in 1938, offered a logistic conceptualization to aid in understanding patients who may present rapidly shifting or fluid symptomatology:

> "I believe it was Freud who used the metaphor of a retreating army to illuminate the mixed clinical picture of libidinal regression. I should like to borrow the metaphor and elaborate for the purpose of illuminating ego-defensive operations. Various segments or detachments of the retreating army may make a stand and conduct holding or delaying operations at various points where the terrain lends itself to such operations, while the main retreating forces may have retired much further to the rear. The defensive operation of the more forward detachments would, thus, actually protect the bulk of the army from disaster; but these forward detachments may not be able to hold their positions and may have to retreat at any time in the face of superior might. On the other hand, the main army may be able to regroup itself, receive reinforcements, or gain new leadership and recapture its morale. In that event, the forward positions may hold long enough for the main forces to move forward to, or even well beyond, the stubbornly defended outposts."

## MALADAPTIVE LIFE STYLE

Another rather complex group of patients who do not fit neatly into any neurosis, psychosis, or borderline state diagnostic categories are individuals who have evolved a rather frozen, often relatively anxiety-free, style of life that encompasses maladaptive or even psychotic ways of interrelating with their everyday life in a seemingly conflict-free way.

For example, one encounters the obsessive, excessively serious, humorless, and compulsive child who grows up to be precisely the same kind of adult. Another fixed pattern is that of the chronically depressed, pessimistic individual who seems to discover constant fulfillment of his disappointing expectations. However, these disappointments are not additive in their consequences, and the patient's depression does not mount but sustains the same magnitude over the years. Such individuals are never happy, but only rarely do they become actually suicidal. Similarly, one may observe patients (usually women) whose life style is characterized by a heavy predominance of hysterical features relentlessly sustained from little girlhood into senescence.

Many of these individuals who have developed highly stylized, conflict-free, maladaptive ways of living have proven to be most refractory to efforts to help them achieve symptomatic relief or modification of behavior patterns.

## THE TREND IN CLASSIFICATIONS

The task of delineating diagnostic categories that will serve more to illuminate than to obscure the mental status and life situation of a given individual is by no means a simple one. Certainly, the trend in thinking about psychiatric diagnosis in recent years has been to stress the dynamic and fluctuating patterns rather than the entity itself. Thus, the American Psychiatric Association classification no longer speaks of neurotic and psychotic states but rather of neurotic and psychotic *reactions*.

Menninger, Mayman, and Pruyser in their book, *The Vital Balance*, propose a unified view of mental illness that dispenses with labels and substitutes a method of diagnosis in which all disturbed states are seen as sequential stages in a single and reversible process. They propose five levels of personality disorganization, extending from a first level marked by "slight but definite impairment of smooth adaptive control, a slight but definite disturbance of organization, a slight but definite failure in coping" and extending to a fifth level of disorganization, "an extremity beyond psychosis in the obsolescent sense, the abandonment of the will to live." These authors feel that it is now time to abandon earlier concepts of psychosis, borderline schizophrenias, neurosis, etc., in favor of a definition of personality that emphasizes personality's special role as system regulator and maintainer of organization and homeostasis. They state: "Threatened disorganization evokes tension which may exceed the powers of the habitual 'normal' coping devices of the organism. Various special devices are called upon in the emergency to maintain the equilibrium, perhaps at a lower level of total functioning, with the best possible facade and with a minimum of discomfort."

This manner of thinking about mental disorder may be more consistent with other medical and biological measures, for example, the functional impairment and capacity scale in heart disease, and may anticipate the nature of psychiatric nomenclature in the future.

## REFERENCES

Hoch, P. H., and Polatin, P. Pseudoneurotic forms of schizophrenia. Psychiat. Quart., 23: 248, 1949.

Knight, R. P. Latent psychosis. Bull. Menninger Clin., 3: 97, 1939.

May, R., Angel, E., and Ellenberger, H. *Existence*. Basic Books, New York, 1958.

Menninger, K., Mayman, M., and Pruyser, P. *The Vital Balance*. Viking Press, New York, 1963.

Miller, M. H. The borderline psychotic patient. Ann. Intern. Med., 46: 736, 1957.

# AREA B

*Assessment of Children*

# CHAPTER THIRTEEN

# *Psychological Testing of Children*

## *ANNE ANASTASI, A.B., Ph.D.*

THE PRINCIPAL focus of this chapter is on the evaluation of psychological tests and the interpretation of test results. Although the major types of ability and personality tests currently available for use with children are described, no comprehensive survey of such instruments has been undertaken. Besides requiring far more space than is available, such a survey would be quickly outdated.

Because of the rapidity with which new tests are developed and revised editions of existing tests are prepared, the test user needs to be familiar with sources of information about tests. The most important of these is undoubtedly the series of *Mental Measurements Yearbooks* edited by Buros.[1] These yearbooks cover nearly all commercially available psychological, educational, and vocational tests published in English. While the coverage is especially complete for paper-and-pencil tests, major performance tests are also included. Each yearbook surveys tests published during a specified period, thus supplementing rather than replacing earlier yearbooks in the series. The *Sixth Mental Measurements Yearbook*, for example, includes tests published between 1959 and 1964. Beginning in 1938, the yearbooks have appeared at intervals of two to six years; understandably, these intervals have tended to lengthen as the volume of published tests has increased. Besides giving such routine information as price, length, general content, and age or other characteristics of persons for whom each test is designed, the yearbooks include critical reviews of the tests by one or more experts.

A comprehensive bibliography covering all published tests currently available in English-speaking countries is provided by *Tests in Print*, also

---

[1] All references cited by name are listed alphabetically at the end of this section. Tests are arranged in Table I, p. 239, and alphabetized by title.

edited by Buros. Information on recent tests published in the years following the last available *Mental Measurements Yearbook* can be found in several other sources. Short abstracts of new tests are regularly included in *Psychological Abstracts*. Reviews of current tests appear in a number of journals, such as the *Journal of Counseling Psychology* and the *Personnel and Guidance Journal*. For more detailed treatment of many of the problems discussed in this chapter, together with more extensive coverage of specific tests, the reader is referred to current textbooks on psychological testing, such as those by Anastasi and Cronbach. An excellent introduction to the use of tests in counseling and clinical practice is provided by Goldman.

## ESSENTIAL TECHNICAL CONSIDERATIONS IN TEST EVALUATION

In evaluating the effectiveness and applicability of any psychological test, we need to ask certain basic questions regarding its reliability, validity, and norms. The information required to answer these questions should be provided in the test manual. When the necessary data are too extensive to fit conveniently into the manual itself, they may be presented in a technical supplement or published in other sources to which references should be given in the manual. This chapter provides an introduction to the principal concepts and techniques required for test evaluation and for the proper interpretation of test results. In this connection, reference is also made to the *Standards for Educational and Psychological Tests and Manuals*, a guide for test evaluation prepared and officially adopted by the American Psychological Association. First published in 1954, this guide was revised in 1966. It presents a summary of desirable practices in test construction, based upon the current state of knowledge in the field.

### RELIABILITY

Test reliability refers essentially to the consistency of scores obtained by the same individual on different occasions. Random fluctuations in test scores may result from several kinds of "chance errors" in test administration, scoring, condition of subject, or selection of items constituting a particular form of a test. Different methods for computing test reliability are influenced by one or more of these types of chance errors. Consequently, not all reliability coefficients have the same meaning. To interpret a reliability coefficient, one must know by what procedure it was found.

The principal procedures for computing test reliability include retest, equivalent form, split-half, and Kuder-Richardson techniques (for references, see Anastasi, 1961, Ch. 5). All these techniques report reliability in the form of a correlation coefficient between independently obtained measures. *Retest reliability* is the correlation between scores on the identical test administered at different times. The interval may vary from a few days to several months. Obviously, this correlation shows degree of temporal stability from one test session to another. When parallel forms of a test are administered on the two occasions, the correlation between them represents *equivalent form reliability*. This measure is influenced by both temporal fluctuation and differences in subjects' responses to the two sets of items constituting the parallel forms.

The latter differences alone are measured by *split-half reliability*. The usual way to compute split-half reliability is to find each person's score on the odd-numbered items and on the even-numbered items. These two scores are then correlated and the reliability of the whole test estimated from this correlation of half tests. Like split-half reliability, *Kuder-Richardson reliability* is derived from a single test session. Being ultimately based on inter-item consistency, however, it is also influenced by homogeneity of test content. For example, in a test consisting of 50 vocabulary and 50 arithmetic items, the Kuder-Richardson reliability would be lower than in a test composed of 100 items of either type alone. Any discrepancy between subjects' performance on the verbal and numerical items would lower the Kuder-Richardson reliability of the first test.

Mention should also be made of *examiner* and *scorer reliability*. Most tests provide such highly standardized procedures for administration and scoring as to leave little room for examiner variance. This is particularly true of group tests designed for mass administration and machine-scoring. However, in most infant and preschool tests and in other individual instruments for clinical testing, there is more opportunity for the examiner's judgment to operate. Under these conditions, some data on examiner reliability should be reported in the form of a correlation between the results obtained by different examiners with the same subjects or through some other statistical index. Certain types of tests, such as projective personality tests, present special problems of scorer reliability. Whenever qualitative judgment is required in scoring, a sample of papers should be independently rescored by another examiner and the degree of agreement determined.

In interpreting the reliability coefficients reported in test manuals, certain precautions should be observed. The first relates to the subjects used in finding reliability. All correlation coefficients are affected by the range of scores or variability within the group. The greater the variability, the higher will be the correlation. Since tests are usually employed to differentiate among individuals within fairly narrow age levels, reliability coefficients should be reported separately for each level. This procedure also makes it possible to see whether the test is equally reliable at all ages. A single reliability coefficient found on a highly heterogeneous standardization sample, on the other hand, may be misleadingly high.

It should also be noted that reliability is directly related to test length. An abbreviated form of a test can thus be expected to show some loss in reliability. Similarly, subtests or parts of a test will have lower reliability than the complete test. If subtest scores are to be separately analyzed, as in a trait profile, reliability coefficients should be reported for each subtest.

With school-age children and older subjects, most well constructed tests of ability yield reliability coefficients clustering around .90. For infant and preschool tests, however, reliabilities tend to run lower. Among the conditions contributing to such low reliability are distractability, shyness, negativism, and other factors interfering with test administration. Reliability may be further lowered by scoring irregularities, since many test responses of the very young child consist of fleeting movements that leave no permanent record. Despite these difficulties, some of the more carefully developed infant tests, such as the Cattell Infant Intelligence Scale and the California First Year Mental Scale, yield split-half reliabilities between .70 and .95 after the first three months of age (for references, see Anastasi, 1961, Ch. 11).

## VALIDITY

The most important property of a test is undoubtedly its validity. The concept of validity concerns the relationships of a test to other data about the individual. An analysis of such relationships makes it possible to state what the test measures and how well it does so. It is meaningless to report that a test is valid or possesses high validity, without indicating the purpose for which it has the specified validity. For the selection of appropriate tests, as well as for the proper interpretation of test scores, full information is required regarding the procedures followed in estimating test validity.

In accordance with current usage, validity may be classified into three categories—namely, content validity, criterion-related validity, and construct validity. *Content validity* is most often used with educational achievement tests, although it also underlies the construction of certain personality inventories. This type of validity concerns primarily the adequacy with which the test items sample the content area to be measured. An achievement test, for example, may be checked against relevant course syllabi, textbooks, and the judgment of subject matter specialists. Coverage of essential topics in the correct proportions is the major consideration.

In *criterion-related validity*, test scores are correlated or otherwise compared with an outside criterion. The criterion is an independent index of those behavioral charcteristics that the test is designed to measure. For example, a test of emotional instability may be validated by administering it to individuals known to have exhibited neurotic behavior, as well as to a normal control group. If the test differentiates significantly between the two groups, it is said to have concurrent validity for this criterion of emotional instability. Or an intelligence test may be administered to school children upon admittance to the first grade and their scores correlated with their educational achievement at the end of the school year. This correlation would represent the test's predictive validity against an academic criterion.

*Construct validity* is a very broad concept, covering a variety of validation procedures. It is concerned primarily with an experimental verification of hypotheses regarding the psychological traits or theoretical constructs that account for performance on the test. The most frequent application of this validation procedure is found in factorial validity. Thus, if a factor of spatial visualization has been identified through factor analysis, the correlation of a test with this factor is its factorial validity. Essentially, this correlation indicates the extent to which the test measures an ability common to a group of similar tests which sample a relatively unified area of performance. Almost any experimental evidence regarding the correlates of test scores would contribute to construct validity. If, for example, a test is designed to detect anxiety, it could be administered to children before and after an anxiety-provoking experience, such as carrying out arithmetic computations under distracting and stressful circumstances. If the anxiety test scores rise significantly on the retest, the initial hypothesis regarding the test is confirmed. Still another example of construct validation is provided by the age differentiation technique in terms of which most infant and preschool intelligence tests are validated. It is part of the construct of intelligence that this function improves with age in childhood. Therefore, individual test items, as well as total test scores, are checked against each child's age to see whether performance does in fact show progressive improvement with advancing age.

## Norms

On any test, a raw score, such as the number of items correct or the time required to complete a problem, is meaningless until compared with a norm or average performance. Psychological tests have no pre-established standards of passing or failing. Each new test must be administered to a large, representative sample of the population for which it is designed. The scores obtained by this group provide the test norms. Test manuals should always include such norms, together with information on the size and nature of the normative sample. The test user will then be able to evaluate the adequacy of the published norms and their applicability to the subjects he plans to test. Owing to differences in the characteristics of the samples on which different tests have been standardized, the same individual may appear to perform much better on one test than on another, although both tests presumably measure the same trait. This is one of the reasons why test scores should always be accompanied by the name of the test with which they were obtained.

An individual's position in relation to the norms may be expressed in several ways. Basically, however, all such derived scores in current use fall into three categories: ratio I.Q.s, percentile ranks, and standard scores. The traditional intelligence quotient, or *ratio I.Q.*, is found by dividing a child's mental age by his chronological age. Theoretically, mental age represents the age of normal children whose test performance the child equals. Thus, if a 10-year-old does as well on a test as the average 12-year-old, his mental age is 12, regardless of his chronological age. If, now, we divide his mental age (M.A. = 12) by his chronological age (C.A. = 10) and multiply by 100 to avoid decimals, we obtain an I.Q. of 120.

Despite its popular appeal, the traditional ratio I.Q. has serious technical deficiencies and has generally been replaced by more suitable measures. Few tests today have retained the ratio I.Q. Such I.Q.s can be properly employed only with age scales specifically constructed to yield comparable I.Q.s at different age levels. The essential requirement for such comparability is that the extent of individual differences, or variability, of I.Q.s shall remain constant at all ages. In statistical terms, this means that the standard deviation $(\sigma)$ of the I.Q. distribution must be equal at all ages. This is a very difficult condition to impose upon the test constructor and has never been completely met in practice. When the condition is not met, an I.Q. of 115 at age 10, for example, might be equivalent to an I.Q. of 140 at age 12, since both might fall at a distance of one standard deviation from the means of their respective age distributions.

A second major type of score is the *percentile rank*, which indicates the percentage of cases in the normative sample falling at or below the subject's score. Percentiles are not to be confused with the ordinary percentage score representing the percentage of items correctly completed. The percentile rank refers to persons, not items. Although satisfactory for crude evaluative purposes, percentiles do not provide a precise measure because of marked inequalities in size of units. Owing to the greater clustering of cases at the center of the range and the decrease in number of persons as the extremes are approached, percentile units near the center (i.e., 50) cover a much smaller distance than do those near the ends of the scale (i.e., 0 and 100). These size discrepancies can be seen by reference to the bottom scale of Figure 1. While percentile ranks correctly indicate the relative position of different individuals, they do not accurately reflect differences in amount of a trait.

The most precise measure is provided by *standard scores* and their various derivatives. In all such scores, the individual's distance from the mean is expressed in standard deviation units $(\sigma)$. Thus if the normative sample has a mean of 38 and a standard deviation of 4, a raw score of 34 would correspond to a standard score of −1.00. Such simple standard scores, utilizing the original $\sigma$ of the distribution as their unit, are called z scores (see Figure 1). Several available derivatives of z scores provide more convenient scales, which avoid the use of negative numbers. An example is the T score, representing standard scores in a normal distribution with a mean of 50 and a $\sigma$ of 10. As can be seen in Figure 1, a T score of 40 corresponds to a z score of −1.00. Another type of standard score is the stanine, which utilizes a single-digit scale ranging from 1 to 9 and having a mean of 5 and a $\sigma$ of 2. Because there are so few cases at the extremes of

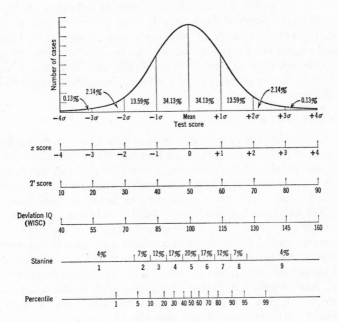

FIGURE 1. *Varieties of test norms.*

the distribution, stanines 9 and 1 represent larger units than the other stanines, extending from +1.75 $\sigma$ to the upper end of the distribution and from −1.75 $\sigma$ to the lower end of the distribution, respectively (see Figure 1).

Of particular interest is the deviation I.Q., currently employed in the Wechsler Intelligence Scale for Children (WISC), the Stanford-Binet, and other recently developed intelligence scales. WISC deviation I.Q.s are actually standard scores with a mean of 100 and a $\sigma$ of 15. Thus a child with a deviation I.Q. of 100 falls exactly at the mean of his age group. Deviation I.Q.s of 115 and 85 correspond to 1 $\sigma$ above and 1 $\sigma$ below the mean, respectively; a deviation I.Q. of 130 falls 2 $\sigma$'s above the mean, and so forth. In the 1960 form of the Stanford-Binet, the earlier ratio I.Q. was replaced with a deviation I.Q. having a mean of 100 and a $\sigma$ of 16. The latter value was chosen because it approximates most closely the standard deviations of the ratio I.Q.s found with the earlier forms of the Stanford-Binet and thus permits continuity of interpretation among forms.

## PROBLEMS OF TEST ADMINISTRATION

Each type of test and each age level presents its own characteristic problems of test administration. The proper use and interpretation of most personality tests, for example, require extensive psychological training and experience. To qualify for the administration of individual intelligence tests such as the Stanford-Binet, as well as for any infant and preschool testing, the examiner needs an intensive course of specialized training. Practical suggestions for testing infants and preschool children are given by Goodenough (Ch. 20) and by Watson (Ch. 12). Terman and Merrill (pp. 46–58) discuss general procedures for the individual examination of older children.

## STANDARDIZED PROCEDURE

Test scores are of little or no value unless obtained under uniform testing conditions. Failure on the part of inadequately trained examiners to realize the susceptibility of test performance to even slight variations in conditions is one of the chief causes of inaccurate test results. The need for uniformity applies not only to such obvious factors as time limits and wording of directions but also to more subtle conditions. In certain tests, for example, performance may be appreciably affected by the rate at which the examiner speaks, where he places emphasis, and when he pauses in his presentation, his facial expression while pronouncing key words that might reveal the correct answer, and the position of materials to be used by the subject. Any unusual condition of the subject, such as illness, fatigue, or excessive worry, may also affect test scores adversely. Even the nature of the subject's activities immediately preceding a test must be taken into account. In two studies with the Goodenough Draw-a-Man Test of Intelligence, the mean scores obtained by school children were significantly higher after an emotionally gratifying experience than after a neutral or depressing activity (for references, see Anastasi, 1961, p. 63).

## EMOTIONAL AND MOTIVATIONAL FACTORS

Underlying the use of all ability tests is the assumption that the individual is "doing his best." Consequently, if conditions are to be kept uniform in this regard, every person should be motivated to put forth his maximum efforts on the test. Among the emotional and motivational conditions found to affect test performance are praise, reproof, ridicule, knowledge of results, presence of observers, competition and rivalry, and various conditions evoking feelings of frustration, failure, and discouragement. With preschool children, experience with adults outside the immediate family is likely to affect performance on individually administered intelligence tests. When a group of children were examined with the Stanford-Binet upon entering kindergarten and retested with a parallel form two months later, a significant mean rise in I.Q. was found (for references, see Anastasi, 1961, pp. 49–50). This gain was attributed largely to the effect of the kindergarten experience in reducing shyness, fear of strangers, and other attitudes inhibiting oral speech. Support for this hypothesis was found in the fact that the mean test-retest improvement was only 4.7 per cent in manipulatory tasks, as contrasted with 11.2 per cent in the oral items.

The nature and effects of test anxiety among school children have also been extensively investigated, particularly by Sarason and his associates at Yale. There is evidence that children vary widely and consistently in their susceptibility to anxiety while taking tests and that high degrees of anxiety have a deleterious effect on test performance.

It is likely that motivational factors in general are especially influential in the test performance of certain types of children, such as preschool children, emotionally maladjusted children, ethnic minorities, and members of lower socioeconomic classes. Juvenile delinquents may approach tests with unfavorable attitudes, such as suspiciousness, insecurity, fear, or cynical indifference. Specific kinds of past experiences in the lives of some children may influence their test performance adversely. Because of early failure and frustration experienced in school work, for example, they may have developed feelings of hostility and inferiority toward any academic task, which most intelligence tests resemble.

## RAPPORT AND EXAMINER VARIABLES

An important aspect of the examiner's function, particularly in the administration of individual clinical instruments, is the establishment of rapport. Essentially, this is a process for arousing interest and eliciting cooperation from the subject so that the objectives of the test will be most fully attained. In the case of an ability test, good rapport means that the subject performs to his fullest capacity. On a self-report personality inventory, it means frank and accurate reporting of personal problems and difficulties rather than choosing answers to create a desired impression. Whether the latter tendency can ever be eliminated through proper rapport is doubtful; but it can at least be reduced.

The specific techniques for establishing rapport vary not only with the objectives of the test but also with the age and other characteristics of the subjects. In testing preschool children, for example, special factors to be considered include shyness with strangers, distractability, and negativism. A friendly, cheerful, and relaxed manner on the part of the examiner helps to reassure the child. The shy, timid child may need more time to become familiar with his surroundings before testing is begun. For this reason, it is better for the examiner not to be too demonstrative at the outset and to wait until the child is ready to make the first contact. At this age level, test sessions should be brief and the tasks should be varied and intrinsically interesting to the child. The testing should be presented as a game and the child's curiosity aroused before each new task is introduced. Some flexibility of procedure is necessary at these ages because of possible refusals, loss of interest, and other instances of negativism.

In the testing of children in the primary grades, the game appeal is still the most effective way of arousing interest in the test. The older school child, on the other hand, can usually be motivated by an appeal to his competitive spirit and his desire to do well on all kinds of tests. It should be kept in mind, however, that every test presents an implied threat to the individual's prestige. Some reassurance is therefore needed at the outset. The examiner should explain, for example, that no one is expected to finish or to get all items right. It should also be remembered that all these procedures for establishing rapport may need to be modified when testing children with special problems or backgrounds.

That test performance, particularly on individually administered intelligence tests and on projective tests, is significantly affected by examiner and situational variables is evidenced in a number of studies surveyed by Sarason (1954) and by Masling (1959, 1960). Among the significant examiner variables are age, sex, professional and social status, appearance, and such behavioral characteristics as self-confidence, aggressiveness, responsiveness, and social warmth. Situational variables are illustrated by the place where the test is given—school, clinic, hospital, prison, psychology laboratory—, the expectations and attitudes established by the way the forthcoming test is presented to the subject, and the nature of specific instructions. The effect of all such conditions can be best conceptualized in terms of interaction between subject variables and examiner or situational variables. For example, such factors as ego-involving instructions and examiner's appearance have a different influence on subjects with different personality characteristics.

## PRACTICE, COACHING, AND TEST SOPHISTICATION

It has been repeatedly demonstrated that scores on intelligence tests can be appreciably improved by practice and coaching (for references, see Anastasi, 1961, pp. 54–57). The effects differ widely, however, with the nature of the test and with the age, ability, and previous experience of the subjects. With certain tests, repetition of the identical form within a few weeks may make the retest score meaningless because of recall of previous responses by the subject. Even retesting with alternate forms generally produces some improvement over short time intervals. In such cases, some adjustment in score should be made to allow for practice effect. General test sophistication must also be considered in interpreting test performance. The child who has had extensive test-taking experience will usually score higher than the one who is taking his first test.

With regard to the effect of coaching on test scores, a fundamental question pertains to the breadth of the resulting improvement. Is the improvement limited to the specific test items, or does it extend to the broader area of behavior that the test is designed to predict? The answer to this question represents the difference between coaching and education. Rote memorization of the correct responses to a list of vocabulary test items can markedly raise a child's score on that particular test without appreciably improving his general appreciation of word meanings. This would be coaching in the narrow sense and would reduce the predictive validity of the test for that child. On the other hand, a year of carefully selected reading, accompanied by a discussion of word meanings, would improve *both* the child's vocabulary test score and his general verbal comprehension, thereby leaving unaltered the test's validity.

## INTELLIGENCE TESTS

### Testing the School Child

It was for the school child that intelligence tests were first designed. In 1904 the French psychologist Alfred Binet was appointed to a commission to study the problem of retardation among Paris school children. Although for many years he had been exploring different approaches to the measurement of intelligence, it was to meet this practical demand that Binet, in collaboration with Simon, developed the first Binet-Simon Scale. Partly because they originated in an educational context and partly because they are commonly validated against academic criteria, intelligence tests measure primarily those abilities essential for academic achievement. For this reason, they are often more accurately described as tests of scholastic aptitude.

Typically, intelligence tests provide a global score, such as an I.Q., purported to indicate the individual's general intellectual level. They include a wide variety of tasks, on the assumption that through "the sinking of shafts at critical points" all important intellectual functions will be sampled. In actual practice, however, intelligence tests are overweighted with certain functions, usually verbal aptitudes, and may completely omit others.

The Binet-Simon tests were translated and adapted for use in many countries. In America the most notable adaptation is the Stanford-Binet, developed by Terman and his associates at Stanford University. The latest revision of this test, published in 1960, is widely used as a clinical instrument. Extending from the two-year level to three superior-adult levels of increasing difficulty, the test yields a mental age and a deviation I.Q. Objects, pictures, and drawings are used largely at the younger ages; printed verbal and numerical materials occur increasingly at the older age levels. Oral questions and answers are common throughout the scale.

Another individual test commonly used in the clinical examination of children is the Wechsler Intelligence Scale for Children (WISC). This scale provides separate verbal and performance I.Q.s based on different sets of tests, as well as a full scale I.Q.

Both the Stanford-Binet and the WISC are individual tests, which must be administered to each subject singly and which require a highly trained examiner. They are essentially clinical instruments for the intensive study of individuals. In addition to the quantitative scores, such tests provide opportunities for observing work methods, social and emotional reactions, and other qualitative aspects of the child's behavior. Group tests, on the other hand, are designed for rapid mass testing. They not

Table I

*Psychological Tests*

This table contains a list of all tests cited in this article. It is *not* to be construed as a comprehensive or recommended list; each test was mentioned only to illustrate a category. For a more complete coverage of available tests and for evaluations of each test, the reader should refer to current textbooks of psychological testing and especially to the *Mental Measurements Yearbooks* cited in the appended references section. It should be noted that the names of tests do not provide a reliable guide to the functions measured by the tests or the uses to which they may be put.

| Title | Major Category[a] | Author(s) | Publisher | Date(s) | Age or Grade Range | MMY[b] |
|---|---|---|---|---|---|---|
| The Blacky Pictures: A Technique for the Exploration of Personality Dynamics | P | G. S. Blum | Psychodynamic Instruments, Ann Arbor | 1950–1962 | 5 yrs. and over | 6, 204 |
| California Test of Personality, 1953 Revision | P | L. P. Thorpe, W. W. Clark, and E. W. Tiegs | California Test Bureau, Monterey, Calif. | 1953 | Kindergarten to adult, in 5 levels | 5, 38 |
| Cattell Infant Intelligence Scale | C | Psyche Cattell | Psychological Corporation, New York | 1940–1960 | 3–30 mos. | 3, 281 |
| Children's Apperception Test (CAT) | P | L. Bellak and Sonya S. Bellak | C. P. S. Co., New York | 1949–1961 | 3–10 yrs. | 6, 206 |
| Differential Aptitude Tests (DAT), Forms L and M, 1963 Edition | C | G. K. Bennett, H. G. Seashore, and A. G. Wesman | Psychological Corporation, New York | 1963 | Grades 8–12 | 6, 767 |
| Gesell Developmental Schedules | C | A. Gesell et al. | Psychological Corporation, New York | 1925–1949 | 4 wks.–6 yrs. | 6, 522 |
| IPAT Children's Personality Questionnaire | P | R. B. Porter and R. B. Cattell | Institute of Personality and Ability Testing, Champaign, Ill. | 1959–1960 | 8–12 yrs. | 6, 122 |
| Jr.-Sr. High School Personality Questionnaire | P | R. B. Cattell and H. Beloff | Institute of Personality and Ability Testing, Champaign, Ill. | 1953–1964 | 12–18 yrs. | 6, 131 |

| Test | C/P[a] | Author | Publisher | Date | Range | Volume, entry[b] |
|---|---|---|---|---|---|---|
| Metropolitan Readiness Tests | C | Gertrude H. Hildreth, Nellie L. Griffiths, and Mary E. McGauvran | Harcourt, Brace & World, New York | 1965 | Grade 1 entrance | (4, 570) |
| Mooney Problem Check List: 1950 Revision | P | R. L. Mooney and L. V. Gordon | Psychological Corporation, New York | 1950 | Grades 7–16 and adult, in 4 levels | 6, 145 |
| Rorschach | P | Hermann Rorschach | Hans Huber (U.S. distributor: Grune & Stratton, New York) | 1921–1960 | Ames et al. norms, 2–16 yrs. | 6, 237 |
| Rosenzweig Picture Frustration Study: Form for Children | P | S. Rosenzweig | S. Rosenzweig, St Louis, Mo. | 1948–1960 | 4–13 yrs. | 6, 238 |
| Sequential Tests of Educational Progress (STEP) | C | Cooperative Test Division, Educational Testing Service | Educational Testing Service, Princeton | 1956–1963 | Grades 4–14, in 4 levels | 6, 25 |
| SRA Junior Inventory, Form S | P | H. H. Remmers and R. H. Bauernfeind | Science Research Associates, Chicago | 1957 | Grades 4–8 | 5, 104 |
| SRA Youth Inventory, Form S | P | H. H. Remmers, B. Shimberg, and A. J. Drucker | Science Research Associates, Chicago | 1956 | Grades 9–12 | 6, 170 |
| Stanford-Binet Intelligence Scale, Form L–M | C | L. M. Terman and Maud A. Merrill | Houghton Mifflin, Boston | 1960 | 2 yrs. and over | 6, 536 |
| Thematic Apperception Test (TAT) | P | H. A. Murray | Harvard University Press, Cambridge, Mass. | 1943 | 4 yrs. and over | 6, 245 |
| Wechsler Intelligence Scale for Children (WISC) | C | D. Wechsler | Psychological Corporation, New York | 1949 | 5–15 yrs. | 6, 540 |

[a] Test designed to measure primarily cognitive (C) or personality (P) traits.

[b] Volume and entry number in *Mental Measurements Yearbooks* where latest information and critical reviews of the test can be located, including references to earlier reviews. When the latest edition of a test has not yet been reviewed in MMY, reference to earlier edition is given in parentheses.

only enable a single examiner to test a large group during one session but are also relatively easy to administer and score. Group tests, of course, may also be administered individually. They are useful when a crude index of intellectual level suffices or when facilities for more intensive testing are unavailable. A number of well constructed and carefully standardized group tests have been developed for use from the first grade to college (for references, see Anastasi, 1961, Ch. 9).

Mention should also be made of nonlanguage and performance tests (for references, see Anastasi, 1961, Ch. 10). Comprising both individual and group tests, these instruments were designed especially for children with hearing, speech, or reading disabilities; the foreign-speaking; and the culturally disadvantaged. Other tests have been adapted for use with the blind or the orthopedically handicapped. Performance tests may also be employed as a supplement to such tests as the Stanford-Binet to provide a fuller picture of the child's intelligence. The inclusion of performance tests in the WISC illustrates this approach.

## PRESCHOOL AND INFANT TESTING

Tests applicable prior to school entrance are conventionally subdivided into infant tests, designed for the first 18 months of life, and preschool tests, covering the ages of 18 to 60 months (for references, see Anastasi, 1961, Ch. 11). The two levels require different procedures of test administration. The infant must be tested while lying down or supported on someone's lap. Speech is of little or no use in giving test instructions, although the child's own speech development provides relevant data. Most of the tests at this level are actually controlled observations of sensorimotor development, as illustrated by the infant's ability to lift his head, turn over, reach for and grasp objects, or follow a moving object with his eyes. At the preschool level, on the other hand, the child can walk, sit at a table, use his hands in manipulating test objects, and communicate by language. At these ages the child is also much more responsive to the examiner as a person, while for the infant the examiner serves chiefly as a means of providing stimulus objects. Preschool testing is a more highly interpersonal process, a fact that increases both its difficulties and its opportunities for observation.

One of the most extensive investigations of infant and preschool behavior is that initiated by Gesell at the Yale Clinic of Child Development. After longitudinal studies of the normal course of development in the human child, Gesell and his associates prepared the Gesell Developmental Schedules (Gesell and Amatruda). These schedules are essentially a refinement and elaboration of the qualitative observations routinely made by pediatricians. Although a few may be properly described as tests, most of the items in the Gesell Schedules are based on observations of the child's everyday behavior. Data are obtained through direct observation of the child's responses to standard toys and other stimulus objects and are supplemented by information provided by the mother. The schedules yield separate scores indicating the level of the child's behavioral development, relative to the norms, in four areas: motor, adaptive, language, and personal-social behavior. While extending from the age of 4 weeks to 6 years, the Gesell Schedules typify the approach usually followed in infant testing. Items from these schedules have been incorporated in several other scales designed for the infant level.

A more highly test-oriented approach is illustrated by the Cattell Infant Intelligence Scale. Extending from 2 to 30 months, this scale was developed as a downward extension of the Stanford-Binet and also includes some items from the Gesell Schedules. If a child passes any test at the 30-month level, testing is continued with the Stanford-Binet, beginning at the 3-year level. Between 22 and 30 months, Stanford-Binet items are intermingled with other items in the Cattell scale. A continuous scale is thus provided from the age of 2 months to the adult level.

A few scales have been developed for the preschool level only. In procedure and content, they have much in common with the lower levels of the Stanford-Binet and of performance tests (for references, see Anastasi, 1961, pp. 289–300).

## LONG-TERM PREDICTION

Theoretically, if a child maintains the same status relative to his age norms, his I.Q. should remain the same at all ages. Empirically, the I.Q. has in fact proved to be fairly constant for most children. In a follow-up of the Stanford-Binet standardization sample, for example, tests administered between the ages of 2 and 5½ years correlated .65 with retests after 10 years and .59 with retests after 25 years (Bradway, Thompson, and Cravens). Other longitudinal studies with preschool and school-age children have yielded similar results (Bayley; Cattell; Honzik, Macfarlane, and Allen). On the other hand, scores on infant tests obtained prior to the age of 18 months are virtually useless in predicting intellectual level in late childhood. The correlations between these tests and I.Q.s during school ages are usually zero or low negative (Bayley). In their present form, infant tests find their chief usefulness in the early detection of severe retardation resulting from organic causes of either hereditary or environmental origin. Among the reasons for the negligible correlations between infant tests and later intellectual performance is the heavy reliance of infant tests on sensorimotor functions. These functions bear little relation to the verbal and other abstract functions that constitute intelligence in later years.

Even in later childhood, however, the I.Q. cannot be regarded as rigidly fixed. A major reason for the usual stability of the I.Q. is that most children remain in the same type of environment throughout their development. Another is that their previous experiences determine their level of attainment in prerequisite intellectual skills needed for subsequent learning. An early deficiency thus becomes cumulative unless corrected by special remedial programs.

Longitudinal studies have demonstrated that in individual cases large upward or downward shifts in I.Q. may occur, depending on the child's subsequent experiences. In one extensive follow-up project, individual I.Q. changes of as much as 50 points were found (Honzik, Macfarlane, and Allen). Between the ages of 6 and 18 years, when retest correlations are usually high, 59 per cent of the cases changed 15 or more I.Q. points, 37 per cent changed 20 or more points, and 9 per cent changed 30 or more points. These changes were not random or erratic but exhibited consistent upward or downward trends over several years. Large shifts in I.Q., moreover, were usually associated with cultural milieu and emotional climate of the home. Children in disadvantaged environments tended to lose with age, while those in superior environments tended to gain in relation to test norms. Changes in I.Q. have also been found to be related to certain personality characteristics of the child, such as emotional independence and achievement motivation (Sontag, Baker, and Nelson).

## APTITUDE TESTS

Shortly after the first intelligence tests came into general use, their limited coverage became apparent and efforts were made to construct tests of special aptitudes to fill the gaps (for references, see Anastasi, 1961, Chs. 14 and 15). Since most intelligence tests concentrate on the more abstract verbal and numerical abilities, a particular need was felt for tests measuring the more concrete and practical intellectual skills. Accordingly, mechanical aptitudes were among the first for which special tests were developed. Tests of clerical aptitude, measuring chiefly perceptual speed and accuracy, and tests of musical and artistic aptitudes followed. Many of these tests are particularly useful in vocational counseling.

After the application of factor analysis to research on the composition of intelligence, it was recognized that intelligence tests themselves cover a limited number of relatively independent aptitudes. As a result of these findings, many recently developed intelligence tests report separate scores on verbal and numerical abilities, either in place of a total composite score or in addition to it. Another related finding is that different intelligence tests may measure different combinations of abilities. Nonlanguage and performance tests, for example, are often heavily loaded with spatial and perceptual abilities; some intelligence tests are almost entirely measures of verbal comprehension; still others combine verbal and numerical functions. Even a single scale, such as the Stanford-Binet, may measure different functions at different age levels (for references, see Anastasi, 1961, pp. 204–205). The diversity of functions measured by different intelligence tests provides one of the reasons for insisting that every test score be accompanied by the name of the test from which it was derived. An unlabeled I.Q. may be quite misleading.

The most direct effect of factor analysis on psychological testing has been the development of multiple aptitude batteries. Rather than yielding a single global score, such as an I.Q., these batteries provide a profile of scores on separate tests, most of which correspond more or less closely to traits identified through factor analysis. Several batteries of this type are now commercially available (for references, see Anastasi, 1961, Ch. 13).

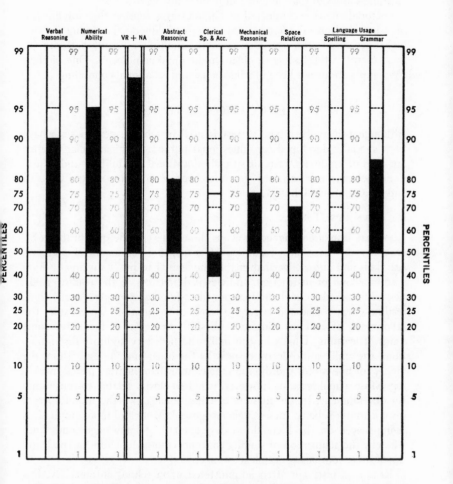

FIGURE 2. *Profile of scores on the Differential Aptitude Tests.* Vertical bars *show distance above or below norm on each test. Percentiles are spaced to correspond to equal distances in a normal distribution.* (*Reproduced by permission. Copyright 1963, The Psychological Corporation.*)

An example is the Differential Aptitude Tests (DAT), for which the largest amount of validity information has so far been gathered. The DAT yields scores in eight abilities: verbal reasoning, numerical ability, abstract reasoning, clerical speed and accuracy, mechanical reasoning, space relations, spelling, and grammar. In Figure 2 is a profile chart showing the DAT scores of a junior high school boy whose greatest strengths are in verbal reasoning and numerical ability. The score in the third column, based on the sum of these two scores, gives a single index of scholastic aptitude similar to that obtained from most intelligence tests.

Factorial analyses conducted at different ages suggest that intelligence may be relatively undifferentiated in early childhood, becoming increasingly specialized with age. Consequently, multiple aptitude batteries are most useful in the testing of older children and adolescents. One of their chief applications has been in educational and vocational counseling.

## EDUCATIONAL TESTS

Although nearly every type of test is used in schools, certain tests have been specially developed for educational purposes. Of particular interest are tests of readiness, tests of special educational disabilities, and educational achievement batteries (for references, see Anastasi, 1961, Chs. 16 and 17; Cronbach, Ch. 13).

### READINESS TESTS

Readiness tests are designed to assess the child's specific qualifications for school work. Essentially, readiness refers to the development of prerequisite skills and knowledge that enable the learner to profit maximally from a certain kind of instruction. Individual differences in the reading readiness of first-grade school children provide a familiar example. At one time, readiness was considered largely in terms of maturation. To be sure, the attainment of certain minimum physical prerequisites facilitates some kinds of learning. Unless he can make the necessary auditory discriminations, the child cannot learn to speak by the usual procedures; without the ability for fine motor coordination, he cannot manipulate a pencil in writing. Most school learning, however, is not so closely related to sensorimotor development. In the mastery of educational tasks, the importance of prior learning is being increasingly recognized. More and more emphasis is being placed on the hierarchical development of knowledges and skills, whereby the acquisition of simpler concepts equips the child for the learning of more complex concepts at any age.

Readiness tests are often administered upon school entrance. At this level, they have much in common with intelligence tests for children in the primary grades. In the readiness tests, however, special emphasis is placed on those abilities found to be most important in learning to read; some attention is also given to the prerequisites of numerical thinking and to the sensorimotor control required in learning to write. Among the specific functions covered are visual and auditory discrimination, motor control, verbal comprehension, vocabulary, quantitative concepts, and general information. A well-known example is the Metropolitan Readiness Tests. Comprising six subtests, this test yields a total readiness score for first-grade work.

## TESTS OF SPECIAL EDUCATIONAL DISABILITIES

At all educational levels, tests are available to aid in the diagnosis and remedial training of children with special educational disabilities, principally in reading and arithmetic. Since the treatment of reading disabilities is of special interest to psychologists, reading tests are probably more often used in clinical examinations than any other type of educational test. Reading tests are customarily classified as survey and diagnostic tests. Survey tests indicate the general level of the child's achievement in reading. They usually provide a single score, although some differentiate between speed of reading and comprehension. These tests serve largely to screen children in need of remedial instruction.

Diagnostic tests are designed to analyze the child's performance and identify specific sources of difficulty. Although all such tests yield more than one score, they range from group tests providing little more information than a survey test to intensive clinical programs for individual case studies. Some include detailed checklists of specific types of errors. The individual batteries frequently employ apparatus, such as tachistoscopes for controlling rate of exposure of printed matter and ophthalmographs for photographing the child's eye movements while he reads. In dealing with reading disabilities, information about possible emotional difficulties and a complete case history are also essential.

## EDUCATIONAL ACHIEVEMENT BATTERIES

Of all tests used in schools, the most numerous are undoubtedly achievement tests, the principal aim of which is to measure the effects of a course of study. Some are comprehensive achievement batteries, designed to assess the pupil's over-all progress in school work; others test for mastery of specific subjects or courses. In keeping with modern curricular trends, many achievement tests today measure the attainment of relatively broad educational goals cutting across different subject matter specialties.

An outstanding example is the Sequential Tests of Educational Progress (STEP). These tests are available at several levels extending from the fourth grade of elementary school to the sophomore year of college. At each level, there are seven tests, including multiple choice tests in reading, writing, mathematics, science, social studies, and listening, as well as an essay writing test. Although the need for specific knowledge in particular fields was recognized in constructing STEP items, major emphasis was placed upon the application of learned skills to the solution of new problems.

Achievement tests have traditionally been contrasted with intelligence tests. From one angle, the difference between them stems from the degree of uniformity of relevant antecedent learning. Achievement tests measure the effects of relatively standardized sets of experiences, such as a course in fourth-grade arithmetic or American history. By contrast, intelligence test performance reflects the cumulative influence of a multiplicity of experiences of daily life. Thus, achievement tests may be said to measure the effects of learning under partially known and controlled conditions, whereas intelligence tests measure the effects of learning under relatively uncontrolled and unknown conditions.

In this connection we should guard against the erroneous assumption that achievement tests are concerned with the effects of learning, while intelligence tests tap innate capacities independently of learning. Although this misconception was prevalent in the early days of psychological testing, it is now recognized that all tests measure current developed abilities, which inevitably reflect the influence of prior learning. It should also be added that several recently developed achievement tests cover relatively broad and unstandardized educational experiences, thus overlapping traditional achievement and intelligence tests. A particularly good example is provided by the previously cited STEP. Stressing broad intellectual skills, STEP resembles intelligence tests more closely than it does the older type of achievement tests with their emphasis on recall of specific factual content.

## CREATIVITY TESTS

The growing recognition that creative talent is not synonymous with academic intelligence, as measured by traditional intelligence tests, has been accompanied by vigorous efforts to develop specialized tests of creativity. An extensive investigation by Guilford and his associates, utilizing the techniques of factor analysis, has produced a variety of new types of tests as well as a theoretical schema for integrating creative functions into a broadened conception of intelligence.

Several tests designed in the Guilford project have been adapted for use with children. The research of Getzels and Jackson with high school students and of Torrance with younger children has utilized such creativity tests and has provided suggestive data on the concomitants of creative achievement in childhood. The tests involve, principally, various aspects of fluency, flexibility, and originality, which Guilford subsumes under the heading of "divergent thinking." Described as "the kind of thinking that goes off in different directions," divergent thinking is contrasted with convergent thinking, which leads to a single right answer determined by the given facts.

An example of a test that is effective with young children is the "Improvements" test, in which the child is given toys—such as nurse kit, fire truck, and dog—and is asked to think of ways for changing each toy so it would be "more fun to play with." Thinking up unusual uses for common objects—such as a tin can, a brick, or a paper clip—illustrates another technique that has proved applicable over a wide age range.

## PERSONALITY TESTS

Although the number of available personality tests is large and their techniques varied and often ingenious, most of these tests must still be regarded as experimental instruments (for references, see Anastasi, 1961, Chs. 18–21). In comparison with tests of ability, personality tests, on the whole, are much less satisfactory with regard to such technical properties as norms, reliability, and validity. For these reasons, any information obtained from personality tests should be verified and supplemented from other sources, such as interviews with the child and his associates, direct observations of behavior in natural situations, and case history material.

The personality tests employed most widely in examining children are of two major types: self-report inventories and projective techniques. In addition, a wide variety of other procedures has been devised, such as situational tests, objective laboratory-type tests, measures of self concepts, and techniques for exploring personal constructs (for references, see Anastasi, 1961, Ch. 21). In their present state of development, however, these instruments are suitable chiefly for research purposes rather than for routine operational use.

### Self-Report Inventories

Self-report inventories originated in an attempt to standardize the psychiatric interview and to provide norms for evaluating the individual's responses. Essentially, they consist of a series of questions, which the individual answers about himself, concerning emotional problems, worries, and other deviant behavior. The technique was later extended to the investigation of individual differences in nonpathological traits, such as interests, motives, values, and interpersonal traits.

Several inventories designed for children and adolescents are basically checklists of personal problems constructed on the principle of content validation. In other words, the questions pertain directly to the information the examiner wishes to elicit about the child's feelings and actions. The responses are thus taken at face value as an indication of the behavior to which they refer. A clear example of this approach is the Mooney Problem Check List. Designed chiefly to identify problems for group discussion or for individual counseling, this checklist drew its items from written statements of problems submitted by about four thousand high school students as well as from case records, counseling interviews, and similar sources. The checklist is available in junior high school, high school, college, and adult levels. The problem areas covered in the junior high school form include health and physical development; school, home, and family;

money, work, and the future; boy and girl relations; relations to people in general; and self-centered concerns. Other examples of this type of inventory include the SRA Junior Inventory, for grades 4 to 8; the SRA Youth Inventory, for grades 9 to 12; and the California Test of Personality, available in five levels extending from kindergarten to college. Several inventories for the detection of anxiety in children are also available (see, for example, Sarason et al.).

A somewhat different approach is illustrated by the IPAT Children's Personality Questionnaire and the Jr.-Sr. High School Personality Questionnaire. Using items selected by factor analysis, these inventories yield scores in a number of different personality traits. In general, questions are used in these inventories not as a means of eliciting specific information but as verbal stimuli, the responses to which are scored in terms of their empirical correlates. Each item retained in the questionnaire serves as an indicator of a cluster of interrelated behavior tendencies. While the basic methodology is promising, the two questionnaires actually developed are limited in their usefulness by the low reliability of several trait scores and by insufficient validity data. Personality inventories today find their major usefulness in screening and identifying children in need of further investigation.

## PROJECTIVE TECHNIQUES

The chief characteristic of projective techniques is that the subject is assigned an unstructured task, which permits an almost unlimited variety of possible responses. The test stimuli are typically vague and equivocal, and the instructions are brief and general. These techniques are based on the hypothesis that the way the individual perceives and interprets the test materials or structures the situation reflects basic characteristics of his personality. The test stimuli thus serve as a sort of screen on which the subject projects his own ideas.

One of the most widely used projective techniques is the Rorschach, in which the subject is shown a set of bilaterally symmetrical inkblots and asked to tell what he sees or what the blot could represent. Although for many years the Rorschach was used principally with adults, Ames and her co-workers (1952 and 1959) at the Yale Institute of Child Development have published Rorschach norms for children between the ages of 2 and 10 years and for adolescents between the ages of 10 and 17. The availability of these norms puts the interpretation of child Rorschach responses on a sounder and more objective basis.

A somewhat more structured test is the Children's Apperception Test (CAT). This test is an adaptation of the Thematic Apperception Test (TAT), developed by Murray. In the CAT, however, pictures of animals are substituted for pictures of people, on the assumption that children respond more readily to animal characters. The animals are portrayed in typically human situations in the anthropomorphic style common in children's storybooks. The pictures are designed to evoke fantasies relating to problems of feeding and other oral activity, sibling rivalry, parent-child relations, aggression, toilet-training, and other childhood experiences. Another example is the Blacky Pictures, a set of cartoons showing a small dog, his parents, and a sibling (see Figure 3). Based on a psychoanalytic theory of psychosexual development, the cartoons depict situations suggesting various types of sexual conflicts. Still another type of picture test is illustrated by the Rosenzweig Picture-Frustration Study. Derived from the author's theory of frustration and aggression, this test presents a series of cartoons in which one person frustrates another. One of these cartoons, from the children's form, is shown in Figure 4. In the blank space provided, the child writes what the frustrated person would reply.

Drawings, toy tests, and other play techniques represent another application of projective methods. Because children are more limited than adults in their facility for verbal communication, these nonverbal procedures are commonly used in the examination of children. Although almost every art medium, technique, and type of subject matter has been investigated in the search for significant diagnostic clues, special attention has centered on drawings of the human figure. Play and dramatic objects—such as puppets, dolls, toys, and miniatures—have also been widely utilized in projective examinations. The objects are usually selected because of their associative value, often including dolls representing adults and children, bathroom and kitchen fixtures, and other household furnishings. Play with such articles is expected to reveal the child's attitudes toward his family, sibling rivalries, fears, aggressions, conflicts, and the like.

When evaluated as standardized tests, most projective techniques have

FIGURE 3. *Sample item from the Blacky Pictures. (Reproduced by permission of Psychodynamic Instruments, Ann Arbor, Michigan.)*

FIGURE 4. *Sample item from Rosenzweig Picture-Frustration Study, Form for Children. (Reproduced by permission of Saul Rosenzweig.)*

fared quite poorly. In their present state of development, these techniques should be regarded not as tests but as aids to the clinical interviewer. They can serve a useful function, particularly with children, in evoking communication regarding emotional problems whose discussion the individual might otherwise eschew for a variety of reasons. The effectiveness of any one projective technique, however, cannot be evaluated independently of the skill of the clinician using it.

## CULTURAL DIFFERENTIALS IN TEST PERFORMANCE

In the measurement of both abilities and personality traits, tests yield significant mean differences between children reared in different cultures or subcultures, such as socioeconomic levels, urban and rural environments, and minority groups (for references, see Anastasi, 1958, Chs. 15–17). For this reason, several attempts have been made to develop so-called culture-free or culture-fair tests. The earliest culture-free tests were designed on the premise that hereditary intellectual potential could be measured independently of the impact of cultural experiences. The individual's behavior was thought to be overlaid with a sort of cultural veneer, whose penetration became the goal of culture-free testing.

It is now generally recognized, however, that hereditary and environmental factors interact at all stages in the organism's development and that their effects are inextricably intertwined in the resulting behavior. For man, culture permeates nearly all environmental contacts and thus affects all behavior development. Since psychological tests are essentially samples of behavior, cultural influences will, and should, be reflected in test performance. It is, therefore, futile to try to devise tests that are *free* from cultural influences. The present objective of cross-cultural testing is, rather, to construct tests that presuppose only experiences *common* to different cultures. Available culture-fair tests eliminate one or more parameters along which specific cultures differ, such as language, reading, speed, or culturally loaded content.

No existing test is universally applicable or equally fair to all cultures. Although less restricted than other tests, culture-fair tests are never completely unrestricted in their cultural reference. Any test tends to favor individuals from the culture in which it was developed. The mere use of paper and pencil or the presentation of abstract tasks having no immediate practical significance favors some cultural groups and handicaps others. Cultural differences in emotional and motivational factors may also influence test performance. Examples include intrinsic interest of test content for the individual, rapport with the examiner (who may be a member of another culture), drive to do well on tests, desire to excel others, and past habits of solving problems individually or cooperatively.

A fundamental question pertains to the validity of culture-fair tests. Whatever the purpose of testing, one should be able to generalize beyond the test itself. Tests are administered so that conclusions may be drawn about what the individual will do in *other* situations. Therefore, whether the elimination of cultural differentials from a test will raise or lower its validity for any group depends on the breadth of the cultural differentials. For example, if a test item requires the interpretation of a proverb familiar to children in one culture but not in another, its inclusion would probably lower the validity of this test against most criteria. On the other hand, if one group performs more poorly than another on certain items because of inadequate linguistic facility, the inclusion of these items would not reduce validity of the test for most purposes. In this case, the same condition that lowered the test score would also handicap the child in his educational progress and other activities of daily life. Similarly, slow work habits, emotional insecurity, low achievement drive, lack of interest in abstract problems, and many other culturally linked conditions affecting test scores are also likely to influence broad areas of criterion behavior.

In the testing of children from varied cultural backgrounds, no universal culture-fair test is suitable. Culture fairness in testing depends on the elimination of relevant cultural parameters. A nonlanguage test may reduce cultural handicap for children from one culture but increase it for children from another culture. Available culture-fair tests, moreover, differ among themselves in the extent to which they measure different abilities. When spatial content is substituted for verbal content, for example, the nature of the abilities sampled by the test may thereby be altered drastically. An I.Q. on one such test may be largely a measure of abstract reasoning, but on another it may depend chiefly on spatial and perceptual abilities. Whether or not cultural differentials should be eliminated from a test depends upon the effect their elimination will have on the test's validity for specific purposes. Cultural handicaps tend to be self-perpetuating and cumulative unless eliminated by special remedial programs. That they *can* be overcome has been widely demonstrated by the many compensatory educational programs for culturally disadvantaged children initiated in America during the 1960's (for references, see Bloom et al.); but the use of tests that fail to detect the handicap is no solution.

## REFERENCES

American Psychological Association. *Standards for Educational and Psychological Tests and Manuals.* American Psychological Association, Washington, 1966.

Ames, L. B., Learned, J., Metraux, R. W., and Walker, R. N. *Child Rorschach Responses: Developmental Trends from Two to Ten Years.* Hoeber Medical Division, Harper & Row, New York, 1952.

Ames, L. B., Metraux, R. W., and Walker, R. N. *Adolescent Rorschach Responses: Developmental Trends from Ten to Sixteen Years.* Hoeber Medical Division, Harper & Row, New York, 1959.

Anastasi, A. *Differential Psychology*, ed. 3. Macmillan, New York, 1958.

Anastasi, A. *Psychological Testing*, ed. 2. Macmillan, New York, 1961.

Bayley, N. On the growth of intelligence. Amer. Psychologist, 10: 805, 1955.

Bloom, B. S., Davis, A., and Hess, R. *Compensatory Education for Cultural Deprivation.* Holt, Rinehart and Winston, New York, 1965.

Bradway, K. P., Thompson, C. W., and Cravens, R. B. Preschool IQ's after twenty-five years. J. Educ. Psychol., 49: 278, 1958.

Buros, O. K., editor. *Tests in Print.* Gryphon Press, Highland Park, N. J., 1961.

Buros, O. K., editor. *The Sixth Mental Measurements Yearbook.* Gryphon Press, Highland Park, N. J., 1965 (see also earlier yearbooks in this series).

Cattell, P. *The Measurement of Intelligence of Infants and Young Children.* Psychological Corporation, New York, 1947.

Cronbach, L. J. *Essentials of Psychological Testing*, ed. 2. Harper & Row, New York, 1960.

Gesell, A., and Amatruda, C. S. *Developmental Diagnosis*, ed. 2. Hoeber Medical Division, Harper & Row, New York, 1947.

Getzels, J. W., and Jackson, P. W. *Creativity and Intelligence: Explorations with Gifted Students.* Wiley, New York, 1962.

Goldman, L. *Using Tests in Counseling.* Appleton-Century-Crofts, New York, 1961.

Goodenough, F. L. *Mental Testing.* Holt, Rinehart and Winston, New York, 1949.

Guilford, J. P. Three faces of intellect. Amer. Psychologist, 14: 469, 1959.

Honzik, M. P., Macfarlane, J. W., and Allen, L. The stability of mental test performance between two and eighteen years. J. Exp. Educ., 17: 309, 1948.

Masling, J. The effects of warm and cold interaction on the administration and scoring of an intelligence test. J. Consult. Psychol., 23: 336, 1959.

Masling, J. The influence of situational and interpersonal variables in projective testing. Psychol. Bull., 57: 65, 1960.

Sarason, S. B. *The Clinical Interaction with Special Reference to the Rorschach.* Harper & Row, New York, 1954.

Sarason, S. B., Davidson, K. S., Lighthall, F. F., Waite, R. R., and Ruebush, B. K. *Anxiety in Elementary School Children.* Wiley, New York, 1960.

Sontag, L. W., Baker, C. T., and Nelson, V. L. Mental growth and personality development: a longitudinal study. Monogr. Soc. Res. Child Develop., 23: No. 2, 1958.

Terman, L. M., and Merrill, M. A. *Stanford-Binet Intelligence Scale: Manual for the Third Revision, Form L-M.* Houghton Mifflin, Boston, 1960.

Torrance, E. P. *Guiding Creative Talent.* Prentice-Hall, Englewood Cliffs, N. J., 1962.

Watson, R. I. *The Clinical Method in Psychology.* Harper & Row, New York, 1951.

# AREA C

*The Field of
Clinical Psychiatry*

# CHAPTER FOURTEEN

# Clinical Psychology

## FRED BROWN, Ph.D.

### HISTORY

CLINICAL PSYCHOLOGY is one of the newest of the mental health specialities, but its accelerated growth and proliferation have established it as a significant component in all planned or operating mental health programs. The first psychological clinic was established in 1896 at the University of Pennsylvania by Lightner Witmer and grew out of the then current interest in individual differences that had already been stimulated by McKeen Cattell's work in psychometrics begun in 1886. Guy Whipple's *Manual of Mental and Physical Tests* appeared in 1910, and in 1911 the Goddard revision of the Binet-Simon intelligence test made its appearance in America, to be superseded by Louis M. Terman's Stanford Revision in 1916. These beginnings, motivated by the urge to objectify psychology by emphasing *measurement* of mental processes and thus to sever all bonds with its subjectivist-philosophical antecedents, were oriented more toward research than toward what are now known as service functions.

In 1918 R. S. Woodworth developed his "Personal Data Sheet" for screening potential military psychiatric casualties, and this instrument, the grandfather of all personality inventories, was later used in civilian clinics. The Rorschach method, which now dominates the field of projective techniques, was created in 1921 and spurred the development of the projective approach to personality analysis and evaluation. Finally, the demands for psychological personnel and techniques in two world wars focused attention on the contributions of the clinical psychologist to the expanding field of mental health, brought him into close contact with psychiatrists and other medical personnel, and established him as a member of the mental health team. The significance of the functions and roles of the clinical psychologist has broadened and deepened as a consequence of the Joint Commission Report, *Action for Mental Health*, and the growing emphasis on comprehensive community mental health programs.

## SCOPE

The 1963 directory of the American Psychological Association lists 2,899 clinical psychologists, of which number 1,300 are diplomates of the American Board of Examiners in Professional Psychology. Not all clinical psychologists are accounted for in this figure, a fact evident in the results of the National Scientific Register survey of psychologists conducted in 1962, which revealed that of 9,348 questionnaires returned by psychologists, 3,441 indentified themselves as clinical psychologists. George Albee reported to the Joint Commission on Mental Illness and Health that there are more than 18,000 psychologists in the American Psychological Association, with only one third of that number engaging in clinical services involving the mentally ill. Albee's estimate of approximately 6,000 psychologists in the United States who constitute a pool of mental health workers would probably be increased to 7,830 if the total 1965 roster of 23,500 fellows, members, and associates of the American Psychological Association is taken into account and if all persons in clinical, counseling, school, educational, and personality psychology are included.

There is considerable overlapping of interests and functions among these subfields. Individual diagnosis and therapy are major specialities of the clinical and school psychologists and supplementary ones for counseling and personality psychologists. Other areas of overlap include educational counseling and measurement, school and personal adjustment, management of behavior problems, vocational counseling, and utilization of objective tests. Only clinical psychologists make extensive use of projective techniques.

At present, clinical psychologists play an important role as psychodiagnosticians, therapists, teachers, and research workers in the psychiatric units of general hospitals, community and private mental health clinics, medical schools, and social agencies. Although there has been a slow increase in the number of training facilities for clinical psychologists, professional progress is uneven because of conflicts with psychiatrists over role and function autonomy, a lack of uniformity in training content and objectives, and unremitting struggles of this relatively new profession to define itself. As a consequence of these and other factors, training and competence levels among clinical psychologists in the areas of psychodiagnostics and therapy vary considerably and have aroused continuing concern on the part of responsible leaders in the field who are devoting themselves to the task of improving education and training. A very important aspect of the American Psychological Association's work in this area is the activities of its Education and Training Board and the Committee on Evaluation concerning approval of doctoral programs in clinical psychology and counseling psychology and of internships for doctoral training in clinical psychology. These activities are supplemented by state and regional psychological associations that concern themselves with the improvement of training and service by establishing licensure and certification standards.

## ACTIVITIES OF CLINICAL PSYCHOLOGISTS

### RESEARCH

This is undoubtedly the most important general contribution of the psychologist and the most valuable one offered to psychiatry by the clinical psychologist. In commenting on William F. Soskin's study for the Joint Commission, *Research Resources in Mental Health*, the Joint Commission Report stated:

> Currently, the major share of systematic investigation on mental health programs is being conducted by psychologists. Dr. Soskin reports that over 50 per cent of all N.I.M.H. grants go to investigators from this discipline. . . . While many of the fundamental concepts and hypotheses of modern psychiatry derive originally from clinical observations and from *what now appear to have been* poorly designed studies, emphasis today is placed increasingly on sophisticated research designs, on highly specialized research techniques and instruments, and on complex statistical procedures for data analysis. Psychologists are likely to have had the requisite training and experience for this type of research and this fact helps to account for their prominent position in this field.

Psychologists contribute theoretical and experimental papers to over 20 basic psychological journals in addition to psychiatric and other journals. A few of the areas covered by this spate of research activity include psychopharmacology, developmental problems, geriatrics, test construction and validation, personality diagnosis and adjustment, psychoanalytic theory, therapeutic processes, brain damage and mental retardation, behavior and habit problems, psychosis, psychoneurosis, psychosomatics, mental health and rehabilitation, and marriage and family problems. The psychologist's special training and competence in the research area make him a valuable consultant and co-worker in hospitals, clinics, and other agencies engaged in mental health research. A good source of condensed information regarding psychological research relevant to the interests of psychiatrists is *Psychological Abstracts*, a monthly publication of the American Psychological Association.

### PSYCHODIAGNOSIS

The clinical psychologist in his psychodiagnostic role uses a battery of appropriate tests and measures, both projective and objective, for the purpose of clarifying the dimensions of the patient's illness. Depending on the reason for referral and the nature of the particular case, a competent clinician can, through the use of such tests, appraise a patient's ego strength, the degree and nature of underlying malignant processes, and his capacity for change.

Very often, covert malignant psychopathological potentialities are not detected in the ordinary psychiatric examination but come into focus through the psychological examination. It may be possible to evaluate the patient's type and mode of thinking; the type and psychoeconomics of his defenses, whether entrenched or resilient; the quality of his affect vis-à-vis object relations; and the diagnostic picture—for example, depression, schizo-affective reaction, psychotic decompensation, or anxiety state. The psychological examination may contribute data useful for the differential diagnosis of organic brain syndromes, neurotic disturbances, and psychotic reactions. The psychodiagnostic test battery has proved useful in delineating focal conflicts that may not have been seen in total perspective in the clinical situation. Psychodiagnostic tests aid also in formulating a therapeutic plan, evaluating the progress and outcome of therapy in longitudinal appraisals, and contributing to an understanding of the patient's reaction to shock, pharmacotherapy, and other therapeutic modalities.

Although it is not imperative that every patient seen by the psychiatrist be referred for psychological evaluation, a comprehensive psychodiagnostic assessment of the patient's resources and liabilities prior to initiation of treatment can, in many instances, prove valuable in helping determine therapeutic approach.

## PSYCHOTHERAPY

This is the most controversial area involving both the clinical psychologist and the psychiatrist. In an early Group for the Advancement of Psychiatry report, the statement was made that psychiatrists should continue to refer some patients to clinical psychologists for such special treatments as vocational guidance, remedial reading, retraining procedures, speech training, and psychotherapy. In addition, it was stated that the type of psychotherapy performed by the clinician is conditioned by his training and competence, by the type of patient, and by the circumstances under which treatment is conducted. It was emphasized that the clinical psychologist must work in close association with the psychiatrist, since independent operation by the clinical psychologist may incur diagnostic error or result in either the failure to detect and treat the early stages of serious psychiatric conditions or the failure to recognize some physical disorder that may be the basis for the maladjustment. The Joint Commission Report of 1961 pointed out:

A narrow enforcement of psychiatric conviction that "nobody should do psychotherapy except psychiatrists" would effectively deny its benefits to patients now receiving it from nonmedical therapists with or without supervision of psychiatrists. Such enforcement would also raise questions regarding the psychotherapeutic nature of other interactions of patient and therapist carried out in the name of "group therapy," "drama therapy," and so on.

Conversely, however, to deny the patient access to a doctor trained in medicine opens up the possibility that a physiological, as opposed to a psychological or social, basis for the illness may be overlooked—unless the psychotherapist has access to and uses medical consultation.

Recognizing the acute shortage of mental health workers and noting that criteria of competence apply equally to psychiatrists and psychologists, the commission recommended the practice of psychoanalysis by professional psychoanalysts and any other professionals who, although lacking a medical education, possess aptitude for and competence and training in techniques of psychotherapy. The commission further recommended that nonmedical mental health workers with such qualifications be allowed to perform short-term psychotherapy "by objective, permissive, nondirective techniques." The report by the commission emphasized that such treatment should be carried on "within the framework of their hospitals and other professional service agencies" and "in all cases should be undertaken under the auspices of recognized mental health agencies."

In reaction, clinical psychologists have taken a more aggressive view in defense of their professional autonomy, rejecting in principle and often in practice the concept of medical supervision. In pursuit of professional independence, many clinicians are establishing their own training centers and clinics. Although some psychologists are not enthusiastic about the prominence given pyschotherapy by their clinical colleagues and feel that this may diminish research motivation by overemphasizing the practitioner role, others concur with this relatively new activity. Shakow has said with regard to psychotherapy that particular professional identification need not necessarily be involved, particularly in areas concerned with human psychology and motivation. He further questioned whether, in certain circumstances, conventional medical training may not hinder rather than aid in preparation for psychotherapy. Some clinical psychologists opposed to the perpetuation of current medical and disease-oriented conceptions of pathological processes have rallied to the view of Szasz that the concept of mental illness is "a logically highly dubious proposition." This view is strongly advocated by George Albee, who stated:

> The plain fact is that nearly all of the people seen in psychologists' offices or on the wards of "mental hospitals" are *not* sick. While the concept of mental illness had a sort of temporary usefulness in counteracting the older explanations of sinfulness and taint, it is now a millstone around our neck.

This intemperate statement represents an extremist view, which is the more significant when propounded by an acknowledged leader in the field.

More cautious opinions, however, suggest a more conservative view and emphasize the need for up-grading the quality of work being done by private practitioners in the field. It should be noted that in 1961 less than 5 per cent of clinical psychologists were in full-time private practice.

In considering the relation of the clinical psychologist to psychotherapy, the crucial, interprofessional issue is whether the clinician is competent to treat psychiatric patients in private practice and, above and beyond professional rivalries, what is best for the patient. Apart from situational difficulties, mild character disturbances, and those conditions listed by the Joint Commission report as capable of being treated by the competent psychologist in his office, close collaboration between psychologists and competent psychiatrists would be in the best interest of the patient, regardless of the particular setting in which therapy is conducted. Direct psychiatric supervision of psychologists engaged in psychotherapy should be provided as a service in relation to the needs of the psychologist and his patient rather than as an inflexible institutional policy.

Although a conscientious psychologist is generally very discriminating in the choice of patients he accepts for treatment, in his private practice with mentally ill persons he is unable to avail himself of antipsychotic medication and other psychochemical agents, to the serious detriment of those patients for whom such medication is indicated. This is especially significant in view of the expanded use of this therapeutic modality by psychiatrists. The clinical psychologist lacks hospitalization privileges, cannot shift to electroconvulsive therapy if this is indicated, and thus lacks the resources available to the psychiatrist for continuing diagnosis and treatment. In addition, he is not trained in the diagnosis and management of psychophysiological reactions. The psychiatrist is a member of a profession that has within itself all the necessary therapeutic modalities. He can prescribe what is best for the patient, whereas the psychologist, when such modalities are required—and one hopes for the patient's sake that recognition of such a need is forthcoming and not belated—must send the patient to members of another profession.

Full and realistic recognition must be given to the clinical psychologist's contribution as a therapist in the collaborative setting of institutions and agencies, where his experience as therapist and psychodiagnostician deepens his understanding of psychodynamics and psychopathology and increases his worth as a teacher in a variety of training programs. However, the role of the clinical psychologist as an independent colleague and as a member of a team where he carries primarily psychodiagnostic and research responsibilities is more clearly defined and less subject, at present, to inherent professional restrictions than is true of his role as a practitioner of psychotherapy, private or otherwise.

## REFERENCES

Albee, G. A declaration of independence for psychology. Ohio Psychol., June 1964.

Ausubel, D. P. Personality disorder *is* disease. Amer. Psychologist, 16: 69, 1961.

Braun, J. R. *Clinical Psychology in Transition.* Howard Allen, Cleveland, 1964.

Brown, F. Contribution of the psychologist to psychiatric problems of diagnosis and therapy. Psychiat. Quart., Suppl., 26: 8, 1952.

Brown, F. The psychodiagnostic battery: use of the test battery for psychodiagnostic appraisal. In *Progress in Clinical Psychology*, L. E. Abt and D. Brower, editors, vol. 3, p. 68. Grune & Stratton, New York, 1958.

Brown, F. Contribution of the psychodiagnostician to problems of therapy. Amer. J. Orthopsychiat., 30: 811, 1960.

Finn, M., and Brown, F. editors. *Training for Clinical Psychology.* International Universities Press, New York, 1959.

Group for the Advancement of Psychiatry. *The Relation of Clinical Psychology to Psychiatry*, Report No. 10. Group for the Advancement of Psychiatry, New York, 1949.

Joint Commission on Mental Illness and Health. *Action for Mental Health.* Basic Books, New York, 1961.

Lockman, R. F. An empirical description of the subfields of psychology. Amer. Psychol., 19: 645, 1964.

Schaffer, G. W., and Lazarus, R. S. *Fundamental Concepts of Clinical Psychology.* McGraw-Hill, New York, 1952.

Shakow, D. The role of the psychologist. In *The Psychiatric Unit in a General Hospital*, M. R. Kaufman, editor, p. 53. International Universities Press, New York, 1965.

Szasz, T. S. The myth of mental illness. Amer. Psychol., 15: 113, 1960.

Szasz, T. S. The uses of naming and the origin of the myth of mental illness. Amer. Psychol., 16: 59, 1961.

# Contributors

### C. KNIGHT ALDRICH, M.D.
Professor and Chairman, Department of Psychiatry, New Jersey College of Medicine, Newark, New Jersey

### ANNE ANASTASI, Ph.D.
Professor and Chairman, Department of Psychology, Fordham University, Bronx, New York.

### ARTHUR L. BENTON, Ph.D.
Professor of Psychology and Neurology, University of Iowa, Iowa City, Iowa

### HENRY BRILL, M.D.
Lecturer, Columbia University College of Physicians and Surgeons; Clinical Professor of Psychiatry, New York School of Psychiatry, New York, New York; Chairman, American Psychiatric Association Task Force in Nomenclature and Classification; Director, Pilgrim State Hospital, West Brentwood, New York

### FRED BROWN, Ph.D.
Professor of Psychiatry (Psychology), Mount Sinai School of Medicine; Head, Division of Psychology, Institute of Psychiatry, Mount Sinai Hospital, New York, New York

### ALFRED M. FREEDMAN, M.D.
Professor of Psychiatry and Chairman of the Department of Psychiatry, New York Medical College; Director of Psychiatric Services, Flower and Fifth Avenue Hospitals, Metropolitan Hospital, and Bird S. Coler Memorial Hospital and Home, New York, New York

### HAROLD I. KAPLAN, M.D.
Professor of Psychiatry and Director of Psychiatric Education and Training, New York Medical College; Attending Psychiatrist, Flower and Fifth Avenue Hospitals; Visiting Psychiatrist, Metropolitan Hospital and Bird S. Coler Memorial Hospital and Home, New York, New York

### MORTON KRAMER, Sc.D.
Chief Medical Record Librarian, Biometry Branch, National Institute Mental Health, Bethesda, Maryland

### VICTOR F. LIEF, M.D.
Associate Professor of Psychiatry, New York Medical College; Associate Attending Psychiatrist, Flower and Fifth Avenue Hospitals; Associate Visiting Psychiatrist, Metropolitan Hospital and Bird S. Coler Memorial Hospital and Home, New York, New York

## LOUIS LINN, M.D.

Clinical Professor of Psychiatry, Mount Sinai School of Medicine of the City University of New York, New York, New York

## MILTON H. MILLER, M.D.

Professor and Chairman, Department of Psychiatry, University of Wisconsin Medical School; Director, Wisconsin Psychiatric Institute, Madison, Wisconsin

## FRANCES C. NEMEC

Medical Record Librarian, Biometry Branch, National Institute Mental Health, Bethesda, Maryland

## ZYGMUNT A. PIOTROWSKY, Ph.D.

Professor Emeritus of Psychiatry (Psychology), Jefferson Medical College; Adjunct Professor of Psychology, Temple University; Director of Personality Research, E. N. Hay and Associates, Philadelphia; Philadelphia, Pennsylvania Area Consultant, Veterans Administration, Philadelphia, Pennsylvania

## HERBERT S. RIPLEY, M.D.

Professor of Psychiatry, Department of Psychiatry, University of Washington School of Medicine; Consultant, Veterans Administration Hospital, Seattle, Washington

## WILLIAM L. SANDS, M.D.

Clinical Professor of Psychiatry and Director of Family Therapy, Albany Medical College of Union University; Attending Psychiatrist, Albany Medical Center Hospital; Consultant in Psychiatry, Albany Veterans Administration Hospital, Albany, New York

## ROBERT L. SPITZER, M.D.

Director, Evaluation Unit, Biometrics Research, New York State Department of Mental Hygiene, New York, New York

## PAUL T. WILSON, M.D.

Principal Investigator, American Psychiatric Association Information Processing Project, Washington, D. C.

# Index

# Alfred M. Freedman

Alfred M. Freedman received his A.B. from Cornell University and his M.D. from the University of Minnesota Medical School. After Army service in World War II, he engaged in neurophysiological and neurochemical research, and trained in general and child psychiatry at Bellevue Hospital. He received his certificate in psychoanalysis from the William Alanson White Institute for Psychoanalysis, and is a Diplomate of the American Board of Psychiatry and Neurology. Since 1960 he has been Professor and Chairman of the Department of Psychiatry at the New York Medical College. Dr. Freedman is Director of the Metropolitan Community Mental Health Center, and Director of Psychiatry at Flower and Fifth Avenue Hospitals, Metropolitan Hospital, and Bird S. Coler Hospital; in addition, he is President of the American Psychopathological Association and President-elect of the American College of Neuropsychopharmacology. He has published over a hundred scientific papers, and is co-editor of the *Comprehensive Textbook of Psychiatry* (1967) and of *Psychopathology of Adolescence* (1970).

# *Harold I. Kaplan*

Harold I. Kaplan received an undergraduate degree from Columbia University and an M.D. from the New York Medical College in 1949. He trained in psychiatry at the Kingsbridge Veterans Hospital and Mount Sinai Hospital in New York and became a Diplomate of the American Board of Psychiatry and Neurology in 1957; presently he is an Associate Examiner of the American Board. He began the practice and teaching of psychiatry and was certified in psychoanalytic medicine at the New York Medical College in 1954. He became Professor of Psychiatry and Director of Psychiatric Training and Education at the New York Medical College in 1961. He is Attending Psychiatrist at Metropolitan Hospital Center, Flower and Fifth Avenue Hospitals and Bird S. Coler Hospital. He is the Principal Investigator of ten National Institute of Mental Health training programs, specializing in the areas of undergraduate and graduate psychiatric education as well as the training of women in medicine. He is the author of over seventy scientific papers and co-editor of the *Comprehensive Textbook of Psychiatry* (1967) and of *Comprehensive Group Psychotherapy* (1971).